An Introduction to

Biophysics

An Introduction to

Biophysics

By

OTTO STUHLMAN, JR. Ph.D.

PROFESSOR OF PHYSICS
UNIVERSITY OF NORTH CAROLINA

New York · JOHN WILEY & SONS, Inc.

London · CHAPMAN & HALL, Limited

PRINTED IN THE UNITED STATES OF AMERICA

PREFACE

As a result of the increased demands for physics by students whose primary interests lie in the biological sciences, this book has been written with the hope that it may lead to a fuller appreciation and understanding of the applications of physics to biological problems.

I trust that it will prove suitable as a textbook for mature students who have had a year's work in college mathematics followed by one year's study of the fundamental principles of physics and chemistry.

In lieu of a more appropriate name, it is proposed to designate all those biological observations which are explainable in terms of physical principles as biophysical phenomena. Which topics are representative of an ideal cross section of the available biophysical material is at present a debatable question. In order to avoid the imputation of superficiality in dealing with this cross section, only such subjects are discussed as are representative of the major subdivisions of physics.

In the general field of radiation no better example can be found of the cooperative effect of the biological and physical sciences than the problem of radiation therapy. Here, as in much of the biophysical research, the tools have been supplied by the physicist so that the medical scientist can use them to point the way in which the physicist should work to make the tools progressively more effective. This cooperative progress in the field of radiation is portrayed in the chapters on the biophysically active x-rays and applied radioactivity.

The influence of physics on physiological optics and acoustics is presented in the chapters discussing the biophysical characteristics of the eye and auditory biophysics.

In the field of physical optics, where its applications merge with the medical sciences, the emission and adsorption of biophysically active light are discussed because of the general desire for information dealing with the effect of ultraviolet radiation on life processes.

The possibility of revealing the nature of the living cell membrane is at present being pushed with great success through the study of the physical properties of molecular-film structures. The chapter discussing structure and properties of surfaces and membranes is introduced to illustrate how the modern molecular concept of matter is influencing the developments in this biophysical field of investigation.

v

To what extent the field of bioelectrical measurements has been enriched since the celebrated investigations of du Bois-Raymond, with the aid of vacuum-tube amplification technique coupled to the modern cathode-ray oscillograph, is discussed as the biophysical problem of nerve conduction.

The final chapter discusses the technical limitations of the optical microscope and points to the electron microscope, with its enormous resolving power, as the instrument which awaits the cooperative interests of experts in the biological sciences as the tool to investigate the structure of organic matter.

The publishers have generously cooperated by subscribing to the pedagogic axiom that one good illustration equals 1000 printed words.

The General Electric X-Ray Corporation, the Victoreen Instrument Company, Bausch and Lomb Optical Company, National Carbon Company, Weston Electrical Instrument Corporation, Kipp and Zonen, Fisher Scientific Company, American Standards Association, Central Scientific Company, Allen B. DuMont Laboratories, Eastman Kodak Company, Electro-Medical Laboratory, Inc., and the R. C. A. Research Laboratories have all been generous in supplying many original photographic illustrations, for which I express my appreciation.

It is a pleasure to thank Dr. S. J. M. Allen for furnishing the new data on x-ray absorption coefficients; Mr. J. L. Weatherwax for the use of his water phantom data; Mrs. E. H. Quimby, of the Memorial Hospital, New York, for clinical data on radiation therapy; Dr. D. B. Lindsley for the original electroencephalograms; and Dr. V. K. Zworykin for the photographs of the electron microscopes.

I am indebted for many excellent suggestions made by my colleagues in the Medical School. For criticisms of various chapters I am indebted to Professors H. A. Blair, H. D. Crockford, J. F. Dashiell, R. B. Lyddane, A. E. Ruark, and P. E. Shearin.

O. S.

Chapel Hill, N. C.
January, 1943

CONTENTS

Chapter I

BIOPHYSICALLY ACTIVE X-RAYS

It was at the University of Würzburg, Bavaria, in November, 1895, that Wilhelm C. Röntgen* discovered x-rays. While experimenting and presumably repeating some of Lenard's contemporary experiments on cathode rays in extreme vacuum he is supposed to have observed that a sheet of paper covered with barium platinocyanide placed near a Hittorf tube (according to Zehnder [1933])† or near a Lenard tube (according to Stark [1935]) became fluorescent although the tube had been enclosed in an opaque cardboard cover.

In accordance with Röntgen's will, all papers and letters bearing dates 1895 to 1900 were destroyed so that no written record of the details of his first experiments is available.

His first publication, " On a New Kind of Ray," which appeared in 1895, contained a description of the three chief properties of the new ray, i.e., its effect on a photographic plate, its ability to produce fluorescence in many substances, and its ability to make the air through which it had passed electrically conductive. He discovered that substances varied in opacity and that flesh was more transparent than bone. He further recognized that x-rays which originated from a tube that possessed a comparatively low air pressure were more easily absorbed by substances than x-rays orginating from a tube exhausted to a very high vacuum. He called the latter " hard " and the former " soft " x-rays; i.e., it was harder to pass a current through the tubes when they were very highly evacuated.

GAS TUBES

The general method of producing roentgen rays is always the same, namely: accelerating electrons to a high velocity in an electrostatic field and then suddenly stopping them by collision with a solid body, the so-called target. The electrons are liberated by the positive-ion bombardment from the surface of a concave aluminum cathode immersed

---

* His signature is written Röntgen; its modern version is Roentgen.

† Brackets enclosing dates [1933] refer to a citation in the bibliography at the end of each chapter.

in a low-pressure gas. They travel in straight lines until they collide with the target, from the surface of which the roentgen rays are emitted.

The thin platinum targets of the early gas tubes were rapidly replaced by thin disks of platinum, backed by massive pieces of copper. The copper support served as a good heat conductor, since it was early recognized that most of the energy of the cathode rays after the rays collided with the target appeared as heat. For a metal to be suitable as material for a practical x-ray target, in medical diagnostic work, it was found that it must possess the following properties: (1) a high melting point, (2) a low vapor pressure, (3) a high thermal conductivity, (4) a high atomic number. Tungsten fulfills all these requirements and hence replaced platinum in most of the later gas tubes.

COOLIDGE HIGH-VACUUM TUBE

No radical changes took place in the construction and method of generating x-rays until the introduction, in 1913, of the Coolidge x-ray tube with a hot tungsten-filament cathode.

By 1909 O. W. Richardson and his students at Princeton had shown under what conditions electrons may be expected to be emitted by high-temperature metal filaments in vacuo. This work terminated in Richardson's thermionic law, which was subsequently slightly modified in its theoretical derivation through the use of the Fermi-Dirac law of distribution of energies in the electrons in the metal, giving

$$I = AT^2e^{-b/T}$$

where I is the saturation current in amperes per square centimeter of the emitting filament surface; A, a universal constant, applicable to all emitting metals; T is the absolute temperature of the filament; and $b = e\phi/300k$, in which k is Boltzmann's constant. $e\phi/300$ is called the work function of the metal emitting the thermoelectrons, and its magnitude is expressed in electron volts. The work function is not the total potential barrier at the surface through which the inner electrons of the metal must pass, but the difference between this energy and the inner energy of the electrons. The value of A for tungsten is 60.2 amp/cm^2/degree^2, and its work function is equal to 4.52 volts.

The electron emission from a metal surface, heated in vacuo, increases exponentially with the temperature of the metal, so that a small change in temperature will result in a very large increase in electron emission. If a metal electrode is placed opposite such an emitting surface and a difference of potential is applied, so as to accelerate the freed electrons toward the plate, it is found that when the temperature of the filament is increased the electron current does not increase as rapidly as the increase in number of thermoelectrons. The electron current moving from filament to plate is said to be limited by " space charge."

Repulsion by the thermoelectrons surrounding the filament prevents all the emitted electrons from moving towards the collecting plate. The electron current has a maximum or saturation value expressed by the relation deduced by Langmuir,

$$i_{\text{max}} = \frac{\sqrt{2}}{4\,\pi} \sqrt{\frac{e}{m}} \frac{V^{3/2}}{x^2}$$

where e and m are the charge and the mass of the electron, x the distance between the electrodes, and V their difference of potential. It is essential to have the electrodes quite close together in order to have electron currents of appreciable magnitudes flow between the electrodes. A close approximation for tungsten is $i = 2.33 \times 10^{-6} \, V^{3/2}/x^2$ amperes per square centimeter of thermoelectron-emitting surface.

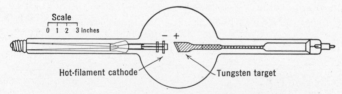

Fɪɢ. I-1. A universal Coolidge tube which may be used up to 200,000 volts with an 8-ma current between target and hot-cathode filament. Solid tungsten target.

Coolidge [1913] designed an x-ray tube using the thermoelectron current from a hot filament *in a high vacuum* to replace the cathode-ray stream for bombarding the target in order to generate the x-rays.

Using a heated tungsten filament as his source of electrons, and a disk of tungsten, backed by copper for heat conduction, as a target, Coolidge found that it was possible to obtain a very stable discharge which permitted more accurate reproducible results, that the tube could be made smaller, that a greater flexibility could be obtained since current through the tube and the voltage across the tube could be varied independently, and that the tube had a comparatively long life.

The commercial form of Coolidge tubes varies in size and shape depending on operating conditions. Figures I-1, 2, and 3 show some available commercial forms. Figure I-1 is an air-cooled type that will carry 8 ma between hot filament and its solid tungsten target when excited at a difference of potential of 200,000 volts. This design of Coolidge tube is used primarily for therapeutic work. Figure I-2 shows an x-ray tube having a copper-backed tungsten target with an air-cooled radiator. It can be designed to operate over a wide range of energy ratings; filament current range 3.5 to 5.0 amp, tube current from 25 to 150 ma, and potentials from 30 to 100 kv.

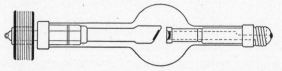

Fig. I-2. A fluoroscopic and radiographic x-ray tube. It will operate at 30 ma for long exposures and will take 100 ma at 85 kv for $\frac{1}{10}$ second. Air-cooled radiator, Pyrex glass bulb.

In an x-ray tube of the stationary-anode type, the electron stream is directed against a fixed area on the target which is known as the focal spot. The rating of a tube is limited by the ability of the target to dissipate the heat generated by the colliding electrons. In practice, the magnitude of the voltage, electron current, and time must be such that the bombarding area is not brought too close to the melting point.

Fig. I-3. A rotating-anode Coolidge (RT 1-2) tube in which a large disk of tungsten replaces the conventional massive copper anode with tungsten button insert. The disk rotates during exposure. Anode speed 3000 rpm. Effective focus 1 mm^2 200 ma, 73 kv peak, exposure $\frac{1}{20}$ sec. A stationary anode with effective focus 3.8 mm^2 uses 200 ma, 82 kv peak, exposure $\frac{1}{20}$ second. (By courtesy of the General Electric X-Ray Corporation.)

If it were possible to move the hot metal target out of, and a cool metal target into, the electron path, the time of operation of the tube could be extended. This is what is done in the General Electric Company's rotating-anode tube, Fig. I-3. The target in this tube is a disk of tungsten fastened to the end of a short shaft of the rotor of an induction motor, mounted in ball bearings. Outside the glass wall of the tube surrounding the circumference of the rotor is the stator of the motor. A 60-cycle current energizes the motor and rotates the target at about 3000 rpm. During excitation the target rotates so that relatively cool metal is brought continuously before the electron stream. This form of target allows an exceedingly small effective focus, 1 mm or 2 mm square, to be used in a tube operating at high electrical energy.

GENERATION OF X-RAYS

X-rays are produced by the sudden stoppage or deceleration of high-speed electrons. In this process the very high kinetic energy of the moving electrons is converted into radiant energy of very short wave-length, while some of the energy due to the deceleration is converted into heat.

In modern practice, the generation of x-rays takes place in an evacuated tube having two electrodes, one emitting electrons and the other acting as a target upon which the electrons are projected by a high difference of potential placed between the electron emitter and the target.

The electron emitter, in a commercial form of x-ray tube, is a spirally or helically wound filament of tungsten wire, which is heated to any desired temperature by means of a variable current from a 6-volt step-down transformer usually connected to a commercial 110-volt alternating-current source. Its operating temperature may be regulated by a current control, which in turn controls the number of electrons emitted.

If the positive accelerating potential of the target is comparatively small, the current flowing from filament to target will be less than that calculable from Richardson's equation. This reduction is due to the repulsion of these negative electrons in the region between filament and target on the electrons coming out of the hot-wire filament. An electron cloud is formed in the space between target and filament with its greatest electron density just in front of the filament. This electron cloud is the space charge.

If the voltage of the target is very great, the electron current passing between filament and target will be appreciably greater than that given by Richardson's equation. This increase is due to the large potential gradient at the surface of the filament which pulls electrons out of the filament and adds them to the normal emission. This so-called field emission may become greater than the thermionic emission calculable from the Richardson equation.

The highly accelerated electron stream is guided by a properly designed electrical field to fall on a small area of the target. The interposed target suddenly decelerates these electrons. Some lose their kinetic energy by a head-on collision with an atom of the target so that at a single encounter they give up all their kinetic energy. Under these circumstances the kinetic energy of the electron is converted into a single quantum of radiant energy of short wavelength. Some of the high-speed electrons do not have such favorable encounters. They may pass close to the nuclei of the atoms of the target and may be deflected. At each such deceleration some kinetic energy is converted into radiant energy, but of longer wavelength. The closer the electron approaches the nucleus, the greater is its loss in velocity and energy and the greater are the energy and frequency of the radiant energy or released photon.

The great majority of the electrons undergo no such collisions but dissipate their energy in penetrating the target. This energy manifests itself as thermal motions of the atoms. Thus much of the kinetic energy of the electron stream appears as heat.

The shortest wavelength of the radiant energy emitted by the target is quantitatively obtainable from the relation proposed by Einstein in 1905 on theoretical grounds and verified experimentally by Duane and Hunt [1915], namely, that the kinetic energy

$$E = \frac{eV}{300} = h\nu = \frac{hc}{\lambda}$$

where E is the kinetic energy of the colliding electron of electrostatic charge e $(4.8025 \times 10^{-10}$ esu), V the difference in potential between filament and target in volts, 300 the conversion factor which makes possible the use of volts for V instead of absolute units, h is Planck's radiation constant $(6.624 \times 10^{-27}$ erg second), ν the frequency of the emitted photon or x-radiation of wavelength λ. The velocity of light c enters the relation because $c = \nu\lambda$.

Upon substituting these values in the above equation, it is found that

$$\lambda V = 12,395$$

where λ is expressed in angstrom units $(1 \text{ Å} = 10^{-8}$ cm) and V in volts.

For instance, it may be desirable to know the shortest x-ray wavelength emitted by the target when an electron, arriving under a difference of potential of 100 kv, between filament and target, is decelerated so that all its energy is converted into one quantum of x-radiation. Under these circumstances

$$\lambda V = \lambda \times 100,000 = 12,395$$

$$\lambda = 0.12 \text{ Å} = 0.12 \times 10^{-8} \text{ cm}$$

When compared with the wavelength of visible light (5500 Å), the x-radiation has a wavelength about 50,000 times smaller.

Of the total energy incident on the target, less than 1 per cent is converted into x-radiation even under a driving potential of 100,000 volts. The remainder, or 99 per cent, of the incident energy of the impinging electrons can raise the temperature of the target even to its melting point. This rise in temperature necessitates a rapid cooling of the target by circulating oil or by radiating fins. Thus, regarded as a machine for producing x-rays, a Coolidge x-ray tube has a very low

TABLE I-1

HARDNESS OF RADIATION
(As used in this book.)

	λ in Å	kv
Very hard	0.05	247
Hard	0.10	123
Medium hard	0.15	82
Soft	0.25	49
Medium soft	0.50	25
Very soft " Grenz rays "	2.0	6.1

efficiency, but the radiant energy emitted has a remarkably high penetrating power because of its high frequency (ν) or short wavelength (λ).

SOFT AND HARD X-RAYS

Soft x-radiations and hard x-radiations correspond to long and short wavelengths, respectively. The soft rays are produced by comparatively low electron-accelerating potentials and the hard by high potentials. Soft x-rays are readily absorbed; those not so readily absorbed by the same substance are qualitatively designated as hard x-rays. These differences are only descriptive and have no quantitative significance.

For all practical purposes the radiations emitted by a tungsten-target x-ray tube in terms of a scale of hardness may be roughly classified as shown in Table I-1.

X-RAY SPECTRAL DISTRIBUTION

Corresponding with a given applied voltage, a definite distribution of intensity at different wavelengths is found, depending on the material of the target. Since in medical or biophysical work ordinarily tungsten

and occasionally molybdenum targets are used, the discussion will be
limited to the emissions from these two metals.

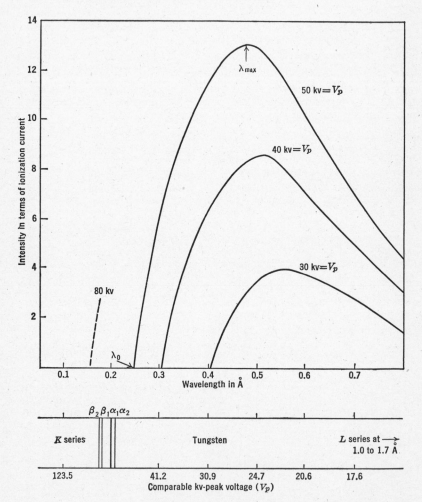

FIG. I–4. These curves show the general radiations from a tungsten target. The
value of the maximum at the peak of each curve moves to longer wavelengths as
the exciting kilovoltage is reduced. The glass bulb if 1 mm thick transmits about
25 per cent of the 1-Å wavelength emitted. The attached characteristic line spectrum of the K series shows relative positions of these emissions with respect to the
general radiation curves. (Curves after C. T. Ulrey [1918].)

Figure I–4 shows the intensity of emission of the x-radiations at
different wavelengths from a tungsten target bombarded by electrons
which had been accelerated by various voltages across a Coolidge tube.

At these low kilovoltages a continuous spectrum, as indicated by the smooth curves, is observed outside the glass-jacketed vacuum tube. Compare these data with those represented in Fig. I–5, and note particularly the sharp peaks which appear in the 110-kv spectrum emitted by a tungsten target.

The continuous spectrum or "general radiation" begins suddenly at the minimum wavelength λ_0 obtainable from

$$\lambda_0 V_p = 12,395$$

where V_p is the maximum potential across the tube. If a rectified alternating potential is used to excite the roentgen tube, then V_p is the peak voltage.

From λ_0 the intensity rises rapidly to a maximum (λ_{max}), from which it gradually declines.

In the roentgenographic region generally used for diagnostic work or superficial therapy, namely, 100 to 50 kv (0.12 to 0.25 Å), the maximum intensity of the general radiation, to a good approximation, is found at

$$\lambda_{max} = 1.6 \lambda_0$$

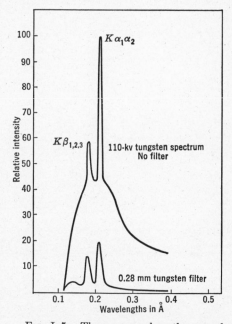

FIG. I–5. These curves show the general x-ray spectrum of tungsten with superimposed characteristic K series. Note that the 0.28-mm tungsten filter does not change the distribution of the wavelengths. Compare these with the curves of Fig. I–14, where filters other than tungsten were used. (By courtesy of A. W. Hull.)

These curves are typical examples of the distribution in intensity of a continuous spectrum emitted by a tungsten target excited by the indicated differences of potential. Note particularly that these are general radiation curves with the bright-line spectra of tungsten missing. They show that the continuous spectrum possesses a rapid intensity increase on the short-wavelength side of the curve and that its maximum intensity shifts to longer wavelengths as the exciting voltage is decreased, and also that the total x-radiant energy, as indicated by the area under each curve, rapidly increases with the increase in exciting potential. This area, when expressed in terms of intensity, is for all practical purposes proportional to the square of the exciting potential.

The overall intensity may also be increased by an increase in the electron current flowing from filament to target. The latter increase may also be obtained by raising the temperature of the filament.

Since the impinging electrons must be decelerated through collision with the atoms of the target, one may conclude that, the greater the density of the atoms in the target, the more frequently will these collisions occur. Broadly speaking, the density increases with the atomic number; hence an increase in the atomic number of the target material should parallel an increase in emitted x-ray intensity.

It has been shown by Nicholas [1930] that the total amount of continuous spectral energy emitted per second

$$I = \text{constant } V^{3/2} zi$$

where V is the potential across the tube, z the atomic number of the element used as a target, and i the current passing from filament to target in the form of the stream of bombarding electrons. This relation is limited to values of V extending from 40 to 150 kv.

CHARACTERISTIC X-RAY EMISSION SPECTRA

The peaks superimposed on the general radiation curves shown in Fig. I–5 compose the K-line spectrum. They make their appearance at certain exciting potentials characteristic of the element out of which the target is constructed. The K series of tungsten makes its first appearance at the characteristic exciting potential of 69.3 kv. Below this voltage it never appears, but at this voltage and above it these radiations are always present. Table I–2 shows the most prominent of the tungsten and molybdenum spectral emissions in angstrom units, classified into their appropriate series with an indication of their relative intensities. The spectrum of tungsten, plotted at the bottom of the intensity-wavelength curves of Fig. I–4, shows the relative wavelength positions of these characteristic emissions with respect to the general radiation.

This so-called K-series radiation of tungsten is caused by a disturbance in the configuration of the innermost K ring of electrons. Suppose that one of the electrons about to collide with a tungsten atom possessed sufficient energy to penetrate to the innermost group of K electrons and succeeded in removing one of them by a collision process. To re-establish the undisturbed normal state an electron from the nearest outer group or L configuration will replace the missing electron. This L configuration, having lost an electron, will have a replacement drop in from the M configuration, etc., until all other electron adjustments have taken place.

Each adjustment necessitates radiation of an x-ray quantum or bundle of energy designated as a " photon " because of the interatomic energy exchange which is involved. The radiations originating as the result of an adjustment of the electrons from the L to the K configuration are called the characteristic K series (Table I–2), i.e., characteristic

TABLE I–2

PROMINENT X-RAY EMISSION LINES

Wavelengths in 10^{-8} cm (Å)

Element		Tungsten	Molybdenum
Atomic Number		74	42
Relative Intensity	K series	λ	λ
50	α_2	0.2135	0.7119
100	α_1	0.2089	0.7076
35	β_1	0.1844	0.6308
15	β_2	0.1794	0.6193
	L series		
11.5	α_2	1.4845	5.400
100	α_1	1.4735	5.394
	M series		
	α_1	6.973	
	Excitation Potentials in Kilovolts of the		
	K series	69.3	20.0
	L series	12.1	2.87
	M series	2.81	

of the tungsten atom. The radiations emitted as the adjustment progresses from the M to the L configuration are called the L series. Because of their long wavelength ($\lambda = 6.9$ Å), these radiations never appear outside of a tungsten-target Coolidge tube owing to the opacity of the glass for these " extremely soft " x-rays.

When the radiations from a tungsten target are examined with the aid of an x-ray spectrometer, sharp peaks are found on the emission curve. These are resolved into four principal homogeneous emissions, the $K\alpha_2$, $K\alpha_1$, $K\beta_1$, and $K\beta_2$, of which the $K\alpha_1$ emission is the most intense (Table I–2).

THE X-RAY SPECTROMETER

An ionization spectrometer of the Bragg type may be used to obtain curves similar to those shown in Figs. I–4 and I–5.

The x-ray beam emitted by the target of the Coolidge tube T (Fig. I–6) is collimated by the narrow slits s. It strikes the surface of a three-dimensional crystal grating G, is deviated, and enters the ionization

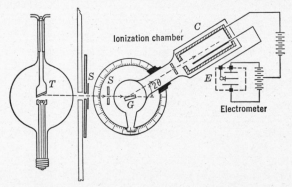

FIG. I–6. A diagrammatic representation of a Bragg x-ray spectrometer using an ionization chamber to measure the intensity of the x-radiations.

chamber C. The gas in the ionization chamber is ionized by the absorbed x-radiation, and this ionization current, which is proportional to the intensity of the deviated beam, is recorded by the electrometer E. The ionization chamber and the crystal may be rotated about the center of the calibrated spectrometer circle. The wavelength of the x-radiation entering the ionization chamber is then obtained from the relation

$$n\lambda = 2d \sin \theta$$

where n is the spectral order, λ the wavelength, 2θ the angle between direct and deviated beams obtained from the spectrometer scale, and d the distance between the reflecting planes of the crystal. If we examine the first-order spectrum for which $n = 1$, the wavelength may be obtained if the crystal constant d is known.

Suppose that we use a rock salt (NaCl) crystal as the three-dimensional grating. This salt crystallizes in a cubic form, the Na and Cl ions occupying alternate positions at the corners of elementary cubes in the cubic lattice characteristic of this crystal. The arrangements of the lattice are similar to the scheme shown in Fig. I–7, which represents a horizontal plane of a three-dimensional array of diffraction centers with the Na and Cl ions located at the bright and dark points.

When the x-ray beam reaches the crystal it encounters an array of ions (points) symbolized by the open and closed circles. A portion of the incident wave train is reflected from some ion P in the face of the crystal; another portion penetrates deeper and is reflected by an

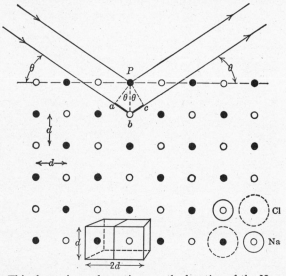

Fig. I–7. This shows, in a schematic way, the location of the Na and Cl ions in a sodium chloride crystal and the reflection by the crystal of a monochromatic beam of x-rays incident at glancing angle θ.

ion at a distance d below P. This latter train travels a longer distance abc, which must be an integral multiple of the wavelength of the x-ray so that on emerging and entering the ionization chamber it reinforces the upper wave train. The geometry of the diagram shows that this path difference is equal to $2d \sin \theta$. For the wave trains to reinforce each other

$$n\lambda = 2d \sin \theta$$

where n is a whole number and is called the spectral "order." This relation is known as Bragg's law.

The value of d may be obtained as follows. There are two ions per molecule, and, as each ion is confined to a volume equal to d^3, a molecule of NaCl occupies a volume equal to $2d^3$. Since one mole of a substance contains 6.06×10^{23} molecules, the number of molecules per cubic centimeter is $\rho \times 6.06 \times 10^{23}/M$, where ρ is the density and M is the molecular weight. Hence

$$d^3 = \frac{M}{2 \times \rho \times 6.06 \times 10^{23}}$$

The value of ρ for a rock salt crystal is 2.165, and its molecular weight is 58.46. Hence the value of the " lattice constant " of NaCl is

$$d = 2.814 \times 10^{-8} \text{ cm}$$

Using this value of d in the Bragg equation when a crystal of rock salt serves as a grating, one may compute the wavelengths for any glancing angle θ observed on the spectrometer table. If at the same time the ionization current due to the absorption of the x-rays in the ionization chamber is observed, one has a measure of the intensity of the x-rays possessing that particular wavelength. The plot of these values gives the curves shown in Figs. I–4 and I–5. Obviously this is a tedious method, and for therapeutic and other practical uses such detailed information is not necessary.

A simplified method of obtaining practically the same information will be outlined after the study of the law of x-ray absorption involved in the procedure.

Absorption

The medical radiologist cannot neglect the phenomena associated with absorption of x-radiation in both diagnostic and therapeutic branches if quantitative reproducible results are to be obtained. In therapeutic work where filters are constantly used to absorb the longer-wavelength radiations, which, for large doses, are dangerous to the patient, a knowledge of the processes involved in absorption is indispensable.

When a beam of x-radiation is incident upon any medium, several effects may occur, all of which result in the reduction of its energy. These effects are:

1. The photoelectric effect. Loss by absorption with the resulting emission of electrons.

2. Scattering of the primary radiation and Compton scattering, collectively classified as secondary radiation. Unfortunately, the removal of energy from the incident beam is not a true additive property of absorption and scattering, but to a good approximation we may write

Energy loss = Loss due to absorption + Loss due to scattering

If the energy loss of an x-ray beam passing through matter followed a true absorption law and were dependent only on the thickness of the absorbing layer, then for a given wavelength the energy would be decreased in each succeeding centimeter of absorbing layer by the same fractional amount. For instance, if the incident beam were composed of hard x-rays and the absorption in the first centimeter were 20 per cent of an incident 100 units of energy, 80 units would pass through this first centimeter. These 80 units would then be incident on the second centimeter of the absorbing medium, and this second centimeter would absorb 20 per cent of the 80 units incident on it and transmit 64 units; the next centimeter would absorb 20 per cent of the 64 units and transmit 51.2 units of energy; and successive centimeter layers would transmit 41, 32.8, 27.2 units, etc.

The energy loss of an x-ray beam passing through matter is, however, also dependent on the wavelength. Long wavelengths (soft x-rays) are absorbed much more readily than short waves (hard x-rays). It has been found experimentally that for restricted wavelength regions the absorption varies as the cube of the wavelength.

Therefore, if the wavelength of the incident radiation on tissue is composed of a beam of soft x-rays, it is found that the first centimeter of tissue absorbs 63 per cent of the incident energy, while successive layers would transmit 37, 13.7, 5.1, 1.9, and 0.7 per cent. To appreciate the difference in opacity in changing from hard to soft x-rays, compare this last value with the effect of the shorter wavelengths where the fifth layer transmitted 32.8 per cent.

The energy loss is also dependent on the kind of material used as an absorber. The loss is proportionally larger for a greater density of the absorbing substance. This implies that absorption is an additive atomic property and depends only upon the number and kind of atoms composing a molecule. The absorption varies as the fourth power of the atomic number, for a given wavelength.

It has been found empirically that the absorption may be represented approximately, over restricted regions of wavelengths, by what is generally known as Owen's law, namely, that the absorption coefficient per atom (μ_a) in the path of the x-ray beam is given by

$$\mu_a = C\lambda^3 z^4$$

in which C is an experimental constant and z the atomic number. When λ is limited to the restricted radiation of wavelengths less than the K characteristic wavelengths of the absorbing atom, as for instance in the use of filters of Al and Cu for λ between 0.50 and 0.71 Å, then the experimental constants C_{Al} and C_{Cu} are 0.0217 and 0.0221, respectively.

Using Owen's absorption law, let us compare the relative opacity of bone and fleshy tissues exposed to the same beam of monochromatic x-rays. Fleshy tissues are composed chiefly of H and O. Their absorption is comparable to water. The molecular absorption of H_2O is proportional to

$$2 \times 1^4 + 8^4 = 4098$$

The absorption of bone, composed chiefly of $Ca_3(PO_4)_2$, is proportional to

$$3 \times 20^4 + 2 \times 15^4 + 8 \times 8^4 = 614,000$$

so that the relative absorption

$$\frac{Bone}{Water} = 152$$

i.e., bone is 152 times more opaque than water.

If a lead bullet is embedded in the bone, then its absorption is proportional to the fourth power of the atomic number of lead, i.e., 82^4. Lead is therefore about 74 times more opaque than bone.

Barium sulphate, $BaSO_4$, which is most commonly used as an alimentary contrast agent, has an absorption proportional to

$$56^4 + 16^4 + 4 \times 8^4$$

It is very opaque because of the high atomic number of Ba.

Two or more adjacent substances transmitting different proportions of the incident energy show intensity contrasts which are very large for long wavelengths and small for shorter ones. Thus when soft x-rays are used, for radiographic work, they will produce a greater contrast between adjacent substances than x-rays of shorter wavelengths.

This contrast effectiveness is illustrated in the use of gases such as sterile oxygen to give radiographic relief effects. In the well-known pneumoperitoneum method, sterile oxygen is injected into the perinephric fatty tissues, and, in consequence of the small absorption of oxygen, the more absorptive kidney is thrown into relief. The same method has been used to inflate the Fallopian tubes. Carbon dioxide has also been employed for this purpose.

QUANTITATIVE STATEMENT OF THE ABSORPTION LAWS

The simple absorption law discussed on the preceding pages is a logarithmic depreciation law of the form

$$I = I_0 e^{-\mu d}$$

where I_0 is the incident intensity, I is the intensity of the x-radiation transmitted by a unit thickness, e is the base of the Napierian logarithms ($e = 2.72$), and μ is a constant for a given medium of thickness d and is called the coefficient of absorption. Its numerical value, in any given medium, depends upon: (a) the nature of the medium, (b) the wavelength of the incident radiation. For logarithms to the base 10 this absorption law may be written

$$\mu = \frac{2.303}{d} \, (\log I_0 - \log I) \; \text{cm}^{-1}$$

The absorption coefficient μ, or " linear absorption," is the fractional decrease in intensity of a beam of unit cross section per unit (linear) path length through the absorbing medium. The " linear absorption coefficient " of a given beam of x-radiation is much greater in water than in steam; hence, its value depends on the nature of the medium. To get a more fundamental constant, an absorption coefficient that is characteristic of the absorbing substance is required; hence a mass absorption coefficient* is used defined by $\mu_m = \mu/\rho$, where ρ is the density of the material. The absorption law in terms of the mass absorption coefficient takes the form

$$I = I_0 e^{-(\mu/\rho) \cdot \rho d} = I_0 e^{-\mu_m \rho d}$$

Experiments have shown that the mass absorption coefficient of a substance for x-radiation is independent of its physical state. Thus the mass absorption coefficient of water is the same whether the water is in the form of liquid or of gas.

The independence of the mass absorption coefficient of the physical and chemical states of an element sharply distinguishes x-radiation from light. For instance, carbon in the form of diamond is optically transparent, whereas in the form of graphite it is opaque. The mass absorption coefficient of both forms for x-radiation, however, is the same.

MASS ABSORPTION COEFFICIENTS INCREASE WITH INCREASE IN WAVE-LENGTH

Figure I-8 shows how the mass absorption coefficient of copper or aluminum, common forms of therapeutic filter material, very rapidly increases with an increase in wavelength. Table I-3 gives tabulated values of the mass absorption coefficients of aluminum and copper in detail. Note the change in the values of μ_m for copper between 1.389 and 1.293×10^{-8} cm.

In x-ray technique an understanding of the comparative opacity of common filter elements like aluminum, copper, and lead is essential for the interpretation of the quality of radiation transmitted by these filters. Attention should be called to the enormous difference in opacity of copper and aluminum for the longer wavelengths.

---

* Mass absorption coefficient is the fraction of a beam 1 cm² cross section absorbed per gram of substance traversed.

TABLE I-3

MASS ABSORPTION COEFFICIENTS $\mu_m = \mu/\rho$ CM^2/GM FOR HOMOGENEOUS X-RAYS ABSORBED IN ALUMINUM AND COPPER

λ is wavelength in 10^{-8} cm

Z	λ	4.0	3.48	3.00	2.50	1.933	1.752	1.539	1.389	1.293	1.235	1.00	0.88	0.710	0.500	0.360	0.200	0.102	0.062
13	Al	760	516	338	194	93.7	72.5	49.5	36.5	29.7	26.4	14.14	9.70	5.22	1.905	0.80	0.270	0.155	0.120
29	Cu	720	500	330	197	96.8	76.0	50.9	38.9	260	222	129	91.2	50.2	18.3	7.1	1.54	0.325	0.162

Private Communication, by courtesy of S. J. M. Allen, 1941.

λ	0.093	0.120	0.135	0.184	0.209	0.234	0.258	0.283	0.332	0.356	0.368	0.381	0.393	0.405	0.417	0.430
Water μm	0.164	0.175	0.199	0.207	0.220	0.234	0.249	0.284	0.306	0.319	0.335	0.348	0.358	0.376	0.394	

By courtesy of F. K. Richtmyer [1921].

It has been found that, if the mass absorption coefficients are plotted as a function of the cube of the wavelength, the curves of Fig. I–8 change to straight lines. This allows us to conclude that

$$\mu_m = c\lambda^3 + b$$

This is shown in Fig. I–8, where c is the slope and b, interpreted as the mass scattering coefficient, is the intercept on the y axis. In this way the practical absorption formulas of Table I–4 were obtained. Note that copper has a slope ten times greater than aluminum.

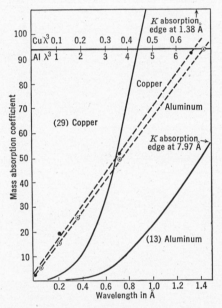

Fig. I–8. These curves show the relatively greater opacity of copper as compared with aluminum when used as therapeutic filters. The broken lines show mass absorption coefficients plotted as a function of wavelength cubed.

X-Ray Filters

In roentgen-ray therapy it is highly desirable to remove the long-wavelength radiations which, failing to penetrate the deeper tissue because of superficial absorption, may give rise to superficial x-ray burn.

Depending upon the excitation voltage aluminum, copper, and mixed metal filters are used of various thicknesses, in order to remove these long-wave radiations. Typical per cent transmission curves for aluminum are shown in Fig. I–9. The aluminum filter is inserted just below the x-ray tube, and the per cent transmission is obtained by means of ionization-chamber measurements.

TABLE I-4

ABSORPTION FORMULAS FOR FILTERS

Filter	Applicable to Wavelength Region Å	Mass Absorption Coefficient $\mu_m = \dfrac{\mu}{\rho}$ $\dfrac{cm^2}{gm}$	Author
Al	0.095 to 0.165	$\mu_m = 15.5\,\lambda^3 + 0.147$	Duane and Mazumder [1922]
Al	0.1 to 0.4	$\mu_m = 14.45\,\lambda^3 + 0.15$	Richtmyer [1921]
Al	0.4 to 0.7	$\mu_m = 14.30\,\lambda^3 + 0.16$	Richtmyer [1921]
Cu	0.1 to 0.6	$\mu_m = 147\,\lambda^3 + 0.5$	Richtmyer [1921]
	0.12 to 0.3	$\mu_m = 153\,\lambda^3 + 0.2$	
Pb	>0.14	$\mu_m = 510\,\lambda^3 + 0.75$	Richtmyer [1921]

ABSORPTION FORMULAS FOR ORGANIC MATERIALS*

Applicable to Wavelength Region Å	Formulas	Absorbing Material
0.05 to 0.5	$\mu_m = 2.5\,\lambda^3 + 0.18$	Blood
0.05 to 0.5	$\mu_m = 11\,\lambda^3 + 0.18$	Bones
0.05 to 0.5	$\mu_m = 1.6\,\lambda^3 + 0.18$	Fat
0.05 to 0.5	$\mu_m = 2.2\,\lambda^3 + 0.18$	Muscle
0.2 to 0.5	$\mu_m = 2.5\,\lambda^3 + 0.18$	Hydrogen

* Compare blood with hydrogen. After Mayneord [1929], attributed to Küstner.

It will be noticed that 1 mm of aluminum allows 36 per cent of the incident energy to be transmitted at 80 kv, 2 mm allows 23 per cent, and 3 mm only 16 per cent to be transmitted. Evidently 3 mm does not transmit one third as much as 1 mm. Neither does the transmission increase linearly with the applied voltage. The absorption governing these phenomena can, however, be represented by the empirical equations shown in Table I-4, where μ_m is the mass absorption coefficient for the wavelength region designated and ρ is the filter density ($\rho_{Al} = 2.70$ grams/cc and $\rho_{Cu} = 8.94$ grams/cc).

SCATTERING COEFFICIENTS

Next the contribution made to the energy loss of the x-ray beam passing through a filter, by scattering, must be considered. Here, as for absorption, an analogous mass scattering coefficient (σ_m) for the elements must be taken into consideration. Representative values are given in Table I–5 for some of the more common therapeutic filters.

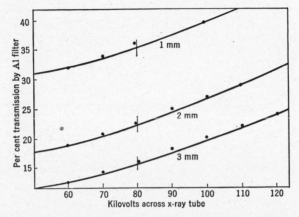

FIG. I–9. The per cent transmission of aluminum filters at increased kilovoltage using a constant source of potential. The tube wall was 1.3 mm cerium glass. (After L. S. Taylor, Natl. Bur. Standards.)

TABLE I–5

| Element | λ = 0.7 Å | | λ = 0.1 Å | |
	Mass Absorption Coefficient μ_m	Mass Scattering Coefficient σ_m	Mass Absorption Coefficient μ_m	Mass Scattering Coefficient σ_m
C	0.605	0.18	0.142	0.14
Al	5.22	0.20	0.156	0.14
Cu	51.0	0.29	0.325	0.18
Ag	Very large	0.48	1.05	0.35
Pb	Very large	0.82	3.50	0.67

By courtesy of C. W. Hewlett [1921].

For all practical purposes the various influences contributing to the scattering of the energy for any given metal are separable into:
1. The influence of thickness on scattering.
2. The influence of density of the filter on scattering.
3. The wavelength of the incident energy.
4. The departure of the incident beam from a parallel column.

The scattering of x-radiation in passing through matter is dependent on the thickness of the filter in such a way that each succeeding centimeter of filter thickness converts the same fractional amount of the incident energy into scattered radiation. If the wavelength is large as compared to the diameters of the atoms composing the absorbing filter, the atomic scattering is independent of the incident wavelength and we may call this an example of true scattering. Under these circumstances the scattered radiation has the same wavelength as the incident radiation, and each atom acts as a source for emitting scattered rays in all directions. Some of the energy is scattered forward, and backward, as well as sideways. The scattered x-radiation may penetrate and be absorbed by the filter in a manner similar to the incident energy. Its intensity is additive to the unabsorbed primary x-radiation at every point in the absorbing substance so that the total intensity at any point in the absorber is increased by the scattering process.

The scattering occurs within the medium; the smaller the density of the absorbing medium, the greater is the possibility that the scattered ray emerges. The scattered radiation which escapes from an absorbing medium of great density is less than that escaping from a less dense medium.

It has been found that the intensity of a beam of hard rays is reduced by scattering more than by mass absorption. Very soft rays are reduced in intensity more because of mass absorption than because of the scattering effect.

Table I–5 shows the relative importance of the mass absorption coefficient and the mass scattering coefficients for various wavelengths and filters. As the wavelengths of the x-radiation decrease, for any given filter, scattering becomes more and more the predominating factor in the absorption of the energy, for the scattering coefficients become increasingly great in comparison to the mass absorption coefficients. For absorbing material containing elements of small atomic number the scattering for any given wavelength is predominantly more effective. On comparing the loss due to scattering with the loss due to absorption, it is found that for light elements and soft rays (0.7 Å) the absorption loss is roughly three times as great as the scattering loss. For hard rays (0.1 Å) the loss is about equally distributed between the two effects. For the heavy elements the loss due to scattering is nearly negligible for soft rays, but it is about 20 per cent or less for the hard rays.

Finally, the scattering is smaller in proportion to the absorption, the greater the density of the absorbing medium.

This loss explains why tissue, owing to the low density and small mass of its constituent atoms, produces so much scattered radiation when subjected to x-ray examination.

SCATTERED X-RADIATIONS AS MODIFIED BY THE COMPTON EFFECT

The preceding section discussed the properties of the scattered x-radiations which possessed the same wavelength as the incident energy. Coexisting with this phenomenon are found scattered x-radiations having longer wavelengths than the incident energy.

In 1922, A. H. Compton first demonstrated experimentally that a modification of the wavelength took place as the result of the scattering of the incident x-ray energy by the electrons in the material. He found, for instance, that, when very soft x-radiation having a wavelength equal to 0.7078 Å was allowed to penetrate a cube of carbon, the scattered radiation emitted by the cube at right angles to the incident beam was composed of two groups of wavelengths. The first was a true, or regularly scattered wave with unmodified wavelength (λ = 0.7078 Å); in addition, he found a *modified* scattered wavelength equal to 0.7320 Å, the increase in wavelength amounting to 0.0242 Å.

Therapeutically speaking, the Compton scattered energy is softer than the incident and regularly scattered energy. If the wavelength of the primary beam is exactly 1.0 Å (very soft radiation), the wavelength of the x-rays emitted at right angles to the incident beam will increase by 0.0242 Å, so that its wavelength becomes 1.0242 Å. This increase in wavelength of about 2 per cent is not very important. If, however, a primary beam whose wavelength is 0.1 Å is examined (hard radiation), the increase in wavelength is also 0.0242 Å, so that the modified scattered wavelength is 0.1242 Å. This increase is nearly 25 per cent, and if any considerable proportion of the modified x-radiation is present, the properties of this scattered beam will be very different from those of an unmodified beam. Such changes in wavelength imply great changes in the mass absorption coefficient. If, in addition, the intensity of the modified portion of the beam is greater than the intensity of the unmodified wavelength of the beam then a serious error arises by not taking the Compton scattering into consideration in biological absorbing material. Table I–6 shows to what dimensions the error may rise when elements of small atomic number are used as absorbing material. In deep therapy where radiations comparable to gamma rays are used, the softening of the scattered beam by the tissues is even more pronounced.

A. H. Compton has shown that it is possible to calculate the increase in wavelength ($\Delta\lambda$) as a function of the angle of scattering ϕ: that is, the angle at which an observer measures the scattered radiation with respect to the direction of the incident ray, from the simple relation

$$\Delta\lambda = \frac{h}{m_0 c} (1 - \cos \phi)$$

where m_0 is the mass of an electron initiating the scattering supposed to be at rest inside the carbon block, c is the velocity of light, and h is the Planck constant. This relation indicates that $\Delta\lambda$ is larger for a greater angle ϕ at which the scattered radiation is measured, being zero in the direction of the incident beam where ϕ is zero.

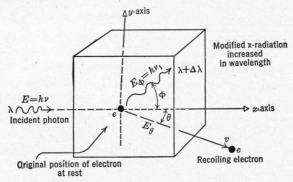

Fig. I–10. A diagrammatic representation of the Compton effect. Note the increase in wavelength ($\lambda + \Delta\lambda$) of the x-ray photon scattered by the stationary free electron e, and the resulting direction and velocity of the electron after the encounter.

Through the explanation of this extraordinary change in wavelength A. H. Compton proved the existence of a collision phenomenon in which an incident quantum of x-radiation or photon of energy content $h\nu$ collides with a free electron in the absorbing material. The photon acts as if it were a perfectly elastic entity colliding with a perfectly elastic electron. The incident photon may be pictured as colliding elastically with a stationary electron, and giving it a glancing blow. In this process it communicates energy and momentum to the deflected electron and in turn loses an amount equal to that passed on to the electron, but in such a way as not to violate the laws of conservation of energy and momentum. This collision is represented pictorially in Fig. I–10. Here the incident x-ray photon, of energy content $E = h\nu$, is shown colliding with an electron at rest of mass m_0. The incident energy E is divided between the modified photon bouncing off at angle ϕ with energy E_ϕ and the electron recoiling at angle θ with energy E_θ. The law of conservation of energy demands that

$$E = E_\phi + E_\theta$$

or that

$$h\nu = h\nu_1 + m_0 c^2 \left(\frac{1}{\sqrt{1 - \beta^2}} - 1 \right)$$

Here $m = m_0/(1 - \beta^2)^{1/2}$ is the relativistic mass of the electron of energy content mc^2, and m_0 is identified as its rest mass. $\beta = v/c$, where v is the recoil velocity of the electron and c the velocity of light. These equations involve relativity calculations because of the high velocity of recoil of the electron, necessitating the use of an effective mass (m) which is greater than the rest mass (m_0).

The next step is to consider the application of the law of conservation of momentum as applied to the collision. This law leads to two equations, one for the momentum along the x axis, or the x component, here chosen in the direction of the incident x-ray photon, and one at right angles to it, the y component.

$$\frac{h\nu}{c} = \frac{h\nu_1}{c} \cos \phi + mv \cos \theta \quad (x \text{ component})$$

$$0 = \frac{h\nu_1}{c} \sin \phi - mv \sin \theta \quad (y \text{ component})$$

The x-ray photon E of energy content $h\nu$, considered as a colliding entity, is moving with the velocity of light c. It has a relativistic mass of $h\nu/c^2$. Its linear momentum is $h\nu/c$. From these relations the increase in wavelength $(\Delta\lambda)$ can be computed, recalling that $c = \nu\lambda$, and is found to be

$$\Delta\lambda = \frac{h}{m_0 c} (1 - \cos \phi)$$

Evaluating h, m_0, and c, we find that

$$\Delta\lambda = 0.0242 (1 - \cos \phi)$$

where λ is expressed in 10^{-8} cm, i.e., angstrom units (Å).

For values of ϕ equal to $90°$

$$\Delta\lambda = 0.0242 \text{ Å}$$

For values of ϕ equal to $0°$

$$\Delta\lambda = 0$$

This result shows that the increase in wavelength is independent of the original or incident wavelength and that the modified scattered radiation depends for its increase in wavelength upon the direction in which it is scattered. For back scattering, where $\phi = 180°$, the increase in wavelength $\Delta\lambda$ amounts to 0.04848 Å.

The conclusion is that the softest scattered radiation appears in the direction $\phi = 180°$, and that this modified scattered radiation hardens as ϕ approaches zero, at which point its wavelength increase is zero.

Therapeutically, the back scattering is therefore a decidedly important phenomenon, especially for very hard x-rays, because of the increase in wavelength and its accompanying greater absorption in this direction.

TABLE I-6

RATIO OF INTENSITIES OF MODIFIED TO UNMODIFIED X-RADIATION IN THE COMPTON EFFECT

Source, Ag K line (0.56 Å)
Observations made at 120° with incident beam

Scattering Element	Atomic Number	Intensity Ratios
Li	3	∞
C	6	5.48
Al	13	2.61
Si	14	2.33
K	19	1.72
Ca	20	1.71
Ni	28	0.40
Cu	29	0.21

For additional data see Y. H. Woo [1926].
Courtesy Physical Review.

The Compton modified scattering varies with the atomic number of the filter or absorber element. Thus for elements of smaller atomic number than lithium all the incident energy is modified and scattered as softer radiation, whereas for lead practically none of it is modified. Table I-6 due to Y. H. Woo [1926] gives some idea of the importance of the ratio of the intensities of the modified to the unmodified x-radiation, especially when tissue and absorbing material of low atomic number are radiated.

THE TRANSLUCENCE OF HUMAN TISSUE

The above discussion on the transmission of x-radiation by matter permits a rather unusual conclusion about matter of low atomic weight: that it is translucent and not transparent to x-radiations. If the human eye were sensitive to x-rays, human tissue, which is composed wholly of elements of low atomic number, would be seen as a bright vaporlike substance if irradiated with x-radiations. An x-ray photograph (radiograph) of an internal organ of the human body is similar to a photograph of a building taken in a fog: the parts of the building nearer the camera would appear more clearly in the photograph, and the distant parts less clearly or not at all; while the larger outlines would be visible with structural details rather indistinct. The photograph lacks contrast and detail. In a similar way the lack of contrast and detail in a radiograph is attributable to the scattering of the x-radiation into the geometrical shadow of the object.

MEASUREMENT OF QUALITY OF X-RADIATION BY ABSORPTION

The radiation emitted by an x-ray tube is heterogeneous. It consists of a continuous spectrum overlaid with a line spectrum characteristic of the metal target, provided that the potential across the tube is sufficiently high to excite the characteristic radiation of the target. The "quality" of the radiation, especially with regard to its therapeutic applications, depends both upon the wavelength content of the spectrum and upon the distribution of the energy over its whole range of wavelengths as measured on the outside of the glass housing of the x-ray tube.

The direct determination of this spectral composition is beset with considerable experimental difficulties, as we have seen. Accordingly, an indirect way of obtaining the same results has recently been developed by L. S. Taylor, and his associates at the Bureau of Standards, by using a so-called filtration method.

The specification of x-radiation quality, with the aid of an absorption curve, has been recommended by the x-ray standardization committee [1934] of the Radiological Society of North America. The committee reported: " *For most practical purposes the quality of x-radiation may be satisfactorily specified in terms of the copper or aluminum absorption curve combined with a statement of the initial filtration. In lieu of an absorption curve, the equivalent constant potential applied to the tube terminals to yield the same curve may be stated as a single numerical magnitude. Up to 100 kv (constant) aluminum absorption curves and above 100 kv (constant) copper absorption curves shall be used to establish the equivalent potential.*"

In order to obtain the complete absorption curve, filters in the form of successively thicker sheets of a metal are placed in the diaphragmed beam of an x-ray tube driven at constant potential and predetermined constant milliamperage. The transmitted intensities are obtained by means of an ionization chamber (spectral distribution of energy assumed constant) placed below the absorber.

Typical results as obtained by Taylor and Singer [1930] are shown in Figs. I–11 and 12, for copper and aluminum filters of increasing thickness for radiations from a tube with tungsten target excited at various potentials.

If the absorption of filters were of the simple exponential type $(I = I_0 e^{-\mu x})$, then plotting log per cent transmission as a function of filter thickness a straight line of slope μ is obtained. The curves in Figs. I–11 and 12 show that the complete absorption curves do degenerate into straight lines, but only at high voltages and large values of filter thickness.

Hence, absorption for thick filters and high potentials can, to a close approximation, be represented by an equivalent composite absorption constant (c), such that $I = I_0 e^{-cx}$ for comparatively large values of x. For copper this result is attained at 150 kv with a 2-mm filter and for aluminum at 110 kv with a 10-mm filter.

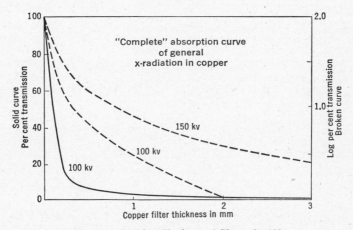

FIG. I–11.   After Taylor and Singer [1930].

The outstanding features of these absorption curves may be interpreted quite readily. The steeper the slope, the softer and more absorbable is the radiation. The slope in the more heavily filtered portion decreases symmetrically with the increase in tube voltage. Monochromatic x-radiation gives a straight-line absorption curve. The degree to which the absorption curve approximates a straight line is a measure of the homogeneity of the radiation. The similarity in the variation of absorption by different materials makes it possible to derive simple relationships between x-ray absorption characteristics of different materials. It is possible to compare the x-radiation output of two x-ray machines by means of the absorption curves obtained from each at various voltages.

EFFECTIVE WAVELENGTH OF A HETEROGENEOUS X-RAY BEAM

The effective wavelength emitted by the target was defined by Duane [1928] as "the wavelength of monochromatic radiation that would produce the same effects (the readings of the instrument employed to detect it) that the actual (heterogeneous) radiation produces."

In order to obtain the quality of an unknown beam of heterogeneous

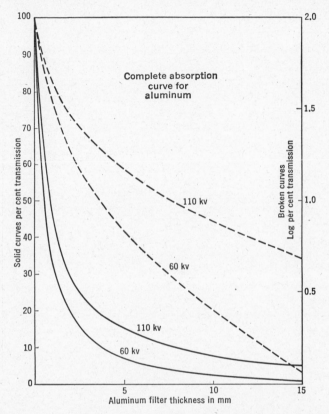

FIG. I-12. Decrease of the per cent transmission with increased filter thickness. From their shape, the solid curves seem to indicate an exponential absorption. Had they followed an exponential law of absorption the broken curves would have been straight lines. Note that at large filter thicknesses the broken curves become linear. (After Taylor and Singer.)

radiation it is possible to make use of absorption measurements. These measurements determine the comparable wavelength of a homogeneous radiation which would be reduced in intensity by a given filter in the same degree as the heterogeneous radiation. The heterogeneous radiation is then designated as having an effective wavelength equal to that of its corresponding homogeneous radiation. This does not imply, however, that the effective wavelength equivalent can produce the same biological results as its comparable heterogeneous beam.

Illustrations of the method for determining the effective wavelength with its composite absorption coefficient are found in Fig. I-13, where with increasing thickness of the copper filter the logarithm of the transmitted energy is plotted against thickness of filter material.

Suppose that one were interested in obtaining a beam of radiation which possessed an effective wavelength of 0.2 Å.   The table of mass absorption coefficients shows that copper possesses a mass absorption coefficient 1.6 for this wavelength.   The broken line in Fig. I–13 is drawn with slope 1.6.   This represents the relation $\log_e (I/I_0) = -cx$, in which $c = 1.6$, or $\log_{10} (I/I_0) = -cx/2.3026$.

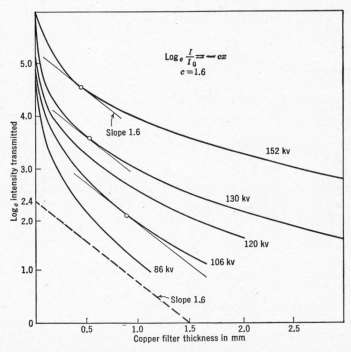

Fɪɢ. I–13.   Taylor's method of evaluating the effective wavelength of a heterogeneous beam of x-radiation.

A line drawn parallel to this broken line contacts the 152-kv curve at 0.4 mm and the 106-kv curve at 0.9 mm.

The conclusion is that, when an x-ray tube is excited at 152 kv and a 0.4-mm copper filter is placed in the beam, the radiation passing through the copper filter has an effective wavelength of 0.2 Å.   A similar effective wavelength may also be produced by a 0.6-mm copper filter introduced into a 130-kv beam or by a 0.9-mm copper filter in a 106-kv beam, if all other factors remain constant.

The converse question may arise: what effective wavelength is transmitted by a 1.0-mm copper filter?   Let us assume the radiation whose quality is to be determined as that produced by 120 kv.   A tangent is drawn to the curve at the 1.0-mm thickness.   The slope of the tangent at this point is 1.13. This is the composite absorption coefficient. Referring to Table I–3 one may observe that the effective wavelength comparable to this mass absorption coefficient of copper is 0.173 Å.

Upon drawing a tangent to the same curve at the 2.0-mm thickness mark it is found that the slope at this point corresponds to a composite absorption coefficient of 0.81 comparable with an effective wavelength of 0.15 Å. Note that, as the thickness of the filter increases, the slope decreases, and hence the effective transmitted wavelength decreases; i.e., successive filters harden the transmitted rays.

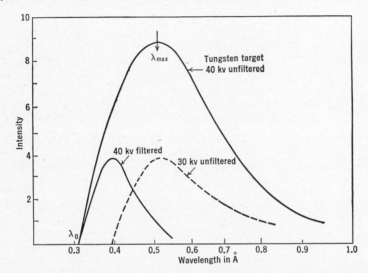

F$_{\mathrm{IG}}$. I–14. A diagrammatic representation of the general radiation emitted from a tungsten target with and without a filter. Note the general hardening of the emission without change in λ_0 but a pronounced change in λ_{max} and loss in intensity of the filtered beam. Compare this with the 30-kv unfiltered beam having about the same area and longer effective wavelength. (After A. W. Hull.)

This general hardening of filtered x-rays was originally observed by Hull. His spectral distribution curves are shown in Fig. I–14. Thus if a copper or aluminum filter is placed in the path of the x-radiation the intensity of the filtered radiation is much decreased but the decrease is proportionally greater in the longer-wavelength region owing to the relatively greater absorption of these wavelengths. As a result the effective value of the wavelength is decreased. This is due to the fact that λ_{max} is transferred to shorter wavelengths without changing the value of λ_0. For comparison a 30-kv unfiltered emission curve is shown having about the same intensity as the 40-kv filtered radiation, but note that its effective wavelength is much longer.

Half-Value Layer

The quality of a heterogeneous x-ray beam can be described by the thickness of a filter which will reduce the intensity of the beam to one half its initial value. The absorption curves shown in Figs. I-11 and I-12 indicate that, the shorter the effective wavelength of the x-radiation, the thicker the half-value layer of the filtering material must be. Inasmuch as the composite absorption coefficient varies with thickness of the added filter, there is no simple direct quantitative relation connecting effective wavelength with half-value layer.

The intensity of a heterogeneous beam of x-radiation, if evaluated by the half-value layer or effective wavelength method, shows that the latter has the advantage, in that it presents a clearer physical picture of the radiation quality.

Action of X-Radiation on Living Tissues

Almost immediately after the discovery of x-rays was announced it was suggested that, by virtue of their penetrating power, they might be used therapeutically to influence deep-seated pathological processes. In order to evaluate their physiological effectiveness it is essential to know the relative penetration, absorption, and resulting ionization of the x-radiation, for the energy must be absorbed to be effective.

The energy penetrating the tissue may be completely absorbed and excite secondary phenomena. It is to these secondary phenomena that the action of the primary radiation is attributed.

The pioneer workers in radiography and roentgen therapy developed cancer of the fingers after exposure to the soft x-rays emitted by the then prevalent gas x-ray tubes. Repeated exposure of the hands to soft radiation results first in keratosis (horny excrescences) that are usually multiple. At first dry and scaly, the surface epithelium in time becomes superficially eroded and the lesions become moist. This condition is an important danger signal indicating activity of the process. The next progressive stage is the development of carcinomata (rarely sarcomata). It is therefore important to appreciate the danger of small, repeated exposures to soft x-radiation.

As in inorganic material, the relative amount of the x-radiation absorbed by tissue in its superficial layers is also determined by its wavelength. Since the absorption is very great for long wavelengths, the superficial layers of tissues irradiated by the entering energy are affected to a greater extent than the deeper-lying tissue. As pointed out in previous sections, the control of physical factors governing the quality and quantity of x-radiation with which a patient is radiated is reproducible, but biological units of dosage contain factors still largely unknown.

Biological units of dosage of x-radiation have been expressed in terms of an erythema of the skin. An erythema may be defined as a reddening of the skin within a week or ten days, followed by tanning within about a month's time.

In human beings the amount of radiation necessary to produce just a mild erythema of the skin seems to depend upon the amount of pigmentation present and the thickness of the skin. An intensity which may produce a mild erythema on the inside of the thigh or forearm of a thin-skinned blond may cause no visible change in the skin of a dark brunette. The palms, soles, and the back of the neck can tolerate much more radiation than the dorsal surface of the forearm.

It is difficult to distinguish the effects due to the changes in the epithelial cells of the skin from the secondary changes brought about by injury to the subcutaneous capillary bed. The basal cells of the skin, or Malpighian* layer, seem to be the most sensitive, and they show vacuoles, pycnosis, and lack of staining power after large doses of radiation.

It has been noted (Packard [1926]) that a sufficient dose of x-radiation may bring the process of growth and repair of the matrix cells of the hair to a standstill with the result that the hair is loosened and falls out.

The single greatest secondary factor in skin changes following radiation exposure is the modification of cell nutrition by the capillaries. It is the engorgement of the capillaries of the area radiated that is identified with the erythema noted at various periods after exposure.

With properly filtered hard rays, the radiation through very small portals (holes in lead plates) does not produce an erythema, probably because there is no participation of adjacent tissues in the general reaction of the capillaries of the skin, so that an increase in blood circulation could not be identified visibly.

Bone and cartilage are resistant to x-radiation. It is common therapeutic knowledge that cartilage may be damaged by very intensive irradiation, especially in the region of the neck if larynx and trachea are subjected to intensive crossfire radiation. Experiments on young rats have shown that, when the jaws are subjected to large doses (Leist [1927]), the odontoblasts, which are especially sensitive, are destroyed; smaller doses produce only pulp injury.

The precursors of the circulating blood cells in bone marrow are very sensitive to irradiation.

---

* The deeper portion of the epidermis, consisting of cells whose protoplasm has not yet changed into horny material.

The coagulating power of the blood (Lindhardt [1924]) is not affected except in therapeutic cases irradiated for castration or hyperthyroidism, where it is found to fluctuate in amount.

The most sensitive cells in the testis, according to Feroux and Regaud [1927], are the basal cells or spermatogonads. The adult sperms are apparently insensitive, since they show no change after irradiation.

S. L. Warren [1928], in a review of the physiological effects of roentgen rays upon normal body tissues, lists the tissues in a descending scale of sensitivity, beginning with a moderate sensitivity, in the following rough order: thymus, stomach, colon, and bladder epithelium; salivary epithelium; probably kidney epithelium; hair papillae; blood-vessel endothelium; fibroblasts; and young connective-tissue cells including collagenous fibrils. Next in order of decreasing sensitivity are: the mucosa of the mouth, esophagus, rectum, and vagina; the lung parenchyma; pleura; skin epithelium; and the structures of the eye. Next come the smooth, striated, and cardiac musculatures; cartilage; bone, including osteoblasts; teeth; normoblasts; Sertoli's cells; and stroma cells of testes and ovary. The most resistant cells may be listed in the following order: adult thyroid, adult pituitary, brain and nerve cells, nerve trunks and endings, tendons and joint capsules, adult sperm cells, and red blood cells.

LATENT PERIOD

In a review of the literature on the latent period Regaud [1925] points out that sensitive cells of the epidermis are the generating cells of the basal layers, and that the changes in the skin occur as these cells are elevated toward the cornified surface. The period of latency is a measure of the time which is necessary for the cells from the basal layer to reach the cornified stage in their progress to the surface. The same is true of the testes, where the sensitive cells are the spermatogonads. Until time has passed to allow successive generations of cells to reach maturity, the injury is not apparent. This is the latent period for the spermatozoa. The thymus cells are very sensitive to radiation and have a very short latent period. This latent period conforms to the interval of time extending from the death of these very sensitive cells, in this case the lymphocytes, to the disintegration and absorption of the cell bodies.

An important biological effect of x-rays and γ-rays is the increase produced by them in the rate of mutation of genes. All types of mutation occur, but none have been observed which may specifically be attributed to x-ray absorption. The interpretation seems to center around the concept that " one direct hit " (Crowther [1924]) suffices for the initiation of mutations. The hit may be supposed to take place in some sensitive region in the chromosome. In the case of *Escherichia coli* (*B. coli*) the volume essential to life as estimated from the area in which the hit took place was less than 6 per cent of the bacterium itself (Wyckoff [1930]). This volume is about 0.75 μ^3. It was concluded from this work that the absorption of a single x-ray photon was sufficient to kill an organism, although on the average only about one in twenty of the absorbed photons was effective.

The biophysical effects of x-rays are due to energy actually absorbed by the tissues. This energy absorption, as previously indicated, does not take place directly, but through secondary processes, i.e., through the production within the tissues of high-velocity electrons and some of lower velocity due to Compton scattering. These electrons give up their energy in producing ionization along their paths (Table I–8). At this point the study must be taken over by the biochemist, who should explain why, as a result of sufficient ionization thus produced, living tissue of all kinds disintegrates.

From the experimental evidence available, one may conclude that absorbed photons in the form of x-rays and γ-rays for equal *ionization doses* produce equal effects. Genetic changes occur in direct proportion to the dose of radiation and are independent of its wavelength.

The biological effects of radiation are intimately related to ionization phenomena produced in a specific region of the living organism. The same number of ions may, however, be produced in the same region and during the same time interval by ionizing radiations of very different frequencies. In general, the biological effect is probably the same in kind but not in degree.

The receptor in which this ionization takes place is fundamentally the living cell. A cell, whether it lives as an isolated entity or as a part of an organism, is enclosed in a membrane which permits the passage into the cell of substances necessary to maintain its normal life and excludes others. The adjustment of the semi-permeability of the cell's membrane is so delicate that it can differentiate between two such very similar elements as sodium and potassium. The living cell is equipped to maintain the physical and chemical characteristics of its cytoplasm in a very constant state. The nucleus, located inside the cell and acting as the controlling center of the cell, is well protected by its environment. The x-ray energy passing through the cell wall, contents, and nucleus, if absorbed, will start a train of well-developed changes. The changes that occur depend on many factors, but primarily on the magnitude of the dose of radiation.

The nucleus contains a certain definite number of threadlike structures known as chromosomes, which carry the hereditary factors in the form of physicochemical units called genes. The remarkable effect following the absorption of the radiant energy is an alteration of the genetic nature of the cell (Goodspeed and Uber [1939]), which results from the ionization accompanying the passage of high-speed electrons through the nucleus and chromosomes. The effect of the ionizing radiations is to increase markedly the frequency of mutations, so that geneticists need not wait for the very rare probability of spontaneous genetic changes in order to study the problems of heredity and variations. For purposes of study those changes which cause differences in the physical appearance of *Drosophila* have been found most convenient.

For a further discussion of these very fundamental problems see Chapter II, " The Biological Roentgen," and Chapter IV, " Effect of Ultraviolet Radiation on Bacteria."

X-Ray Protection

The protective materials commonly used in radiology are: (1) sheet lead; (2) lead-impregnated glass and rubber; (3) concrete.

The absorptive values of sheet lead for various thicknesses and various wavelengths of radiation are given by Mutscheller [1925] and reproduced in Table I–7. These results show that absolute protection is impossible even with 8 mm of lead.

Under practical conditions faced by an x-ray operator, a protection comparable to 8 mm of lead is seldom attainable. Mutscheller has, however, found that an operator can safely subject himself to a " tolerance dose " of 1/100 of an erythema dose in 30 days' exposure.

On the basis of this definition we can assume that during radiographic work with an effective wavelength equal to 0.17 Å, with 50 exposures per day, each of 5 seconds at 20 milliamperes current, the operator standing 10 feet from the tube would receive about 1 erythema dose in 1 month. To reduce this to 1/100 of an erythema dose, lead protection of 1.2 mm is needed. If fluoroscopic work is undertaken during 2 hours per day, using 4 ma, about 6 erythema doses would be received in the same time and distance. Under these working conditions 1.8 mm of lead as a protection is necessary.

During radiotherapy work, where 4 ma for 10 hours a day may be used, 28.5 erythema doses per month under similar conditions are received and from 5 to 6 mm of lead are needed for protection.

Protective gloves or gauntlets and aprons are constructed of rubber impregnated with 55 per cent lead oxide. They are comparatively heavy but ensure protection. Lead-rubber aprons can be obtained in different weights. The usual 7-lb apron is made of $\frac{1}{16}$-in. leaded rubber

TABLE I–7

PERCENTAGE OF ENERGY TRANSMITTED THROUGH VARIOUS THICKNESSES OF LEAD

Tungsten target excited at kilovolt peak indicated

mm Pb	124	113	103	95.4	88.9	82.7	77.8	73	70	65	62 kv peak
1.0	23.9	19.8	15.7	11.9	8.61	6.00	3.94	2.44	1.45	0.794	0.410
1.2	17.9	14.3	10.8	7.74	5.27	3.42	2.06	1.16	0.62	0.302	0.137
1.4	13.5	10.3	7.48	5.05	3.23	1.95	1.08	0.55	0.27	0.115	0.046
1.6	10.1	7.47	5.17	3.30	1.98	1.11	0.566	0.26	0.114	0.044	0.015
1.8	7.60	5.40	3.57	2.15	1.21	0.63	0.297	0.13	0.049	0.017	0.005
2.0	5.71	3.90	2.46	1.41	0.74	0.36	0.155	0.059	0.021	0.006	
2.6	2.42	1.48	0.81	0.39	0.17	0.07	0.02				
3.0	1.364	0.77	0.39	0.17	0.064	0.02					
3.6	0.578	0.29	0.13	0.05	0.015						
4.0	0.326	0.15	0.06	0.02							
4.6	0.138	0.058	0.02								
5.0	0.078	0.030	0.01								
6.0	0.019	0.006	0.001								
7.0	0.004	0.001									
8.0	0.001										

weighing about 1.5 lb per sq ft, and is equivalent to 0.5 mm of lead. They should be frequently tested for holes and cracks.

Lead glass is merely a glass into which lead salts have been introduced. A thickness of 15 to 20 mm has an opacity equivalent of about 2.5 mm of lead. Some of the commercial lead glasses are $\frac{3}{16}$ in. thick and have a protective value equal to $\frac{1}{5}$ their thickness in sheet lead. The glass must be entirely free from air holes and other flaws. For proper protection 2.0 mm lead equivalent is recommended.

MEASUREMENT OF LEAD EQUIVALENT

The " lead equivalent " of a given thickness of absorbing material to be used as a protective layer is the ratio of the thickness of lead to the thickness of the material which absorbs a given x-ray beam to the same extent. The protective lead equivalent of gloves, aprons, and other guards is very simple to determine in practice. It can be obtained by means of a lead foil echelon under the actual working conditions to which the operator is subjected.

An echelon or step wedge is constructed of layers of plane parallel lead foils so arranged that the edges, each overlapping its neighbor, resemble a flight of stairs. Such a series of equally spaced steps may be built up of 25 layers, each with a thickness of 0.2 mm. The echelon and sample protective material are then placed on a paper-covered photographic film of suitable size so that sample and echelon are in contact along their long sides. The whole is exposed to the particular radiation against which the operator wishes to protect himself.

The developed photographic image then shows the relative transparency of lead and protective material. The photographic density of the image of this protective material is matched against the image of one of the steps of the echelon. A sufficiently accurate estimate of matched density can be obtained by direct observation. The lead layer having the same photographic blackening as the unknown material is chosen as representing its lead equivalent.

Concrete as a protective material was investigated by Singer, Taylor, and Charlton [1938], who found that the thickness of a concrete barrier which will provide adequate protection at 400 kv is about 26.5 cm, and the required thickness at 200 kv is 22 cm.

The radiation due to scattering is often so widespread that the whole room is filled with it, since it is emitted from floors, walls, table, attached metal parts, and patient. This emission may be a source of great danger in specific x-ray installations and apparatus. The best practice for protection during radiographic and radiotherapeutic technique is unquestionably to enclose the operator and controls in a booth protected by lead or barium plaster. This protection cannot be obtained in fluoroscopic work, and it is here that the most danger arises. A simple test shows the possible extent to which the operator is exposed to x-radiation. With patient placed upon an x-ray couch and with undercouch tube box, a fluorescent screen between patient and operator at right angles to the couch top will be found to be brightly illuminated if scattering danger exists. It is very probable that under these circumstances the usual lead equivalent of the operator's apron is insufficient protection. For proper protection 1.5 mm lead equivalent is recommended.

It has been suggested that, since the region of the operator so radiated is that of the hypochondrium, it is very probable that the overfrequent occurrence of duodenal ulcer in radiologists may be attributed to the direct effect of radiation upon the mucosa of the duodenum, resulting at first in a generalized inflammation and later in definite ulceration.

The United States Department of Commerce, National Bureau of Standards, issues a handbook HB 20, " Protection from X-Rays," price 10 cents, containing the recommendations of a committee representing the International Safety Committee and National Bureau of Standards.

IONIZATION OF A GAS BY X-RADIATION

Since, in therapeutic work, speed and comparative ease of operation are essential, ionization measurements are being used as the most direct method of determining the intensity of an x-ray beam under practical conditions.

In order to evaluate the intensity of the x-radiation in terms of the ionization produced in a gas, it is necessary to have some understanding of this process. Thus, when a beam of x-rays traverses matter, three things are observed: a certain fraction of the incident energy is transmitted; a second fraction of the energy is absorbed with the resulting emission of photoelectrons; a third fraction is scattered in all directions and then absorbed and additional photoelectrons are emitted. The volume ionized by these photoelectrons is much larger than that penetrated by the primary rays. The total number of ions which the photoelectrons in turn produce in the gas is far greater than their own number. X-ray absorption by the gas is to a great extent, therefore, an indirect process. It is the absorbed portion that is responsible for ionization.

Let us first examine an ideal condition: A very large volume of gas, oxygen for example, is contained in a metal vessel, at 760 mm pressure and $0°$ C. A monochromatic beam of x-radiation of frequency ν in passing through the gas will lose part of its energy through absorption. The energy extracted from the beam manifests itself by the appearance of a large number of atoms, ions, and electrons mixed with the gas molecules. The electrons are photoelectrons which are emitted by an atom when it absorbs a photon of energy $h\nu$. Their kinetic energy of emission is proportional to the frequency of the absorbed photon and is $\frac{1}{2}mv^2 = h\nu$. Using x-radiation of 1.0-Å wavelength, we can calculate the velocity of emission to be of the order of 6.5×10^9 cm/sec. When these high-speed photoelectrons traverse the gas they may collide with neighboring molecules and atoms and ionize them, each electron making many collisions. At each collision additional ions are produced, until after frequent collisions the energy is so reduced that the power of ionization is lost. This is the fundamental energy exchange process involved in ionization of a gas, and it is essentially an indirect process because of the emission of photoelectrons when x-radiation is the instigator of the process.

This ionization process is even more complicated when hard x-rays are used. Under these circumstances a quantum of energy $h\nu$ may collide with an electron, resulting in Compton scattering accompanied by the usual recoil electrons. These recoiling electrons may possess enough kinetic energy to ionize a molecule or atom with which they collide before their available ionization energy is dissipated. X-radiation excited at 200 kv or more may produce ionization of greater abundance by means of these recoil electrons than through the liberated photoelectrons. A third effect, though a practically negligible one, is the possibility of exciting the gas to emit its characteristic radiation through electron collisions. The characteristic radiation emitted under these circumstances, however, is of such long wavelength that it is reabsorbed before traveling very far.

Let us next introduce electrodes, in the form of two parallel metal plates, into the gas. Then connect these electrodes to the terminals of a battery having a difference of potential of several hundred volts, and insert a very sensitive ammeter in the circuit. If the beam of x-radiation is now passed through that volume of gas lying between the two plates, the ionized condition of the gas manifests itself by a current flowing through the ammeter. Such an ionization current is very small and for best results must be measured by a sensitive electrostatic instrument in the form of an electrometer.

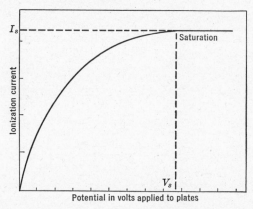

FIG. I–15. A typical saturation curve obtained by means of an ionization chamber. The extended curve becomes asymptotic to the potential axis. This asymptotic value is the saturation value I_s attained when the applied potential is V_s.

The variation of the current with successively greater potentials applied to the electrodes is shown in Fig. I–15. It will be noted that, although the intensity of the x-ray beam is kept constant, the ionization current increases with the voltage applied to the plates, but reaches a flat maximum, where it remains despite further increase in plate voltage. This maximum value to which the current rises is called its " saturation " value I_s. This saturation value of current is attained when all the ions are removed from the gas as fast as they are formed as a result of absorption of energy from the x-ray beam. The removal of all the electrons and ions from the gas is accomplished by applying a minimum voltage V_s across the ionization chamber. The minimum voltage is called the *saturation voltage*, and the resulting ionization current is said to have reached its saturation value.

It has been found that several factors such as distance between the plates, their shape, their size, and their enclosure influence the potential at which the saturation current value is attained. For a specific design of apparatus, however, the potential at which saturation takes place depends only on the degree of ionization, which in turn depends on the intensity of the x-radiation.

As a practical guide for determining the distance between the electrode plates one must possess some information about the distance high-speed photoelectrons may travel in a gas.

TABLE I–8

RANGE OF HIGH–SPEED ELECTRONS

Air, $p = 1012.9$ millibars, $t = 0°$ C

kv	10	50	100	500	1000
Range in air, cm	0.2	5.2	21	160	360
Range in water, cm	2.3×10^{-4}	...	1.3×10^{-2}	...	0.42

After Kulenkampff [1926].

Kulenkampff's [1926] experiments have shown that the energy of ionization is nearly independent of the wavelength of the absorbed x-radiation in the region 0.56 to 2.0 Å and is equal to 35 volts per ion pair. The *range* of the electron in its passage through the gas before its ionization ability has been exhausted is shown in Table I–8. These data also show that, when the energy of a photon of wavelength 0.12 Å (100-kv) is absorbed, the emitted electron has a velocity of 16.45×10^9 cm/sec and ceases to ionize after having attained a range of 21 cm.

These data were taken into consideration in designing the "standard parallel-plate ionization chamber" when the international unit of x-ray quantity, the roentgen (r), was established.

A source of error encountered in ionization measurements is attributable to the x-radiation striking the walls of the chamber. The radiation falling on the metal produces an emission both of high-speed photoelectrons and of x-radiations characteristic of the metal. These effects, if not eliminated, are measured as part of the ionization recorded by the current-measuring instrument.

In order that the ionization current recorded shall be a true measure of the intensity of the x-radiation, three conditions must be fulfilled by an ionization measurement:

1. No radiation must strike the walls of the ionization chamber.
2. Sufficient volume of a gas must be interposed into the path of

the beam of x-radiation so that all high-speed electrons may have sufficient range in which to dissipate their energy.

3. A saturation current value must be utilized to measure the ionization.

INTERNATIONAL UNIT OF X-RAY QUANTITY. THE ROENTGEN

In the report of the Committee on the Standardization of X-ray Measurements as published in *Radiology*, Vol. 22, p. 289, 1934, a definition for a unit effective intensity for biological purpose is set up called the roentgen (" r " unit). It has been accepted in the United States and defined as follows: " *The roentgen is the quantity of x-radiation which, when the secondary electrons are fully utilized and the effects of all scattered radiation avoided, produces in* 1 *cc of atmospheric air at* 0° *C and* 76 *cm mercury pressure such a degree of conductivity that* 1 *esu of charge is measured under saturation conditions.*"*

What is wanted in roentgen therapy work or in biological reactions to x-radiation is not the energy content of an x-ray beam but rather the amount that will be utilized in the tissue. For example, suppose that one considers the biological effectiveness of two beams of different wavelengths. The beam having the greater biological effect is not the one with the greater energy content but the one that will lose the greater amount of energy in 1 cc of tissue. If the total energy content were available, to decide which beam was biologically more effective, it would be necessary to know the distributions of energy in each beam for each wavelength and the coefficients of absorption and scattering for each wavelength. Ionization measurements, however, include all these factors, since an electrometer, introduced into the electrical circuit, indicates a current proportional to the energy absorbed.

PARALLEL-PLATE STANDARD IONIZATION CHAMBER

The Bureau of Standards has constructed a standard ionization chamber under the direction of L. S. Taylor [1930]. Figure I–16 shows the assembled chamber diagrammatically. In the standard chamber the plate spacing P_1P_2 must be sufficiently great so that if any photoelectrons strike them their contribution to the ionization is negligibly small. It was found that, for a parallel-plate ionization chamber with a 200-kv

* The Fifth International Congress of Radiology held in Chicago [1937] provisionally adopted the following definition: " The roentgen shall be the quantity of X- or gamma-radiation such that the associated corpuscular emission per 0.001293 gram of air produces, in air, ions carrying 1 esu of quantity of electricity of either sign." This definition rules out any possible ionization by scattered x-rays, a matter left uncertain in the original definition.

beam passing centrally between the plates, a spacing of 12 cm was satisfactory. Since a guard ring GG surrounds the collector plate P_2, and since a perfectly parallel electric field across the whole width of the collector electrode P_1P_2 was desirable, the widths of the guard plates were made from one and one half to two times the plate spacing. Thus for a plate spacing of 12 cm the guards must be about 20 cm wide. The standard chamber is rather large and unwieldy. In order to reduce the guard-ring dimensions to 5 cm a guard wire system was added.

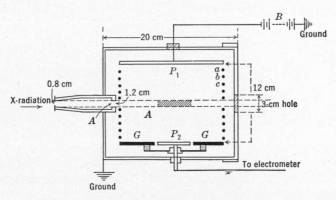

Fig. I–16. Diagrammatic section to scale of the National Bureau of Standards guarded-field ionization chamber. For use with 50- to 200-kv x-radiation. Guard wires a, b, c, etc., used to aid in creating a parallel field between electrodes P_1P_2G. P_2 aluminum collector electrode, shielded by guard ring G.

The electric field between the plates is rendered parallel by placing ten small aluminum guard wires (a, b, c, $\cdots$) across the ends of the chamber parallel to the electrodes about 1.1 cm apart, except for the center pair which are spaced about 1.6 cm apart. The electrode system is completely surrounded by a lead box. The diaphragm system used with this design is held in place by a lead-lined brass tube which fastens in front of the ionization chamber. The limiting diaphragm has a diameter of 0.8 cm; the inner end is diaphragmed to 1.2 cm. At the back of the chamber the beam passes out through a 3-cm hole covered with a thin sheet of celluloid to eliminate air drafts.

X-radiation, in passing through the diaphragms and then between the plates P_1P_2, produces ions in this space. They are drawn to the plates along the paths of the lines of force. The effective volume of air ionized is that of a cylinder of cross section equal to the area A and length equal to the effective length of the collector electode P_2. The electric field must also be of sufficient magnitude, as provided by the battery B, so that all the ions are removed before any are lost by recombination.   For this purpose a field strength of about 150 volts/cm is sufficient.

Since the degree of ionization is determined by the mass absorption coefficient of x-radiation by the gas, corrections must be made for the temperature and pressure of the air in the chamber, for by definition the air must represent conditions at 0° C and 1012.9 millibars (760 mm) pressure.

Under these circumstances, if I is the current, measured by the electrometer, in electrostatic units, L the effective length of the collector electrode P_2, A the area of the limiting diaphragm in square centimeters, T the absolute temperature, and p the pressure in millimeters of mercury, then the intensity of the x-ray beam as measured in roentgens per second is

$$\frac{r}{sec} = \frac{I}{L \times A} \cdot \frac{T}{273} \cdot \frac{760}{p}$$

Thus, if the area A and the length L are each unity, so that we are considering 1 cc of air at $T = 273°$ K, and if $p = 760$ mm, then r/sec $= I$.   If now I is 1 esu of current (1/3,000 microampere), then, since $Q = It$, r has the dimensions of quantity.   The unit of quantity of radiation defined this way is a unit of dosage.   In order to get a clearer conception of the magnitude of 1 roentgen, we may choose a technical x-ray tube with glass walls, driven at 100-kv constant potential and 5-ma current.   At a distance of 2 meters, using no filter, this tube emits in 1 second about 0.1 r, and at 180 kv its intensity is about 0.2 r/sec.

1 r is equal to 1 esu × 1 second

SMALL IONIZATION CHAMBERS

For therapeutic or biological purposes it is, of course, impracticable to handle such a large instrument as the one discussed above, because it lacks mobility.   A portable instrument has been developed with a small ionization chamber, an electrostatic current-measuring device with calibrated scale, and an electrostatic charger for supplying the potential for the saturation current measurements, all housed as a self-contained unit.

The ionization chamber may be cylindrical, with the ion collector in the form of a coaxial rod of graphite.   The outer shell of the ionization chamber is usually some very thin material comparable to an " air wall," as for instance Bakelite, whose effective atomic number closely approximates that of air.*   This outer shell, with its internally conducting layer

---

* Effective atomic number of air is 7.69.

of graphite, is earthed to the apparatus, and the central graphite electrode of the " thimble chamber " is connected to a potential recording device usually in the form of an electroscope or string electrometer.

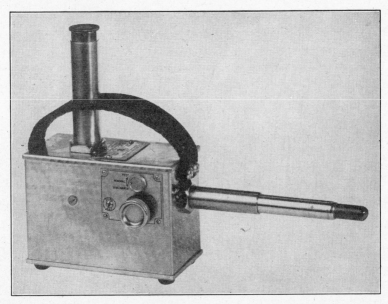

Fig. I–17. The Victoreen condenser r-meter. A portable instrument for measuring roentgens per minute. Its detachable chamber tube facilitates measurement directly on the patient and simplifies phantom measurements. (By courtesy of the Victoreen Instrument Company, Cleveland, Ohio.)

Figure I–17 shows one form of r-meter with a thimble chamber of the condenser type, with its string electrometer calibrated in roentgen units. It is a practical dosage instrument having a range from zero to 25 r.

VICTOREEN CONDENSER-METER

In this type of instrument, shown in detail in Fig. I–18, the chamber at C is made of any substance having a effective low atomic number (Bakelite). The thin chamber wall with its internally conducting deposit of graphite, Fig. I–19, constitutes one electrode of the ionization chamber which is grounded to the case. The internal rod electrode C of graphite is connected by a well-shielded conductor to the string electrometer F. The string of the electrometer F, its connection, and the graphite electrode are charged by means of a rotating amber wheel A. The position of the deflected (charged) string is viewed through the low-power microscope T. The image of the string is seen in the plane of the calibrated transparent scale situated below the eyepiece. This scale is calibrated to read 0–25 r in half r units. It is illuminated from below by the small lamp L connected to a small dry cell. The whole

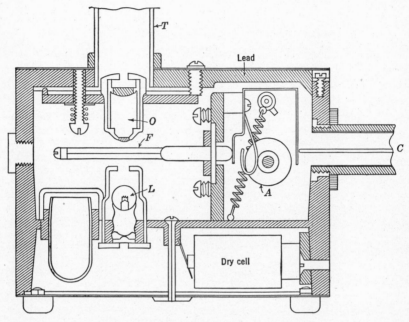

FIG. I–18. Detailed construction of the Victoreen condenser r-meter. Small thimble ionization chamber attached at C. String electrometer F is charged by frictional electricity from wheel A. Huygens' eyepiece with transparent scale calibrated in roentgens inserted above T. Lamp L illuminates F and calibrated scale through low-power objective O.

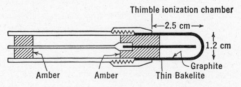

FIG. I–19. Removable thimble ionization chamber of the Victoreen condenser r-meter.

weighs 10 pounds. Most of the weight is attributable to the lead-shielded construction.

After the string electrometer has been charged, to read zero on the r scale, the charged chamber tube (condenser), Fig. I–19, can be removed and placed in the path of the x-ray beam whose intensity one wishes to measure. The x-ray tube is then activated for 1 minute. The chamber tube is then reinserted into its socket. This connects the partly discharged graphite electrode to the electrometer, and the string drops to a point on the r scale indicating directly the roentgens per minute emitted by the tube at the point in space previously occupied by the chamber tube.

The ionization produced in the small thimble chamber by the x-radiation neutralizes the charge given to the insulated graphite rod, and it is this decrease in charge that is recorded by the electrometer, which has been previously calibrated in r units by means of a standard ionization chamber. Usually the capacitance of these instruments is small. The loss in charge due to the ionization is $Q = CV$. The capacitance is constant, but the potential of the graphite rod has dropped from V_2, its charged potential, to V_1, its partially discharged potential state, during the 1-minute exposure to the x-radiation. Since $Q = It = C(V_2 - V_1)$,

$$\frac{r}{t} = \frac{C}{t}(V_2 - V_1) = I$$

it follows that the roentgens per minute are proportional only to the change in potential.

In order that the above thimble chamber may effectively simulate the standard open-air chamber, it is necessary to construct the walls of this chamber from material of low atomic number so that the so-called " wall effect " of this chamber is equivalent to a comparable mass of air. The x-radiation incident on this chamber wall and internal collector electrode produces, owing to absorption, secondary x-rays and photoelectrons. These contribute to the ionization within the chamber in a manner different from that in the standard open-air chamber. The ionization contributed by these sources depends upon the atomic number of the materials of which wall and electrode are constructed. The walls of the chamber, therefore, must be made out of a material whose effective ionization is that of the free air. Accordingly horn, celluloid, or Bakelite is used in the construction of these small ionization chambers.

IONIZATION MEASUREMENTS IN A WATER PHANTOM

Small ionization chambers such as have been described above are especially well adapted for intensity measurements within a " water phantom."

A water phantom consists merely of a water container, constructed to simulate human tissue. A small water-tight ionization chamber may be used to measure the effective penetration of an x-ray beam. According to Kulenkampff [1926], the relative absorption of average human tissue to water is about 800/830, which is sufficiently near to unity so that, for all purposes, water may be substituted as an absorbing medium for tissue in measurements of intensity at varying situations and distances from an x-ray tube.   In order to avoid errors arising from the effects contributed by the walls and bottom of the water container, the phantom is preferably constructed of a material having a scattering power approximating that of water (Quimby [1939]), such as sheets of wax or " presswood."

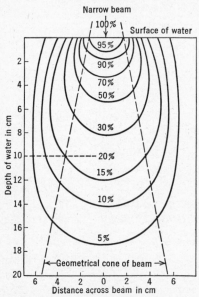

The procedure in determining depth dosage is then as follows. Ionization measurements are made at various depths below the surface of the water to determine the variation of intensity with depth. The intensity at a point beneath the surface will also depend upon the horizontal and vertical coordinates of the point, since we are dealing with a volume effect. This intensity will depend on the hardness of the radiation, the distance of the x-ray tube above the surface of the water, and the size of the portal of entry.   The size of the portal is determined by a lead diaphragm placed at the surface of the water.   The distribution of the intensity with depth for a narrow cone of x-rays is shown in Fig. I–20.

Fig. I–20. A narrow beam of x-rays is directed perpendicularly to the water surface.   These so-called "Isodose" curves were obtained from a water phantom using a thimble chamber ionization meter. (By courtesy of J. L. Weatherwax [1934]).

The radiation observed at the points outside the geometric beam, indicated by the dotted lines, is due to scattered radiation produced by the material lying in the path of the primary beam, while the radiation intensity inside the geometrical beam is due to unabsorbed radiation reaching that depth plus that due to scattering.   Weatherwax [1934] has shown with the aid of water phantoms that when large ports of entry are used 30 to 35 per cent of the intensity just below the surface is due to scattered radiation, coming from the deeper layers of water, while 50 to 60 per cent of the radiation reaching 10-cm depth is made up of scattered radiation.   These results show the impossibility of predicting predetermined intensities in irradiated tissue on the basis of absorption alone.

FLUOROSCOPE

A fluoroscope is an instrument used for the roentgenoscopic examination of a patient. Certain minerals have the property of absorbing x-radiation and re-emitting radiant energy of longer wavelengths which may be of sufficient length to be classed as ordinary light. This property we designate as photoluminescence or fluorescence.

Stokes established the fact that the wavelength of the emitted energy was always greater than that of the exciting energy.

It was through the luminescence of a platinum salt that Röntgen in 1895 discovered x-rays. When light is used as the exciting source of luminescence, the luminous radiations originate in the superficial molecular layers and then only on that side of the material turned towards the source of the radiation. If x-radiation, however, is the source of the excitation, fluorescent radiations from all sides of the material may be obtained. The effect may be represented to be a resonance phenomenon between the frequency of vibration of the exciting absorbed radiant energy and the frequency of the electrons revolving about the radiated atoms. That fluorescence is associated with the property of the peripheral electrons is supported by the changes in fluorescence due to temperature variations and by the presence or absence of fluorescence in chemical combinations of the same elements. $BaCl_2$ and $BaPtCN_4$ are fluorescent; $BaCO_3$, Ba_2CO_3, and Ba_2FeCN_6 are non-fluorescent. The platinocyanides in general exhibit varying degrees of fluorescence, especially the above-mentioned barium and calcium salts, but the magnesium salt is non-fluorescent.

TABLE I–9

Compound	Fluorescent Band Wavelength Range Å	Maximum of Emission Band at Å
$CaWO_4$*	4800–3750	4330
$BaPtCN_4$†	5090–4420	4800
K_2PtCN_4	4900–4120	4500
$CaPtCN_4$	5090–4550	4800

Compounds	Colors of Fluorescence
$CaWO_4$, calcium tungstate (white salt)	Light blue
$CdWO_4$, cadmium tungstate	Light blue
Zn_2SiO_4, zinc silicate (willemite)	Green
Cadmium zinc sulfide (silver-activated)	Yellow-green

*Used in radiographic intensifying screens.
†Used in visual intensifying screens.

The color of the fluorescence is greatly dependent upon the wavelength of the x-radiation. If too short a wavelength is used, practically no fluorescence occurs.

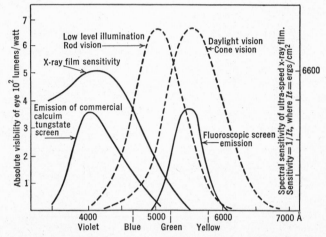

FIG. I–21. These curves show the relative spectral distribution of the emissions from a commercial form of fluoroscopic screen with its maximum in the region of most sensitive cone vision. Wavelength 5560 Å; color yellow-green. The calcium tungstate screen with its blue emission is used for photographic roentgenological examination of body structures. Note the position of its emission spectrum in relation to the curve for sensitivity of high-speed x-ray photographic film.

Each type of luminescent compound emits a definite spectral range of fluorescent radiation with one or more spectral bands possessing maxima of rather definite wavelengths. The more common forms of salts that are used in the construction of fluoroscope screens are shown in Table I–9.

The relative position of the fluorescent bands emitted by a commercial fluoroscopic and roentgenographic screen and their relative visibility as compared with the photographic spectral sensitivity of a high-speed x-ray film are shown in Fig. I–21. From these curves it becomes apparent that a fluorescent screen with an emission maximum in the yellow green is eminently well adapted for radioscopic work, and that calcium tungstate with its blue fluorescence is best adapted for photographic work.

APPLICATION OF FLUORESCENT SCREENS TO RADIOLOGY

If the luminescent material is applied in a thin layer to a cardboard screen support, and if the mounted compounds emit visible radiations when excited by x-rays, we have a technical radioscopic screen. These screens are used in visual fluoroscopic examinations of body structure. If the mounted compounds emit radiations predominantly in the blue, photographically sensitive wavelength region, then these mounts are designated as intensifying screens and are used for roentgenographic work.

In the construction of a screen the compound is carefully sifted for uniformity of fragments. Marcotte (British patent 184,485; 1921) claims that the fluorescence varies with crystal size, first rising to a maximum and then decreasing. He also maintains that the color of the fluorescent light from the tungstates of calcium and cadmium undergoes a parallel variation with crystal size, changing from yellow-green, blue-green, to blue-white, and that ungraded crystals in consequence give a luminosity of mixed color.

The proper grade of crystals is mixed with a binder of cellulose, acetone, or amyl or methyl acetate (20 per cent); the resulting mass is heated to 45° C and then poured into molds and rolled to a thickness of 0.02 in. These screens are claimed to be inert to soap and alkali. In the trade they are referred to as " washable screens."

For radioscopic work the screens must satisfy the following requirements:

1. Brilliancy. A yellow-green with maximum intensity at 5560 Å is recommended.

2. Clearness of definition. Coarse crystals produce great brilliancy but poor definition. Small crystals give less brilliancy and better definition.

3. Contrast. This depends on the use of a fluorescent material of heavy atomic weight, such as $BaPtCN_4$, in which the fluorescent atom is the platinum atom and not the barium atom, since absorption takes place in the region of the K and L platinum spectral lines. With the presence of this heavy atom, variations of absorption and fluorescence can be obtained as the hardness of the exciting radiation varies. Additional contrast may be obtained if greenish fluorescent emission screens are used and if the general illumination in the x-ray room is strong red light such as supplied by a bright photographic ruby light bulb.

4. Absence of after-glow. Successive exposures to the exciting x-radiation must be spaced for sufficient time to elapse so that the accompanying phosphorescence, if present, has had time to decay below the threshold of absolute visibility of the eye. The after-glow phosphorescence can be controlled by dilution of the sensitive material with insensitive crystals, but unfortunately at the expense of its original brilliancy.

5. Protection. The fluoroscopic screen is mounted in a frame covered with a lead glass plate $\frac{3}{16}$ in. or more in thickness, to protect the

operator from x-radiations. A fine-focus x-ray tube driven at 88 to 105 kv peak and 3 to 5 ma is usually recommended to give sharp images.

INTENSIFYING SCREENS

The blue fluorescing screens are used for roentgenographic work. The x-ray film is pressed in close contact between the active faces of two such screens. X-ray photographic films are coated on both sides (duplitized), thus permitting the photographically active blue fluorescent emissions from the activated surface of each screen to irradiate the film. Calcium tungstate is nearly universally used in the production of intensifying screens because its region of maximum fluorescence is between 3570 and 5100 Å. As seen in Fig. I-21 this emission band lies within the spectral photographic-sensitivity region of the x-ray film.

The older forms of intensifying screens were merely sheets of cardboard coated with the fluorescent material. In the present type of intensifying screens the calcium tungstate is introduced into the celluloid binding material itself. This type of screen is washable and flexible, and it can be closely pressed to the photographic material so as to reduce distortion of the photographic image.

In the manufacture of intensifying screens the following factors are kept in mind for high-quality work.

1. Speed refers to the relative amount of x-radiation required to produce a developable photographic image when films are used with or without screens. If a given product, distance × milliampere × kilovolt-peak × time, produces a desired photographic density with no screens, and the same density can be obtained with the aid of screens in one fifth the time, using the same x-ray intensity, then the screens are said to have a speed factor of 5 to 1 at that intensity. A cassette containing a good double screen should possess a speed factor from 5 or 6 to 1.

The major factor used in controlling the speed of screens is the size of the calcium tungstate crystals. Ordinarily, the larger the crystals (other factors being constant), the faster the screens. The screen speed also varies with the x-ray tube's peak voltage excitation, i.e., effective wavelength; in general, the higher the kilovolt-peak, the faster are the screens.

2. Grain is usually caused by the use of too large crystals of calcium tungstate or the presence of impurities. Screens of very high speed must of necessity be grainy, owing to the large crystals used. A compromise is always made by the manufacturer in the size of the crystals in order that maximum speed may be obtained with minimum of grain. Too much grain will materially mar the diagnostic value of a film in

radiographs of the chest, sinus, mastoid, or small-body localization, or in industrial work where castings and welded seams are examined for blow holes or faults.

3. Lag due to phosphorescence of the crystals after the x-radiation exposure has ceased is caused by impurities in the calcium tungstate. A cassette fitted with a screen possessing lag should be unloaded immediately after an exposure and not reloaded with photographic film until the phosphorescence has entirely disappeared. A screen may be tested for lag as follows: Lay a small piece of lead, a bunch of keys, or some metal object on a cassette containing the screens under examination, but with no film between the screens. Subject the empty cassette with superimposed opaque metal objects to a moderately long exposure. Take the cassette to the photographic dark room and place a film in the cassette. Close the screens over the film and allow it to stand for ten minutes. Develop the film in the normal manner. If any appreciable lag is present, an image of the opaque metal object will be visible on the film.

BIBLIOGRAPHY

1913   COOLIDGE, W. D., *Phys. Rev.*, **2**, 409.
1915   DUANE, W., and F. L. HUNT, *Phys. Rev.*, **6**, 166.
1916   HULL, A. W., *Gen. Elec. Rev.*, **19**, 603.
1918   ULREY, C. T., *Phys. Rev.*, **11**, 401.
1921   HEWLETT, C. W., *Phys. Rev.*, **17**, 284.
1921   RICHTMYER, F. K., *Phys. Rev.*, **18**, 13.
1922   DUANE, W., and K. C. MAZUMDER, *Proc. Natl. Acad. Sci.*, **8**, 45.
1924   CROWTHER, J. A., *Proc. Roy. Soc.*, **B96**, 207.
1924   LINDHARDT, S. V., *Strahlentherapie*, **16**, 754.
1925   MUTSCHELLER, A., *Am. J. Roentgenol.*, **13**, 65.
1925   REGAUD, C., *Paris Med.*, **1**, 113.
1926   KULENKAMPFF, H., *Ann. Physik*, **79**, 97.
1926   PACKARD, C., *J. Cancer Research*, **10**, 319.
1926   WOO, Y. H., *Phys. Rev.*, **28**, 426.
1927   FEROUX, R., and C. REGAUD, *Compt. rend.*, **97**, 330.
1927   LEIST, M., *Strahlentherapie*, **24**, 268.
1928   DUANE, W., *Am. J. Roentgenol.*, **20**, 241.
1928   WARREN, S. L., *Physiol. Rev.*, **8**, 92.
1929   MAYNEORD, W. V., *The Physics of X-Ray Therapy*, J. and A. Churchill, London.
1930   NICHOLAS, W. W., *J. Research Natl. Bur. Standards*, **5**, 843.
1930   TAYLOR, L. S., *J. Research Natl. Bur. Standards*, **5**, 517.
1930   TAYLOR, L. S., and G. SINGER, *J. Research Natl. Bur. Standards*, **5**, 507.
1930   WYCKOFF, R. W. G., *J. Exptl. Med.*, **52**, 435.
1933   ZEHNDER, L., *Helv. Phys. Acta*, **6**, 608.
1934   RADIOLOGICAL SOCIETY OF NORTH AMERICA, " Report of Committee on Standardization of X-Ray Measurements," *Radiology*, **22**, 289.

1934 WEATHERWAX, J. L., *Physics of Radiology*, Paul B. Hoeber, New York, N.Y.
1935 STARK, J., *Physik. Z.*, **36**, 280.
1937 FIFTH INTERNATIONAL CONGRESS OF RADIOLOGY, *Radiology*, **29**, 634.
1938 SINGER, G., L. S. TAYLOR, and A. L. CHARLTON, *J. Research Natl. Bur. Standards*, **21**, 783.
1939 GOODSPEED, T. H., and F. M. UBER, *Bot. Rev.*, **5**, 1.
1939 QUIMBY, E. H., *The Physical Basis of Radiation Therapy, A Syllabus of Lectures*, Memorial Hospital, New York, New York.
1941 FAILLA, G., " Biological Effects of Ionizing Radiations," a review, *J. Applied Phys.*, **12**, 279.

Chapter II

APPLIED RADIOACTIVITY

At the meeting of the Academy of Science in Paris, on the twenty-fourth of February, 1896, Henri Becquerel read his epoch-making paper in which he announced that compounds of uranium emitted radiations that were able to affect a photographic plate through an envelope opaque to light.

Röntgen had just previously announced (1895) that x-rays appeared to originate from those parts of his discharge tubes which fluoresced intensely. Becquerel at this time was investigating the cause of phosphorescent emissions. He apparently reasoned that a direct connection must exist between the cause of phosphorescence and the x-rays producing the fluorescence in Röntgen's vacuum tubes, since both fogged a photographic plate enclosed in a light-tight envelope. It was, however, the accidental fogging of a photographic plate by means of a sample of uranium mineral not previously activated to fluorescence by sunlight that led him to the conclusion that fluorescence had nothing to do with the fogging of a covered photographic plate. His conclusion was that some active radiation was emitted spontaneously from the uranium mineral. He coined the word " radioactive " to designate this type of active radiation.

After Becquerel's discovery, numerous substances were examined for similar properties, and as a result the radioactive properties of the uranium-radium, actinium, and thorium families of elements were established. Mme. Curie, for instance, succeeded in isolating minute quantities of two highly radioactive substances from uranium minerals, to which she gave the names polonium and radium.

Rutherford, by 1899, through a series of brilliant investigations, conclusively showed that the radiations continuously emitted by uranium could be separated into two types. He called the first " alpha rays." These were easily absorbed by a few thin sheets of paper and produced intense ionization in the air through which they passed. The second, a more penetrating type, he called " beta rays." These beta rays have speeds ranging from three to ten times the speed of alpha rays and are able to penetrate several centimeters of air or even 1 mm of aluminum.

Subsequently Villard (1900) discovered that a third and very penetrating type of radiation was also associated with beta-ray emissions from uranium minerals, and these were designated by the third letter in the alphabet, namely, " gamma rays."

By 1913 Rutherford and Soddy had coordinated the various radioactive processes and proposed an acceptable theory of spontaneous disintegration of their " nuclear atom model " to account for the radioactivity of the atom. They suggested that the nuclear disintegration was explosive and was accompanied by the ejection of an alpha particle or if the explosion resulted in the ejection of a beta particle then the disintegration was accompanied by the emission of a gamma ray. The ejected alpha particle was shown to be a particle of matter comparable to a helium atom which had lost its two planetary electrons, i.e., a helium nucleus. The beta particles were found to be high-speed negative electrons, and the accompanying gamma-ray emission was discovered to have the properties of x-radiation of exceptionally short wavelength.

As the result of the explosive emission of an alpha particle, any atom drops in the scale of atomic numbers by two units and there is a loss in atomic weight equal to the atomic weight of a helium nucleus. Since the helium nucleus is equal to four mass units, its loss will reduce the mass of the parent atom by four units. This residue is a new, but less massive, atom having physical and chemical properties different from its parent atom.

DISINTEGRATION OF RADIUM

Radioactive changes are accompanied by the emission of alpha or beta particles. They are never emitted simultaneously. All radium salts actively emit alpha and beta particles with the accompanying gamma radiations. Usually gamma radiations accompany beta-particle ejections. Sometimes weak gamma radiations also accompany alpha-particle emissions.

The radium atom is an unstable complex structure. Its atomic weight is 226, and its atomic number is 88. Its compact unstable massive nucleus can be represented pictorially as surrounded by 88 planetary electrons. We can imagine this nucleus undergoing a sudden explosive readjustment with the emission of an alpha particle of characteristic speed. The residue is the radon atom of atomic weight 222. It is a radioactive inert gas sometimes called radium emanation.

This and the subsequent transformations are shown schematically in Fig. II-1; all but the last atoms contain radioactive nuclei. A radioactive nucleus is one which spontaneously changes itself into another nucleus of another element by emitting a charged particle.

Radon gas is a short-lived residue which rapidly disintegrates with the liberation of alpha particles and changes into a solid, radium A. In turn, this element breaks up into radium B in an analogous way. These and subsequent decomposition products are found adhering to the walls of a vessel which originally contained radon gas and which make these surfaces radioactive.

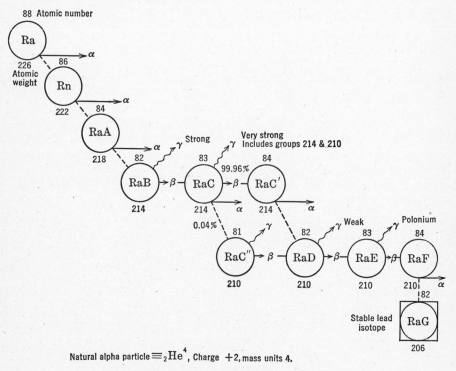

Fig. II–1. Radium and its family of products.

Radium B, however, undergoes a different type of change, one accompanied by the emission of a gamma radiation and of a high-speed beta particle. Since the gamma ray is a short-wave x-radiation, its emission results in no appreciable loss in mass. The beta particle is a high-speed negative electron. The ejection of such an electron is accompanied by an inappreciable loss in atomic mass; the new element, radium C, is therefore considered as having the same atomic mass as its parent atom radium B.

Biophysically speaking, this and the next group of radioactive nuclear changes are the most important links in this chain of reactions. We depend upon the characteristic gamma radiations at this stage of the degenerating process to furnish the necessary effective, deeply penetrating radiations used in gamma-radiation therapy.

The schematic disintegration diagram indicates that radium C may undergo disintegration in either of two ways. By the emission of an alpha particle it degenerates to RaC'', or by the emission of a beta particle and a gamma ray it changes to radium C'. As the alpha-ray process of degeneration occurs in only 0.04 per cent of the atoms present, for all practical purposes this transformation product is negligible. The other 99.96 per cent of the radium C atoms participating undergo a high-speed beta-particle ejection with its accompanying gamma radiation. The resulting product is radium C', of atomic weight 214. Radium C' in turn degenerates with the emission of an alpha particle to radium D. By successive steps radium D degenerates into radium G, a stable isotope of lead of atomic weight 206, which is the end of the uranium-radium chain.

DECAY CONSTANT

In the process of disintegration of a radioactive element, we are in reality observing only the statistical nature of the disintegration of a large group of atoms, in which, on the average, the number of atoms that are disintegrating each second is a constant fraction of those present at any given moment.

For instance, if we isolate 10,000 atoms which possess the property of disintegration at the rate of 2 per cent per second, then during the first second we would lose 200 atoms, leaving 9800. During the second second we would lose 2 per cent of 9800 or 196, leaving 9604. In the next second we again lose 2 per cent of these, etc.

We are here dealing with the exponential law of depreciation. Thus, if we let N be the number of atoms which survive after a time t, and N_0 the number originally present at time zero, then the above exponential law of depreciation of number is expressed thus:

$$N = N_0 e^{-\lambda t}$$

where λ is the constant indicating the rate of disintegration of the atoms.

The radioactive decay constant λ is defined as *that proportion of active matter which undergoes change each second*. The larger the value of this constant, the greater will be the activity of disintegration.

The magnitude of the decay constant of each of the therapeutically valuable radioactive atoms is shown in Table II-1.

TABLE II-1

Substance	Decay Constant λ per sec	Half-Value Period or Half-Life	Amount in Milligrams in Equilibrium with 1 Gram of Radium
Ra	1.38×10^{-11}	1590 yr.	1,000
Radon	2.097×10^{-6}	3.825 days	0.00625
RaA	3.79×10^{-3}	3.05 min	0.0000034
RaB	4.31×10^{-4}	26.8 min	0.000030
RaC	5.86×10^{-4}	19.7 min	0.000022
RaC '	10^{6}	10^{-6} sec	Negligible
RaC ''	8.75×10^{-3}	1.32 min	0.0000015
RaD	1.0×10^{-9}	22 yr	
RaE	1.61×10^{-6}	5.0 days	0.0081
RaF (polonium)	5.73×10^{-8}	140 days	0.22
RaG	Stable		

The decay constant (λ) for radium is 1.38×10^{-11} per sec. This means that, in a group of 10^{11} atoms, 1.38 on the average disintegrate per second. One gram of radium contains $6.07 \times 10^{23}/226$, or 26.8×10^{20} atoms. Then $26.8 \times 10^{20} \times 1.38 \times 10^{-11}$ or 3.7×10^{10} atoms in each gram of radium disintegrate per second.

The decay constant for radon is 2.097×10^{-6} per sec, which means that approximately 2 atoms in every million disintegrate per second. In 1 gram of radon gas, $570,000 \times 10^{10}$ atoms disintegrate per second, a rate which indicates that radon is more than 150,000 times as active as an equal mass of radium.

Suppose that we have 1000 relative units of radon and 1 hour later we wish to use this material; how many units will still be available? The following formula can be used to calculate N, the number of units available after 1 hour for which $t = 3600$ sec.

$$N = N_0 e^{-\lambda t}$$

$$N = 1000 e^{-2.097 \times 10^{-6} \times 3600}$$

$$\log_e \left(\frac{N}{1000} \right) = -75.06 \times 10^{-4}$$

$$\log_{10} \left(\frac{N}{1000} \right) = -\frac{75.06 \times 10^{-4}}{2.3026} = -32.5 \times 10^{-4}$$

$$N = 993$$

HALF-LIFE

The number of seconds required for the radioactivity of a substance to fall to half its original value is called its half-life or half-value period. This value of t may be obtained by setting

$$\frac{N}{N_0} = e^{-\lambda t} = \frac{1}{2}$$

Then

$$\log_e 2 = \lambda t$$

or

$$\log_{10} 2 = \frac{\lambda t}{2.3026}$$

To illustrate what is meant by half-life of a radioactive substance one may use that therapeutically valuable radioactive gas radon. It disintegrates in a typical way by the emission of an alpha particle. Its decay constant is 2.097×10^{-6} per sec. Figure II–2 shows graphically

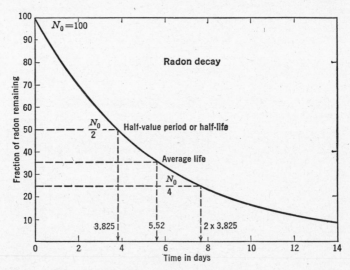

FIG. II–2. The percentage of radon remaining after any time recorded in days. N_0 is taken as an arbitrary activity of 100 units.

how radon disintegrates in the course of 14 days. Note that half of the original number N_0 remains after 3.825 days, and one-fourth after 7.65 days. It is simpler to calculate the number of days it takes for the original amount to reduce to half-value, by using the above decay law. For λ substitute the value 2.097×10^{-6}, and solve for t.

$$\log_{10} 2 = \frac{2.097 \times 10^{-6}t}{2.3026}$$

$$t = 3.825 \text{ days}$$

The quantity $1/\lambda$ is that average time in seconds in which the number of original atoms is reduced to $1/e$ ($= 0.36788$) of their original count. This is called the *average life* of a radioactive substance, even though some of its atoms may exist for only a short time and others for a long time. The average life of radon is $1/\lambda = 1/(2.097 \times 10^{-6})$ sec $=$ 476,871 sec $= 5.52$ days.

Radioactive Equilibrium

The following example illustrates what is meant by an equilibrium state. Suppose that you are given a closed vessel containing many millions of microorganisms. At the close of each day you are asked to investigate the number of deaths and the number of births. Suppose that at the end of 30 days you find that the birth rate equals the death rate. You have found that an equilibrium state has been established if from then on the death rate equals the birth rate.

Similarly the population content of 1 gram of freshly prepared radium sulphate is about 26.8×10^{20} molecules. In the first day (about one-millionth of these) 3.2×10^{15} of the radium atoms will disintegrate to form the atoms of the radon gas. As soon as some radon atoms are formed, however, some of them will disintegrate, so that by the end of 3.825 days half of them have disintegrated. In this process about 16 per cent of the radon atoms disintegrate per day. Hence at the end of the first day 16 per cent of 3.2×10^{15} atoms have disintegrated, leaving 2.7×10^{15} radon atoms. By the end of the second day 3.2×10^{15} $+ 2.7 \times 10^{15}$, or 5.9×10^{15}, are present, of which 0.9×10^{15} disintegrate, leaving 5×10^{15} atoms. By the end of the third day there are 8.2×10^{15} atoms, of which 1.3×10^{15} disintegrate. At the end of about 30 days nearly as many radon atoms are disintegrating as are supplied by the disintegrating radium atoms. Radioactive equilibrium has then been established between radium and radon. The maximum amount of radon that can accumulate from a given quantity of radium under these circumstances is called its equilibrium amount. Table II–1 shows the various amounts of the radioactive substances in equilibrium with 1 gm of radium.

Figure II–3 shows the increase in number of radon atoms, despite their decomposition in the presence of the more slowly decomposing

radium, during the course of 35 days.   Note particularly how the growth
of radon conforms to an exponential rise in time, and that for all practical purposes it attains its maximum value in about 30 days.

A mathematical analysis of radon equilibrating in the presence of
radium leads to the following general law

$$N = N_{max} \left(1 - e^{-\lambda_2 t} \right)$$

where $N_{max} = (\lambda_1/\lambda_2)N_0$.   Here N_0 is the number of radium atoms
originally present, λ_1 the decay constant of radium, and λ_2 the decay
constant of radon.   Since the radium atom has a very long life compared
to the radon atom $(\lambda_2 > \lambda_1)$ and no radon is present initially, the above
expression describes the results accurately.

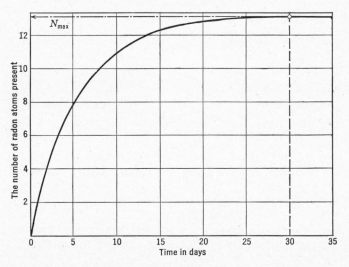

Fig. II–3.   The net increase in number of radon atoms in the presence of radium.
Despite the rapid decay, radon is formed at the same rate as it disintegrates at about
the thirtieth day.   After this N_{max} maintains its constant value.

Radon, when used for therapeutic purposes, is pumped off the radium
and sealed in small capsules.   Initially such a capsule contains only
radon gas.   Radon progressively disintegrates, and the successive
products of decay are RaA, RaB, RaC, etc.   The state of equilibrium
between radon and its products is reached in about 4 hours.   The rate
of decay of radon cannot be neglected in calculating the equilibrium
of the end products despite its rapid decay.   The relative number of
these atoms is therefore different when in equilibrium with radon than
when in equilibrium with radium.   This type of equilibrium is referred
to as " transient."   In *transient equilibrium* the products RaA, RaB,

and RaC (in the presence of radon) are about 0.05 per cent, 0.5 per cent, and 1.0 per cent greater, respectively, than those corresponding with the equilibrium mixture values of radium shown in Table II–1.

NATURE OF THE RADIATIONS

A sample of radium salt, after radioactive equilibrium has been attained, will emit alpha rays, beta rays, and gamma radiation. The alpha rays are rather massive particles carrying a positive charge of electricity; the beta rays are negative electrons with rather large velocities of ejection.

To demonstrate these properties put a small sample of radium salt in the bottom of a cylindrical hole in a lead block and then place the block so that the vertically emitted rays pass at right angles through an intense magnetic field furnished by a powerful electromagnet, as shown in Fig. II–4.

The magnetic lines of force are represented as entering into and perpendicular to the plane of the paper. It is found that the beta particles are deflected to the right and the alpha particles to the left. The beta particles are observed to move on the arc of a circle while they are in the magnetic field. Their deflection to the right proves them to be negatively charged. The alpha particles are observed to undergo a similar deflection to the left; hence they are positively charged. The relative curvature of the paths depends on their relative values of e/m and velocity, such that $Hev = mv^2/R$. Here H is the intensity of the magnetic field, and R the radius of curvature of the circular paths.

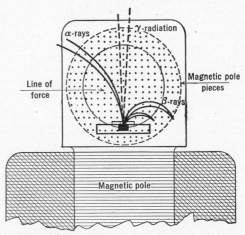

Fig. II–4. Depicting the deflection of alpha and beta rays in a uniform magnetic field, set perpendicularly to the paper and directed downward. Gamma rays not deflectable.

The vertically emitted group of rays, called gamma radiations, suffer no deflection. This lack of deflection shows that they carry no net charge. They have been identified as radiant energy comparable to very short-wave x-rays.

Alpha Rays

Alpha particles are ejected as if they were high-velocity projectiles originating in the nucleus. They are doubly charged positive fragments of matter and have a structure like that of the helium nucleus. On the average they have a velocity equal to about one-twentieth the velocity of light. They are able to penetrate about 6.97 cm of air at standard atmospheric pressure before dissipating their energy. A single particle during its passage through air produces as many as 150,000 ions by collision.

TABLE II–2

Ranges in Solid Elements as Compared with Water and Mica

Alpha particles of RaC′. Units of range are 10^{-4} cm.

Element	Al	Ag	Ni	Au	Pt	Water	Mica
Range	40.6	19.2	18.4	14.0	12.8	60.0	36

TABLE II–3

Beta-Ray Absorption Coefficients (μ) in Aluminum

Elements	RaB	RaC + RaC″	RaD	RaE
μ cm^{-1}	890 80 13	50	5500	45.5
Velocity, 10^{10} cm/sec	1.08–2.47	1.14–2.96	0.96–1.20	2.05–2.84

Velocity of light is 3×10^{10} cm/sec.

The number of alpha particles emitted from 1 gram of pure radium per second is 3.7×10^{10}. When radium is in radioactive equilibrium with its products, the same number of particles is also emitted per second by each of its important alpha rayers, viz., Rn, RaA, RaC′, and RaF. Consequently, the number of alpha particles from 1 gram of radium in radioactive equilibrium is $5 \times 3.7 \times 10^{10}$, or 18.5×10^{10}.

We are now in a position to appreciate the terrific bombardment that the walls of a glass ampule are subjected to when they enclose as little as a milligram of radium salt.

The ranges in some metals used as alpha-ray filters are listed in Table II–2. These data show what thickness of metallic capsules can be used for radium containers which will completely absorb the alpha particles. The range in mica is about 0.036 mm. Since mica and glass may be considered comparable it can be appreciated why a glass radium needle with 0.04-mm wall thickness is sufficient to absorb all the alpha particles. An aluminum filter 0.04 mm thick is sufficient protection against the physiological effects of alpha particles when open radium applicators are used in dermatology.

BETA RAYS

The beta rays from the disintegration products of radium consist of streams of negative electrons possessing a wide range of velocities, the swiftest having a velocity nearly equal to that of light. RaC is outstanding in this respect, as seen in Table II-3.

One naturally is curious about the origin of such very high-speed electrons. It has been determined experimentally that, on the average, for every pair of disintegrating RaB and RaC atoms, 2.3 electrons are emitted, about 1.25 coming from RaB and 1.05 from RaC. These electrons may be either nuclear electrons or planetary electrons. The accompanying gamma rays have their origin in the nucleus. The number of electrons in excess of the one coming from the nucleus are planetary electrons, emitted as the result of the absorption of the gamma rays as they pass through the planetary electrons, and are referred to as photoelectrons.

RaE emits only extremely weak gamma radiation. No photoelectrons are mixed in with the disintegration electrons which come from the nucleus. Emeleus [1924] actually found that, in the disintegration of each RaE atom, only one electron was emitted.

RaD emits statistically about 1.5 electrons at each atomic disintegration. It was found that two of every three electrons are slow disintegration electrons, and the third is emitted with high speed because of the internal conversion of the gamma radiation into electron emissions.

BETA-RAY DISTRIBUTION OF ENERGY

The distribution of energy among the emitted beta rays is determined by their electron spectra, obtained by means of their relative deflections by a magnetic field. As shown in Fig. II-5, the strong magnetic field bends the negative electrons into arcs of circles. Their radii of curvature are proportional to their momentum (mv) of emission. Chadwick as early as 1914 showed that the magnetic field acted as a lens to focus all those electrons leaving the source with the same velocity. Advantage is taken of this fact in the design of a device for measuring the velocity distribution of a source of beta-ray electrons. The source, in the form of some radioactive material deposited on a fine wire, is fixed at S, Fig. II-5, perpendicular to the plane of the diagram. A wide slit is placed at A. Beyond, in the same plane with the slit is placed a photographic plate. The whole is contained in a light-tight evacuated box and placed between the poles of an electromagnet, with its field perpendicular to the plane of the paper. The magnetic field intensity

H is varied by the current exciting the pole pieces of the electromagnet. The result is that electrons of the same velocity, though shot up at different angles, will describe circles of radius *R*, and converge to a line focus on the photographic plate.   Groups of low-velocity electrons

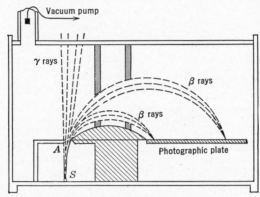

Fɪɢ. II–5.   A form of beta-ray spectrograph.   This shows how the magnetic field, perpendicular to the plane of the paper, acts as a lens to focus the electrons.   First used by Chadwick in 1914.

converge nearer to the source than the high-velocity groups.   For low-speed electrons the relative curvature of path is determined by $Hev = m_0v^2/R$.   For the very high-speed electrons the relativity mass of the electron must be used, so that

$$HR = \frac{m_0c}{e} \frac{v/c}{\sqrt{1 - v^2/c^2}}$$

where m_0 is the rest mass of the electron of charge *e* and velocity *v*, and *c* is the velocity of light.

The photographic images of the radiative source are lines lying parallel to the linear source of the beta rays.   The line images due to the higher-velocity electrons are found farther from the slit.   If radon had been used as the beta-ray source, the developed photographic plate would have shown a composite effect, a general background darkening with superimposed sharp linear images.   A photometric analysis of such a plate is shown diagrammatically in Fig. II–6.   The line images appear as humps on the curve.   These are homogeneous velocity groups of emission.   This curve indicates that theirs is a relatively small effect as compared to the numbers producing the continuous electron spectrum.   The latter produce the general background darkening of the photographic plate and are represented by the area under the broken curve.

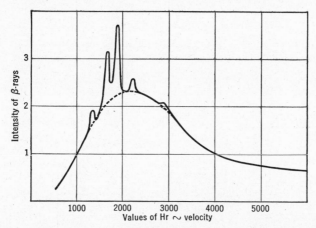

FIG. II-6. This is the beta-ray spectrum of radium B originally obtained by R. W. Gurney [1925]. It shows the velocity distribution of the beta rays from a radon source. The humps are homogeneous velocity groups superimposed on the general electron emission limited by the broken curve. The number of electrons composing the humps are small compared with those in the continuous spectrum, so that one practically always deals with a decidedly non-homogeneous distribution of velocities.

TABLE II-4

PROMINENT HOMOGENEOUS BETA-RAY VELOCITY GROUPS

Relative Intensity	Energy in Kilovolts
Radium B	
17	37.25
11	49.83
80	152.9
91	206.7
100	263.8
16	337.9
Radium C	
7.6	519.9
2.4	1037
4.7	1334
Radium D	
50	30.9
20	43.3
10	46.1

The relative intensity of these radiations is very small as compared with the general total background radiation. Composite results of Ellis and Skinner, *Proc. Roy. Soc.*, **A 105**, 60, 1924; Ellis and Astor, *ibid.*, **119**, 645, 1928; Ellis and Wooster, *ibid.*, **114**, 276, 1927; Ellis and Astor, *ibid.*, **129**, 180, 1930.

The beta-ray electron spectrum, therefore, may be divided into two parts: (1) the disintegration electrons forming the continuous velocity spectrum, and (2) the photoelectrons, the characteristic line spectral images composing the homogeneous velocity groups.

Figure II–7 shows the relative intensities of the continuous beta-ray spectral velocity distributions emitted by RaB, RaC, and RaE without the superimposed photoelectric emissions. They all possess different but definite upper limits of velocity. These upper limits can also be

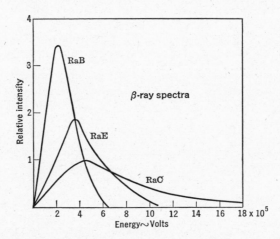

FIG. II–7. These are the beta-ray spectra of RaB, RaE, and RaC with homogeneous velocity groups omitted. RaB and RaC are from data by Gurney [1925], and RaE is reduced to the same scale from data by Madgwick [1927].

shown to exist by absorption methods. If aluminum is used as the absorber of the beta rays from RaE, it is found that a layer of aluminum 1.7 mm thick must be used to absorb the electrons having the highest velocity. The highest velocity electron emitted by RaC are stopped by 5 mm of aluminum.

Radium B (Table II–4) shows prominent photoelectric emission groups in the neighborhood of 263 kv; the very simple electron spectrum of RaD possesses a moderately prominent emission of electrons at 31 kv.

For therapeutic use these homogeneous velocity groups are not separated from the continuous velocity distribution groups, but they must be kept in mind when beta-ray filters are used.

ABSORPTION OF BETA RAYS

A thin-walled glass tube of radium salt or radon gas will emit beta rays and gamma radiations due to the decay products. The beta-ray emission, as shown above, is not a homogeneous velocity group. If the electronic emission were, for simplicity's sake, confined to a narrow cylindrical pencil and were allowed to impinge normally on a metal filter, the electrons would be subject to so much scattering in their passage through the metal that some of them would be found to be re-emitted on the incident side of the filter. Even under these simplified conditions it would be found that an original parallel beam had become diffused very rapidly.

TABLE II–5

RELATIVE AMOUNTS OF RADIATION TRANSMITTED BY VARIOUS METAL FILTERS

Metal	Thickness mm	Amount of Radiation Relative to Amount through 0.5 mm Pt Considered 100	Composition of Radiation	
			% Beta	% Gamma
Brass	0.5	160	33	67
	1.0	111	8	92
	2.0	100	0	100
	3.0	95	0	100
	4.0	92	0	100
Silver	0.5	128	17	83
	1.0	103	0	100
	2.0	94	0	100
	3.0	90	0	100
Lead	0.5	118	12	88
	1.0	97	0	100
	2.0	88	0	100
	3.0	83	0	100
Gold or platinum	0.2	135	22	78
	0.3	111	9	91
	0.5	100	0	100
	1.0	88	0	100
	1.5	82	0	100
	2.0	78	0	100
	3.0	73	0	100

By Courtesy of E. H. Quimby, Memorial Hospital, New York.

The absorption laws governing the loss of electrons, possessing random velocities, as they pass through matter are very complicated. For all practical therapeutic purposes the electrons which pass through a filtering metal can be considered as suffering an exponential reduction in number.

When a flat radium salt " applicator " possessing a cover impervious to alpha rays is applied to the skin under clinical conditions, it is of importance to know the filter thickness that must be used to remove all the low-velocity beta particles in order to control the therapeutic effects.

It has been found that 1 mm of aluminum reduces a 100 per cent electron intensity to 1.3 per cent, indicating that probably only the high-velocity electrons from RaB and RaC are coming through. The data of Table II–5 obtained by E. H. Quimby [1939] show that for all practical purposes a 2-mm brass, 1.0-mm silver, 1.0-mm lead, 0.5-mm gold, or 0.5-mm platinum filter will remove all the beta rays emitted by a radium source.

ENERGY OF GAMMA RADIATIONS

Radium will attain its radioactive equilibrium with its products in about one month. Under these conditions it will emit about 88.8 per cent of the radioactive energy as alpha rays, 4.5 per cent as beta rays, and 6.7 per cent as gamma radiation. The short-wavelength gamma radiation is primarily due to the disintegration of RaB and RaC. Of these two, the gamma radiations from RaB are much more easily absorbed than those from RaC. The gamma radiations from RaD are also comparatively soft, and moderate filtering removes them completely.

TABLE II–6

GAMMA RAYS FROM RaB → RaC. MOST INTENSE RADIATIONS

Energy in Kilovolts	Relative Intensity	Wavelengths 10^{-8} cm
53.8	53	0.22
243	25	0.050
297	30	0.041
354	40	0.035

GAMMA RAYS FROM RaC → RaC′, RaC → RaC″, RaC → RaD, AND RaC″ → RaD

612	30	0.020
941	7	0.013
1130	13	0.0109
1426	16	0.0086

Composite results from Ellis and Aston, *Proc. Roy. Soc.*, **A 129**, 180, 1930.

Gamma radiations are comparable to x-rays but of shorter wavelength. Table II–6 shows some of their wavelengths and their equivalent energies in electron volts. They range from 50 to 1400 kv. An x-ray tube driven at 1.5 million volts difference of potential will emit wavelengths approaching the shortest wavelengths of the gamma radiations emitted by RaC.

ABSORPTION OF GAMMA RADIATION BY MATTER

The reduction in intensity of gamma radiations by an absorbing substance takes place, like the reduction of intensity of x-rays, in two distinct ways: by true absorption and by scattering. In true absorption the energy of the gamma beam is completely absorbed by an atomic structure, and the result is emission of planetary electrons (photoelectric emission). The scattering loss takes place as if the gamma radiation were composed of photons or bundles of energy.

Photons colliding with electrons in the filter material communicate energy to the electrons, so that the electrons are set in motion. The penetrating photon is deflected by the electron from its path (see Compton effect) after collision, and hence scattered. The scattered photon in this act, having lost some of its energy by the collision, moves off with less energy content. The number of photons emitted by radioactive material used in radiotherapy that suffer no energy loss in this scattering process is inappreciable.

When gamma radiation of very short wavelength (hard gamma rays) passes through low-atomic-weight filters composed of aluminum, water, or tissue, the reduction in intensity of the beam is almost entirely due to scattering. This explains the comparative loss in different kinds of tissue as shown in Table II–7. As the atomic number of the absorber increases, the loss due to the photoelectric process becomes more pronounced.

TABLE II–7

ABSORPTION OF GAMMA RAYS BY VARIOUS KINDS OF BEEF TISSUE

Type of Tissue	Per Cent of Gamma Rays Absorbed in First Centimeter
Solid bone	13.0
Porous bone	7.5
Liver	7.4
Spleen	7.3
Muscle	6.9
Brain	6.6
Fat	6.5
Lung	4.5

By Courtesy of G. Failla [1921].

TABLE II-8

ABSORPTION BY LEAD OF GAMMA RAYS FROM RADIUM C

Thickness of Lead cm	Ionization Arbitrary Units
0.3	100
1.0*	61.6
2.0	33.1
3.0	19.9
4.0	11.7
5.0	7.07
6.0	4.26
7.0	2.57
8.0	1.62
9.0	1.00
10.0	0.63
15.0	0.07
20.0	0.01

* A 0.1-cm lead filter removes all beta rays.

TABLE II-9

COEFFICIENTS OF ABSORPTION

Gamma radiation
Value of μ after having traversed an 8-mm lead fore-filter

Filter	0–2.5 mm	2.5–5.0 mm	5–10 mm	10–15 mm
Platinum	1.17	....	....	....
Lead	0.64	0.56	0.48	0.44
Zinc	0.28	0.27	0.25	0.27
Aluminum	0.11	0.11	0.11	0.11
Glass	0.087	0.087	0.087	0.087
Water	0.34	0.34	0.34	0.34

For gamma as well as x-rays the photoelectric absorption in high-atomic-number elements is approximately proportional to the fourth power of the atomic number of the filter and to the cube of the wavelength of the incident radiation. The *total absorption coefficient* μ is therefore made up of two parts, the coefficient of photoelectric absorption τ, plus the coefficient of diffusion or scattering σ, so that $\mu = \tau + \sigma$.

A useful table of transmission characteristics in the form of the relative amounts of radiation transmitted by various metal filters, complied by E. H. Quimby, is reproduced in detail in Table II-5. Table II-8 and Table II-9 show what may be expected in the way of absorption by different practical filters. The protective value of 20 cm of lead used in the construction of radium storage vaults is quite obvious from Table II–8. The data in Table II–9 are presented to show the effect of increased filter thickness on the coefficients of absorption of gamma radiations after having passed through 8 mm of preliminary filtering by lead. These data show that there is practically no change in the total absorption coefficient (μ) with increased filter thickness up to 1.5 cm for the low-atomic-number elements, and therefore no hardening in the rays can take place through the use of these filters.

The absorption is very nearly proportional to the density of the filter, and for comparison it can be stated that gamma radiations are approximately 200 times more penetrating than beta rays.

If the total radiations from Ra(B + C), after passing through 5 cm of lead, are examined it will be found that the total absorption coefficient no longer decreases with increase in filter thickness, and that no further hardening of the gamma radiation takes place if greater filter thicknesses are used.

In external radium therapy, where only gamma radiations are desired, the metal capsule containing the radioactive material can be used to remove all alpha and beta rays. Further filtration much beyond this point in order to obtain harder gamma radiation is, according to many authorities, of little practical value.

In the absorption process the frequency of a scattering process increases rapidly with hardness of the incident gamma radiation as compared with that of the photoelectric process. For the hard gamma radiations from RaC with wavelength 0.005 Å a scattering process occurs 20 times more frequently than an absorption process. In absorbers of low atomic number, such as carbon, the above ratio may be from 3000 to 8000 times as large. In very-low-atomic-weight material comparable to tissue or water the photoelectric process is negligible as compared with scattering.

Gamma Radiations Are Not Homogeneous

None of the gamma radiators of radium emit a homogeneous gamma radiation. The emissions, however, can be resolved into a few prominent, practically homogeneous wavelength groups, each possessing an appreciably different absorption coefficient, or what should be designated as a coefficient of reduction of intensity. For instance, Table II–11 shows that in the decomposition of the radium products absorption measurements indicate roughly four groups of more or less homogeneous radiations. For comparison, the radiations are designated as soft, medium, hard, and very hard. In Table II–12 are listed the comparable

TABLE II–11

COEFFICIENT OF REDUCTION OF INTENSITY OF GAMMA RADIATION IN
ALUMINUM (μ cm^{-1})

Element	Soft	Medium	Hard	Very Hard
RaB	230	40	0.57	
RaC + RaC''			1.49	0.23, 0.127
RaD		45	1.17	
RaE				0.24
RaF	2700	46		

TABLE II–12

WAVELENGTH LIMITS OF GAMMA RAYS

Element	λ in 10^{-8} cm	Energy in Electron Volts
RaB	0.23 –0.035	5.36×10^4–3.51×10^5
RaC + RaC''	0.209–0.0056	5.9×10^4–2.22×10^6
RaD	0.269	4.59×10^4

spectroscopic results obtained by Ellis and Skinner [1924]. These are
the therapeutically useful gamma radiations of more than average
intensity. For comparison, the equivalent calculated energy in electron
volts that must be used to excite an x-ray tube to produce the same
minimum wavelengths is shown in the last column.

ATOMIC NUCLEUS THE SOURCE OF GAMMA RAYS

In the process of radioactive disintegration it has been found that a
beta particle in the form of a nuclear electron is ejected. This ejection
is followed by the emission of a gamma ray. The emission of the disintegration electron leaves the new nucleus in a disturbed or " excited "
state, and as the nucleus settles down to its normal state it becomes the
nucleus of the next product. In the same way that optical and x-ray
spectra are characteristic frequencies emitted as the result of readjustment in the electron configuration of the atom, the gamma rays represent characteristic frequencies associated with the readjustment of the
structure of the nucleus. The greater proportion of the radiant energy,
because of nuclear readjustment after the emission of a nuclear electron,
escapes from the atom, but some of it is absorbed by its planetary electronic structure. Consequently planetary or photoelectrons are also
emitted. Their energy depends on the frequency of the gamma radiation and on the level from which the planetary electron is liberated.

If the nucleus emits gamma rays of several different frequencies, the result will be a series of groups of electrons emitted with velocities characteristic of their orbital origins. These orbital electrons account for the *beta-ray line spectrum* of the radioactive elements. In addition, further secondary effects take place. The removal of an electron from its orbital level will be followed by adjustment transitions giving rise to very hard x-radiations also characteristic of the electron configuration of the element.

The beta-ray photoelectron spectrum is a clue to the relative wavelength of the nuclear gamma radiation. Suppose that a gamma photon of energy content $h\nu$ is emitted as a result of a beta-particle ejection from the nucleus. The absorption of this energy in the K, L, $\cdots$ electron levels of the resulting atom will lead to electron emissions having energy $E_1 = h\nu - w_K$, $E_2 = h\nu - w_L$, $\cdots$, respectively, where w_K, w_L $\cdots$ denote the energies necessary to remove the photoelectron from its level. The energy of each electron group can be found from measurements of its magnetic deflection, and the absorption energies which are known from x-ray data. The frequency ν, and hence the wavelength of the gamma radiation which gives rise to the group, can therefore be calculated.

PHYSICAL PROPERTIES OF RADON

Radium, upon the emission of an alpha particle from its nucleus, degenerates into the inert gas radon.

Radon is the heaviest of the inert rare gases. Its boiling point is $-62°$ C, and its freezing point $-71°$ C.

Its coefficient of distribution between water and air at 20° C amounts to 0.255. It is readily soluble in water. It is easily occluded by solids such as hard rubber, celluloid, wax, carbon, and especially platinum and palladium. Solid salts of radium occlude as much as 65 per cent of radon. With increase in temperature the solubility decreases in strict accordance with Henry's law. The solubility is also reduced by the addition of salts to the water.

USES OF RADON

Radon is primarily used for medical purposes. The gas is compressed into small volumes containing sufficient radioactive material for the widely different requirements that have to be met in particular surgical and experimental needs. If placed under pressure it is confined in capillary tubes cut to various lengths, which are referred to as seeds.

Sources of Radon

Radium metal or any of its salts is a source of radon. Radium salts may be obtained commercially as chloride, bromide, nitrate, carbonate, or sulphate. The solubility at 20° C as bromide is 41.4, chloride 19.7, and nitrate 12.2 per cent by weight. Since the radioactive disintegration of radium is independent of its chemical combination and since the radon production depends only upon the actual amount of radium element present, one should refer to the content of a radium container as so many milligrams of radium element. For instance:

1 gram $RaCl_2$	contains 761 mg Ra element
1 gram $RaCl_2 \cdot 2H_2O$	contains 679 mg Ra element
1 gram $RaBr_2$	contains 586 mg Ra element
1 gram $RaBr_2 \cdot 2H_2O$	contains 536 mg Ra element
1 gram $RaCO_3$	contains 790 mg Ra element
1 gram $RaSO_4$	contains 702 mg Ra element

Definition of Curie

One curie is defined as the amount of radon in equilibrium with 1 gram of radium. The amount in equilibrium with 1 mg is 1 millicurie (1 mc). The number of atoms in 1 curie is 1.71×10^{16}.

The volume of radon in equilibrium with 1 gram of radium is 0.65 cu mm (6.5×10^{-6} gram).

TABLE II–13

Transient Activity of Radon

Initial increase in beta- and gamma-ray activity in a radon preparation, due to accumulation of RaA, RaB, and RaC

Time		Transient Activity
Hours	Minutes	Maximum equals 100
0	0	0
0	10	3.9
0	20	11.9
0	30	21.8
0	40	32.1
0	50	42.0
1	0	51.1
1	30	72.3
2	0	85.2
2	30	92.3
3	0	97.0
3	30	About 100

One gram of radium will produce 166 mc of radon daily. This amount will reduce by radioactive disintegration to 138.5 mc by the end of the first day and will disintegrate to 115.5 mc by the end of the second day. In the meantime, more radon will have been generated and will decompose in the same way, so that by the end of a month there will be available 995 mc in equilibrium with 1 gram of radium. For all practical purposes this amount is taken as 1000 mc, although 60 days are required for radium to come into complete equilibrium with all its disintegrative products.

A sample of the gas removed from the radium salt and concentrated into a capillary tube by pressure may have a " strength " as great as 100 mc. Owing to its disintegration, it will fall to a strength of 83.4 mc at the end of 1 day, to 69.6 mc at the end of 2 days, until at the end of 30 days its strength is only 0.45 mc. For its detailed change in strength refer to Table II–14.

RADON EXTRACTION PLANTS

Radon extraction and purification plants of a semi-automatic design were introduced in America by the late Professor William Duane of Harvard, and subsequently modified by Failla of the Memorial Hospital, New York City.

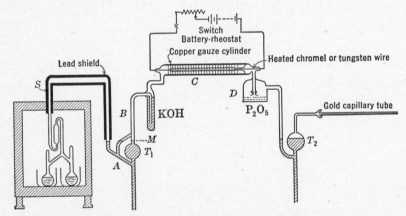

FIG. II–8. A semi-diagrammatic representation of a radon-extraction plant.

A typical installation may use 1 or more grams of radium bromide dissolved in dilute hydrochloric acid. It is usually divided into two portions of about 100 cc each and stored in 200-cc long-necked flasks. The flasks are joined at the top in such a way (Fig. II–8) that the accumulated gases can be led off through a continuous train of glass tubing through the top of a fireproof lead-lined safe to the purification apparatus. The safe may be 32 by 18 by 16 in., with 5-in. walls.

The whole purification plant is first well exhausted by a quick-action vacuum pump. Then the radon gas accumulates over the solutions and spreads into the lead-covered glass chamber S. The mercury trap T_1 must be lowered so as to allow the gas to fill the chambers A, B, C, D. When T_1 is raised the gas in A is pushed into the purification chambers B, C, D. Here the accumulated and compressed gases are passed over caustic potash to remove carbon dioxide. The chamber C contains a heated tungsten filament surrounded by a well-oxidized copper gauze. When the gases pass through this chamber the oxygen and hydrogen combine to form water vapor, which is removed by the phosphorus pentoxide tube D. This purification process takes about one-half hour.

The purified gas is then allowed to expand into trap T_2, from where it is compressed into the capillary tubes.

One gram of radium in solution produces about 15 cc of mixed gas per day. It is well known that the alpha rays rapidly decompose water. As a result the gas contains about 1 part radon to 2500 parts of hydrogen and oxygen. The hydrogen and oxygen must be removed in order to provide a sufficiently active radon supply to be compressed into the capillary tubes.

Formerly, when the capillary tubes were made of glass, the wall thickness was 0.5 mm, and the tubes were placed in hollow silver needles for radiation therapy. The present practice is to compress the radon into gold capillary tubing without glass lining. The gold tubes, cut into 4- or 5-mm sections, are the " seeds " used in radium therapy. Their external diameter is about 0.75 mm with wall thickness 0.3 mm. Platinum seeds from 5 to 6 mm long are also employed; their radioactive strength varies from 1 to 5 mc.

These seeds are standardized three and a half hours after they have been sealed off at the radon plant. In this time the decomposition products RaA, RaB, and RaC have reached their "transient" equilibrium (Table II–13) with the radon, after which the activity decays with the decay period characteristic of radon. The activity of the seeds follows the usual decay law (see Table II–14), decreasing in activity 22.08 per cent by the end of the first day and dropping to half strength in 3.825 days. A common hospital practice is to have 20 to 50 seeds available and to calibrate them daily when not in use.

RADON SEED IMPLANTS

If the seed is introduced into an incision in tissue, when its calibrated strength is 1 mc, then Table II–14 can be consulted to determine its strength after any subsequent time, and the column labeled millicurie-hours (mc-hr) indicates the percentage of the radiation used up to the time of removal of the seed. If the seed is 4 days old, it will possess a potential activity of 48.42 per cent of its original maximum strength of 1 mc. In this time interval it has emitted 68.60 mc-hr. If this seed is used during the next 6 days on a second patient, its activity will reduce to 16.32 per cent of its initial value, and during these 6 days it has delivered 42.8 mc-hr to the second patient.

TABLE II–14

DECAY OF RADON

The number of millicuries (mc) available after any lapse of time if the original strength at time zero is 1 mc

Time Day	Hours	Per Cent Remaining	Mc-hr Used
	0	100.00	0.00
	1	99.25	1.00
	2	98.50	1.99
	3	97.76	2.98
	4	97.02	3.96
	5	96.29	4.94
	10	92.72	9.62
	15	89.29	14.25
	20	85.98	18.64
1	0	83.42	22.08
1	5	80.32	26.18
1	10	77.35	30.15
1	15	74.48	33.98
1	20	71.72	37.60
2	0	69.59	40.45
2	10	64.52	47.12
2	20	59.82	53.42
3	0	58.05	55.80
4	0	48.42	68.60
5	0	40.43	79.30
6	0	33.70	88.40
7	0	28.11	95.78
8	0	23.45	102.1
9	0	19.56	107.0
10	0	16.32	111.4
15	0	6.59	124.4
20	0	2.66	129.4
25	0	1.1	131.8
30	0	0.4	132.7
Complete		0.0	133.3

The quantity or intensity of the radiation delivered by a seed is expressed in either of two ways. The fraction of the original activity used is stated in terms of the percentage of millicuries remaining in the seed, or the amount of radon disintegrating during tissue exposure is given as millicurie-hours delivered. Recently, the second notation is being used in America to denote the quantity of radiation delivered interstitially.

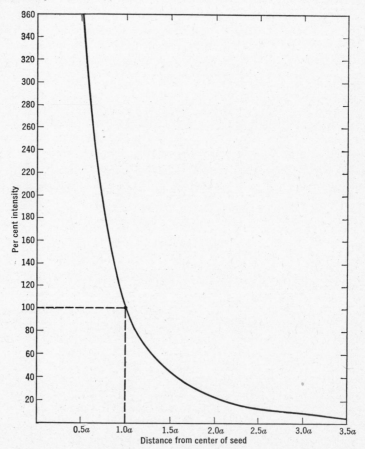

Fig. II–9. Percentage intensity of radiation reaching different distances, from a buried gold seed. (By courtesy of E. Quimby [1928].)

Intensity of Radiation in the Vicinity of Radon Seed Implants

Since the radiations from radon must pass through the 0.3-mm gold envelope of the seed, the emitted energy will be composed primarily of gamma radiations, and the curve of Fig. II–9 reproduced from

Quimby's [1928] data shows how the intensity decreased with distance from such a seed buried in tissue.

Some of Quimby's illustrations serve to show how the empirical data represented by this curve can be used.

Suppose that a preliminary experiment shows that a seed of 4 mc will bleach butter to a radius of 3.5 mm. How many millicuries will bleach butter to a radius of 5 mm? A distance from the center of the seed marked 1a on the curve is the radius of a full bleaching dose, here called 100 per cent intensity. Then 1a = 3.5 mm, or 5 mm = 1.43a. The curve shows that, at the distance 1.43a, bleaching of 46 per cent is produced. Thus x millicuries are necessary to produce 100 per cent bleaching when 4 mc produces 46 per cent bleaching. Hence $x/4$ = 100/46, or x = 8.7 mc.

It has been found that 110 mc-hr produces an erythema at 10 mm. What is the erythema dose at a distance of 6 mm? Here 1a = 10 mm; 6 mm = 0.6a. The curve shows that 300 per cent intensity is equal to 0.6a. Hence $x/110$ = 100/300, or x = 36.6 mc-hr.

It has been found that a seed of 5 mc produced necrosis in a rabbit muscle at a distance of 3.1 mm. How far will a tube of 8 mc be effective? *Ans.* 3.85 mm.

RADIUM SALTS AS A SOURCE OF GAMMA RADIATION

Radium sulphate may also be used as a source of biologically effective gamma radiation. It was commercially available before 1911 at £20 to £25 per milligram. In 1911 it was quoted at £18. In America it could be obtained for $120 per milligram in 1913 and for about $100 in 1914. With the discovery of the Canadian deposits, the price sank to $70 in 1933. Recently it could be obtained at $20 per milligram.

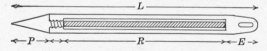

FIG. II–10. Diagram of a typical radium needle. *L*, overall length of needle 36.5 mm; *R*, length of radium chamber 25 mm; *E*, length of eye 5 mm; *P*, length of point 6.5 mm.

For interstitial radiation the salt is placed in a capillary needle-shaped tube containing from 1 to 25 mg of radium element. The radium tube is then placed as a core in the hollow cylindrical needle, 1 to 6 cm long, made of platinum or Monel metal.

The construction of a typical needle is shown in Fig. II–10. The hollow metal cylindrical tube contains the cell filled with the radium sulphate. The total thickness of the radium container and the wall of the needle is about 0.5 mm. If platinum is used, this is a sufficient thickness to absorb all beta rays. The internal cylindrical opening has a diameter of 0.6 mm. The diameter of the needle is 1.6 mm. The total overall length of the needle is 36.5 mm. If the radium chamber is to be longer than 25 mm it is good practice to use two or more radium tubes. Usually these contain 1 or 2 mg of radium each.

In dermatology, flat " applicators " are often used. They are in the form of very shallow round or square boxes. The radium salt is either placed under silver covers about 0.05 mm thick, to allow for considerable beta-ray transmission, or mixed with a varnish-like base and packed into the shallow opening, to give a uniform thickness of radiating material. Applicators vary in radium content from 2.5 to 10.0 mg of radium element per square centimeter.

The intensity of the gamma radiation with increase in distance of either of the above sources does not follow the inverse-square law, since neither of them is a point source of radiation. Available data, however, indicate that the relative intensity varies with size, shape, and changes in distance from the skin. The emission characteristics are reliable, for the quality of the radiation is always the same under identical physical conditions.

In practice, it has been found that gold radon seeds may be considered point sources. When these seeds are used for interstitial irradiation the amount of radiation passing through a unit area at any tissue depth is modified by absorption and scattering in the tissue. Actually, according to Quimby [1939], for the distances involved in practice, the absorption and the scattering approximately compensate each other, so that the intensity of radiation within the tissues is about the same for a given source as its intensity at the same distance in air.

TISSUE REACTION TO GAMMA RADIATIONS

If a given amount of radiation is administered slowly, either by continuous irradiation of low intensity or in fractions with rest periods of some hours or days between exposures, it is less effective in producing tissue changes than if it is delivered continuously at high intensity. Normal living tissue can tolerate a larger dose if the destructive radiation is administered slowly or administered in fractions with time intervals, and this tolerance is attributable to the recovery or life process of the type of cell radiated. Living tissue possesses dynamic recuperative properties which are not possessed by non-living material. It appears to resist the action of destructive agents. If the destructive radiation is applied slowly, it is to be expected that recuperation will be more effective than when the same amount is applied over a shorter period of time. If the destructive radiation is applied to normal cells and diseased cells alike, and the recuperative process of the normal cell is faster than that of the abnormal cell, then the division of a proposed dose into small doses with sufficient time intervals to allow the normal cells to recuperate completely will make it possible to produce regression of the abnormal cells without marked permanent damage to the normal structure.

The data available seem to point to the conclusion that normal tissue recuperates faster from exposure to soft x-rays than to hard x-rays and that tissue recuperates definitely with less rapidity from the destructive effects of gamma rays.

RADIUM DOSAGE

It is highly desirable to have a common unit of dosage in radium and roentgen therapy. Recent attempts to do this have been made by Gray [1936], Mayneord and Roberts [1936], and Failla and Marinelli [1937].

To construct a standard gamma-ray ionization chamber somewhat after the specifications laid down by the definition for the roentgen has led to complications. Secondary electrons, due to gamma-ray absorption, have very long paths in air, a fact which makes it necessary to use a large chamber. If the chamber is made large enough for the electron paths other difficulties are introduced that have not been completely solved.

An indirect method of measuring gamma-ray intensities using small thimble-type ionization chambers, though unsatisfactory, appears to avoid some of the difficulties. The procedure is usually as follows: The small chamber is calibrated in terms of the standard air chamber in roentgens. It is then exposed to gamma radiation, and the calibrated roentgen scale is compared with the ionization produced by the gamma radiation in milligram-hours. The results thus obtained vary more than 13 per cent among seven independent investigations. Failla and Marinelli [1937] who reviewed these results concluded that the ionization dose and the roentgen dose do not bear the same relation to each other when the quality of the radiation varies over any considerable range. Further complications result from the fact that the ionization dose and the roentgen dose do not bear the same relation to each other even in the gamma-ray region, since the roentgen applies to a beam of radiation in which the scattered energy does not contribute to the ionization of the air of the standard chamber. The roentgen cannot be used as a unit of tissue dose where scattering is a predominant phenomenon. Since tissue dose is what the radiologist desires for his work, Failla suggested the following definition: " The roentgen is the quantity of any ionizing radiation capable of producing 1.615×10^{12} ion pairs per gram of air at a given point in a given medium under the conditions in which the radiation is to be utilized."*

The unit thus defined can be used for measurements of radiation in air or tissues.

It has been suggested that, as a temporary expedient, the gamma-ray quantity of 1 mg-hr measured at a distance of 1 cm from a point source of radium filtered through 0.5 mm platinum be adopted as equivalent to 8.3 " effective " roentgens.

THE BIOLOGICAL ROENTGEN

Living organisms have been used as dosage indicators of both x-rays and gamma rays. The reaction most often used is the effect of the radiation upon the rate of cell growth and repair.

Since the absorbed radiation can slow down the rate of cell division, a sufficient dose can stop cell division. This results in the death of the organism.

A large variety of biological material has been used to test the lethal action of radiant energy, among them bacteria, yeasts, and spores of many kinds; algae and a great variety of seeds; protozoa; the eggs of salamanders, insects, and frogs.

In order to get quantitatively reproducible results, large colonies of small organisms must be used so that the results may be handled statistically. If small enough, the entire organism can be considered as having been irradiated uniformly, and if the organism is properly suspended scattered radiation can be disregarded.

The technique involved in evaluating the gamma radiation in terms of the roentgen is illustrated by some typical results obtained with *Drosophila* eggs. The lethal effects of 120-kv x-rays filtered with 0.25 mm Cu plus 1 mm Al will be compared with gamma rays from radon filtered with 0.5 mm Pt and 4 mm Bakelite.

The criterion of the effect produced is the proportion of eggs, in a standard sample colony, which survive and hatch as larvae. A typical survival curve, as obtained by Packard [1936], is reproduced in Fig. II-11. This shows the effect of various doses, of the above-specified

* For the provisional definition of the roentgen for gamma radiation see Chapter I.

x-radiation measured in roentgens, in terms of the percentage of eggs which survived and were subsequently hatched.

The form of the graph is that of a typical biophysical sigmoid-shaped response curve with its approximate constant slope at the point of inflection. In this restricted region the percentage of eggs surviving per dose administered was nearly constant. The response to the radiation apparently differed greatly among similar individuals. Some were killed by small doses yet others remained alive even after exposure to large doses. These and other results also indicated that damage caused by ionizing

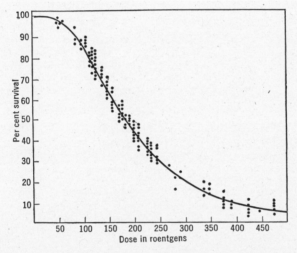

Fig. II–11. A typical survival curve of *Drosophila* eggs after eggs have been subjected to the lethal effect of 120-kv x-rays. Fifty per cent of the eggs survive when exposed to 190 roentgens. (By courtesy of C. Packard.)

radiations was probably traceable to chemical changes in the cell or in its surface structure which manifested themselves by changes in osmotic pressure, because expanded cells were frequently observed after irradiation both of tissue and of microorganisms.

The experiments were then repeated with gamma-ray doses measured in millicurie-hours. Such an experiment is difficult because the eggs must be exposed at very short distances from the source and the intensity must be uniform over the field occupied by the eggs. Exner and Packard [1935] used highly compressed radon gas in a sufficiently small tube, with platinum walls 0.5 mm thick, so that it could be considered a point source. This was placed at the center of a spherical shell of Bakelite 4 mm thick. The eggs were placed on the outer surface of the shell, so that all eggs were 1 cm from the radiating source. The eggs were exposed to gamma radiations filtered by 0.5 mm of Pt and 4 mm of Bakelite. They were tested for survival after exposures varying from 1 to 55 mc-hr. The results are shown in Fig. II–12.

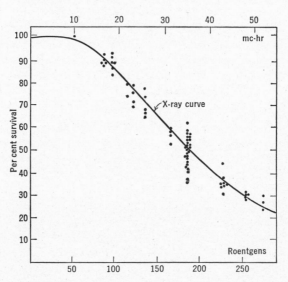

FIG. II–12. Survival of *Drosophila* eggs after exposure to gamma rays in millicurie-hours. The x-ray survival curve is shown superimposed on the gamma-ray survival data. Fifty per cent of the eggs survive when exposed to a dose of 38 mc-hr. (By courtesy of C. Packard.)

If the x-ray survival data are superimposed on the gamma-ray data, it is found that a single curve fits the two sets of data equally well. Figure II–12 shows how well the x-ray survival curve fits the gamma-ray data.

These composite data show that 50 per cent of the eggs survive an exposure of 38 mc-hr and also 190 roentgens. These two doses are therefore biologically equivalent, if *Drosophila* eggs are acceptable as a standard test substance and if the response is independent of the wavelength of the radiant energy.

The millicurie-hour is therefore equal to 5 "biological" roentgens (1 mc-hr ≡ 5 br).

Other recent attempts to measure x-rays and gamma rays in the same biological unit were made by Braun [1930]. Using *Ascaris* eggs, he obtained 1 mc-hr ≡ 5.3 br. Henshaw and Francis [1936], using *Drosophila* eggs, obtained 1 mc-hr ≡ 5.4 br.

ARTIFICIAL TRANSMUTATION

The complex nucleus of radium contains 88 protons; therefore, its atomic number is 88. In addition, this nucleus contains 138 neutrons, making a total of 226 entities of atomic weight 226. The neutrons are supposed to play the role of a binding cement which holds the nucleus together in spite of the very strong electrostatic repulsive forces which the positive protons exert upon one another.

Radium, like many of the natural radioactive types of atomic number greater than 80, does not possess a completely stable nuclear configuration. It can, however, become more stable by splitting off a nuclear fragment in the form of an alpha particle.

Since radioactivity is a quality of the nucleus, it varies from one isotope to another of any element. This nuclear quality of a radioactive atom is the same whether the atom is part of a solid, a liquid, or a gas. It is the same whether the radioactive element is isolated or part of a chemical compound.

Elements of small atomic number like Li, B, and N have stable nuclei. If, for instance, nitrogen is bombarded with sufficiently high-speed atomic projectiles, it might be possible to dislodge a nuclear proton fragment. The resulting " artificial " nucleus with its complement of planetary electrons would be a " transmuted " element. A transmutation may also be brought about by changing the number of neutrons, or by a combination of neutrons and protons in the nucleus. Thus, transmutation is not always a destruction of the nucleus, but frequently a synthesis in which neutrons or protons are added to an original nucleus.

As early as 1919 Rutherford succeeded in producing the artificial transmutation of an element, although the isotopic elements thus produced were not radioactive. In his first experiments he subjected nitrogen to an intensive bombardment of alpha particles from RaC' to see if he could disintegrate the nucleus of the nitrogen atom. He was successful in breaking down the nucleus, and the products of disintegration were an isotopic atom of oxygen and a nuclear proton. The proton was ejected with a large amount of kinetic energy.

This classic experiment is shown pictorially in Fig. II–13. At the time of Rutherford's experiment the constitution of the nucleus was thought to be only protons and negative electrons. They were supposed to be closely and tightly bound together. Disruption of the nucleus was thought to be accomplished by the shooting of a high-speed projectile in the form of an alpha particle at the very small nuclear target. The high-speed alpha particle colliding with the nucleus of the nitrogen atom occasionally succeeded in penetrating this nucleus. When it did this, a proton was ejected with high kinetic energy.

For the purpose of this discussion an atomic nucleus is sufficiently specified by giving its atomic number, which is numerically equal to the positive charge of the nucleus, in integral multiples of the proton charge, and the mass number in multiples of the proton mass. Actually, the atomic nuclei do not have masses that are exact multiples

$$_2\mathrm{He}^4 + {_7}\mathrm{N}^{14} \longrightarrow {_8}\mathrm{O}^{17} + {_1}\mathrm{H}^1 + \text{Energy}$$

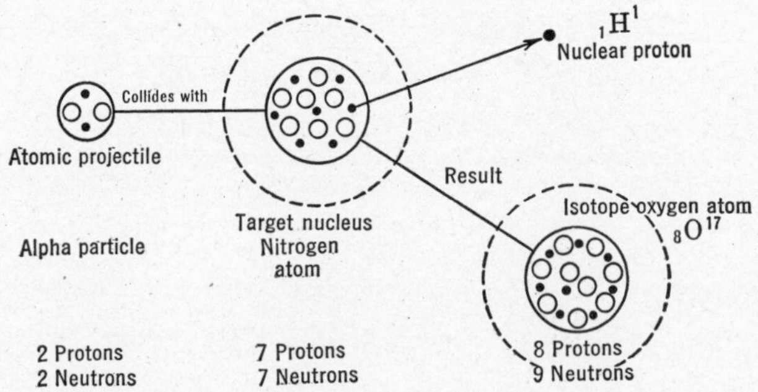

FIG. II–13. Rutherford's classic experiment. Nitrogen bombarded with alpha particles from RaC'.

of the mass of the proton, but the correction factor is not involved here. In the notation used in describing these disintegration phenomena, the upper right-hand corner of the symbol of the element is reserved for the isotopic mass ($_8\mathrm{O}^{17}$) and the lower left-hand corner for the atomic number.

Since the discovery of the neutron by Chadwick in 1932, the accepted conclusion is that the alpha particle is made up of two neutrons and two protons bound tightly together as in the nucleus of the helium atom. The alpha-particle projectile is designated as $_2\mathrm{He}^4$. This mass, with its equivalent of 4 proton masses (neglect mass of nuclear electrons), joins the 14 protons of the nitrogen nucleus, which then loses 1 nuclear mass unit. This mass unit appears as an ejected high-velocity hydrogen nucleus $_1\mathrm{H}^1$. The decomposition product has gained 3 mass units and forms a nucleus of 17 mass units. This is identified as O^{17}, an atom of oxygen whose nucleus is 1 mass unit greater than normal oxygen (O^{16}). Hence it is an oxygen isotope.

After this first definite example of the artificial transmutation of an element, many other transmutations were accomplished. By 1932 the Curie-Joliots had discovered that charged and uncharged particles were emitted when boron was bombarded with alpha particles. The charged particles were electronic in nature but carried a positive charge. These positive charged electrons had just previously been discovered by Anderson at the California Institute of Technology and named *positrons* by him. The uncharged particles were shown to have protonic mass. These neutral particles of protonic mass had been identified only a few months before by Chadwick in England, who gave them the name *neutrons*.

The unusual part about the emissions discovered by the Curie-Joliots was the continued positron emission even after the bombardment by alpha particles had ceased. Thus the first artificial radioactivity had been produced as a property of a disintegration product.

The reaction equation for this experiment is shown in Fig. II–14. The alpha particle joins the boron nucleus, with the emission of a neutron. An unstable nitrogen nucleus results, which in turn explodes

$$_2He^4 + _5B^{10} \longrightarrow _7N^{13} + \text{Neutron}$$
$$\text{then } _7N^{13} \dashrightarrow _6C^{13} + _{+1}e^0 + \text{Energy}$$

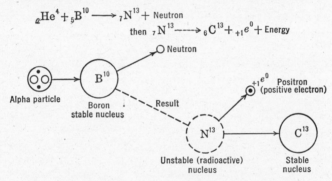

Fig. II–14.   The Curie-Joliot experiment.

with the emission of a positron $(_{+1}e^0)$ and the formation of a new stable nucleus carbon, C^{13}.

The success of the Curie-Joliot experiment raised a question of fundamental importance. If the boron atom can be converted by alpha-particle bombardment into a new radioactive element, what would prevent other atoms from becoming radioactive if bombarded with any form of high-speed atomic projectile?

The alpha particles, emitted by RaC′, used in the above experiments possess kinetic energy of 1.23×10^{-5} erg, corresponding with the energy acquired by an electron in passing between two points in a vacuum differing in potential by 7.66 million volts. It is obviously impracticable to impart to a charged particle, by a single high-voltage operation, energy comparable to that possessed by an alpha particle emitted by natural radioactive elements. It is practicable, however, for a voltage

1/nth as great to operate n successive times on a charged particle in the form of an ion and impart to it a prescribed amount of energy.

An ingenious solution to this problem was proposed by E. O. Lawrence, in 1930, in the form of a magnetic resonance accelerator, or cyclotron. This instrument can produce extremely high-speed ions of various sorts by means of relatively small differences of potential applied a large number of consecutive times.

THE CYCLOTRON

The instrument finally adopted by Lawrence and Livingston [1934], and their co-workers, consists of a large, shallow, cylindrical metal vacuum chamber (Fig. II–15) in which are inserted two insulated semi-

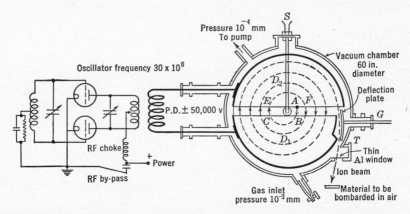

FIG. II–15. Cyclotron. General view of a 60-in. D-shaped accelerating chamber which is placed between the magnetic pole pieces of the cyclotron. Direction of magnetic field perpendicular to paper.

With the support of the Rockefeller Foundation a " Giant Cyclotron " is under construction at the University of California. It will contain 4900 tons of steel and copper, will have a 30-ft. vacuum chamber, and is expected to produce a beam of ions of more than 200 million electron volts.

circular, flat, hollow D-shaped brass electrodes. The vacuum chamber can, for example, be 60 in. in diameter and about 18 in. high. The two electrodes, or " dees," are made of spun copper, and insulated from each other. They clear the vacuum-chamber walls by about 2 in. The vacuum chamber with its flat circular steel ends is supported between the pole pieces of a powerful electromagnet. These pole pieces are also 60 in. in diameter. The magnetic field acts in a direction normal to the radial plane of the dees, i.e., perpendicular to the plane of the paper in Fig. II–15.

Dees D_1 and D_2 are connected through an inductance in the manner shown, so that they form a capacitance in an oscillatory circuit. If a high-frequency potential is applied to the dees so that an alternating voltage ($\pm$ 50,000 volts) is operative between them while the electrical center of the dee circuit is always at zero potential, an accelerating force is developed by the electric field across the diametral gap between the dees. Within the hollow dees, however, there exists a nearly field-free region.

An insulator is inserted through the port at S to carry the connections to the hot tungsten spiral filament situated at the center of the vacuum chamber. This filament is kept at about 1000 volts negative with respect to the earth potential.

The vacuum chamber may be filled with hydrogen, deuterium, or helium at low pressure. Positive ions are produced at the center of the vacuum chamber by collisions of the thermoelectrons with the gas molecules.

A positive ion in the gap between the two dees will be accelerated by the intense electric field across this gap. In Fig. II–15 is shown such an ion accelerated across the gap from A to B, after which it will pass into the field-free interior of D_1. Under the influence of the perpendicular magnetic field the ion will trace out a semicircular path BC within the dee and arrive at C. If the time which the ion has spent within D_1 is equal to half of the periodic time of oscillation of the high-frequency driving circuit, then, when the ion emerges into the gap between the dees at C, the electric high-frequency field will be reversed and the ion will be given a second acceleration from C to E. It then enters the field-free region inside of D_2 with a greater velocity than it had when it passed through D_1. Having a greater entrance velocity at E, it will describe a half-circle of greater radius and arrive at F to receive a further acceleration. As the speed increases, the ion describes larger and larger semicircles until it reaches the periphery of the chamber at G.

The magnetic intensity H will deflect the ion to describe a semicircle of radius R such that $mv^2/R = Hev$, where v is the velocity of the ion of net charge e and mass m. After a large number of accelerations the energy of the ion is $\frac{1}{2}mv^2 = eV$, so that

$$V = \frac{H^2R^2e}{2m}$$

If e is expressed in electrostatic units and V in volts

$$V = H^2R^2\frac{e}{m}\ (16.7 \times 10^{-20})\ \text{volt}$$

and if H and R are equal to 10,000 oersteds* and 10 cm, respectively, and the value of e/m for protons is used, it will be observed that the protons found traveling in a semicircle of 10-cm radius are those which possess energy equal to that produced by an electric field between two points in a vacuum of nearly half a million volts.

These very high-speed ions emerge at G, where the edge of the dee is cut away. Here they are deflected by the oil-cooled copper deflection plate G, which is maintained at a steady potential of 50,000 volts negative relative to the vacuum chamber, at earth potential.

The ions are deflected into the target chamber T, where they can either be used for the bombardment of a substance mounted as a target or be passed through a thin metal window out of the vacuum chamber into the air.

ARTIFICIAL RADIOACTIVITY

The cyclotron is therefore a source which can supply controlled charged-particle projectiles of enormous energy content. With these projectiles it becomes possible to penetrate the nuclear barrier of many atoms so that in their union they may enter into a reaction with each other, and convert them into artificially radioactive bodies.

Among the artificially radioactive processes, beta-ray radioactivity is most common. This consists of the emission either of negative electrons or of positrons. A second type of spontaneous transmutation is electron capture, in which the atomic nucleus combines with and destroys one of its atomic electrons. Finally, there is the so-called isomeric transition, which involves only a shift in the configuration of the neutrons and protons in the nucleus without any change in their numbers.

The experimental results obtained with the aid of high-speed deuteron projectiles show that radioactive nuclei were formed in which neutrons or alpha particles were emitted. In many cases it was found that the neutron of the deutron was captured and the proton emitted with high speed. This general type, the neutron-capture reaction, is illustrated by the radiosodium and radiophosphorus reactions.

Radiosodium may be obtained by bombarding sodium chloride by a beam of high-speed deuterous from a cyclotron. The sodium atom captures the high-speed deuteron, as illustrated in Fig. II–16, with the emission of a proton, and forms an unstable isotope nucleus, Na^{24}. This radiosodium disintegration product has a half-life of 14.8 hours (Van

* Unit field intensity. The oersted (formerly called the gauss) is that field which exerts a force of 1 dyne on unit magnetic pole.

Voorhis [1936]). It ejects a high-speed (1.4-Mev) beta particle from its nucleus. This ejection is followed by the emission of a very hard gamma ray, and the end product is a stable magnesium nucleus. The

$$_1H^2 + _{11}Na^{23} \longrightarrow _{11}Na^{24} + _1H^1 + \text{Energy}$$

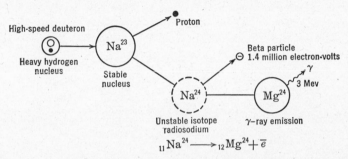

High-speed deuteron

Proton

Heavy hydrogen nucleus

Na^{23}

Stable nucleus

Beta particle 1.4 million electron-volts

γ

3 Mev

Na^{24}

Mg^{24}

Unstable isotope radiosodium

γ-ray emission

$$_{11}Na^{24} \longrightarrow _{12}Mg^{24} + \overline{e}$$

Fig. II–16. Radiosodium produced by deuteron bombardment. A possible substitute for radium. Its gamma ray is more energetic than any emitted by radium.

beta particle and gamma radiation possess energy of 1.4 and 3 million electron volts respectively. The latter artificially induced radioactive emission is more penetrating than any of the natural radium radiations.

Radiophosphorus preparations may be obtained by bombarding red

$$_1H^2 + _{15}P^{31} \longrightarrow _{15}P^{32} + _1H^1 + \text{Energy}$$

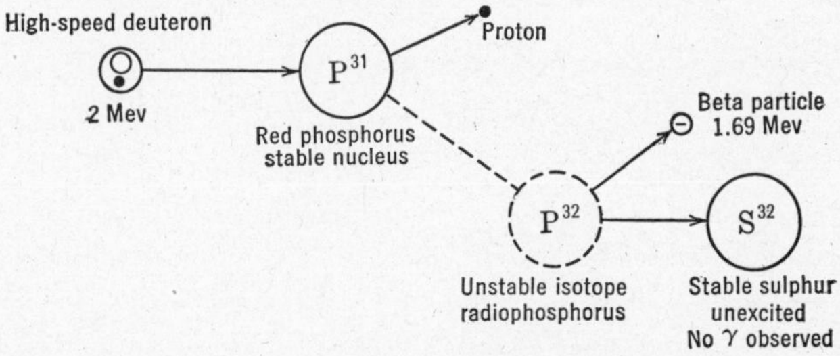

High-speed deuteron

Proton

2 Mev

P^{31}

Red phosphorus stable nucleus

Beta particle 1.69 Mev

P^{32}

S^{32}

Unstable isotope radiophosphorus

Stable sulphur unexcited No γ observed

$$_{15}P^{32} \longrightarrow _{16}S^{32} + \overline{e}$$

Fig. II–17. Radiophosphorus produced by bombarding red phosphorus with high-speed deuterium ions, from a cyclotron.

phosphorus with high-speed deuterium ions, obtained by means of the cyclotron. The reaction is shown in Fig. II–17. This reaction involves a beta decay emission without the accompanying gamma radiation. The resulting radiophosphorus ($_{15}P^{32}$) has a half-life of 14.30 days (Cacciapuoti [1938]).

RADIOACTIVE TRACERS

Certain chemical compounds, when administered orally or intravenously, tend to concentrate themselves in certain organs of the body. It has recently become possible to make such chemical compounds radioactive, so that these specific regions where the radioactive chemical compound has concentrated may be irradiated without producing a large systemic effect or any skin injuries. If the radioactivity has a comparatively short half-life and the decomposition products of the artificially radioactive material are not toxic, no harm will result from its presence in the body, even if it is not promptly eliminated.

If certain foodstuffs, such as, for instance, those containing calcium and phosphorus, are made temporarily radioactive, then they can be used as tracers by measuring the relative radioactivity of the tissue in which deposits have taken place. Such radioactive indicators or tracers have helped in the solution of certain therapeutic and physiological problems.

When radiophosphorus is used as a tracer, a small amount of activated sodium phosphate is added to ordinary sodium phosphate solution. The path and deposition of sodium phosphate are traced and located by the 1.7-million-volt electronic emissions. Estimates of deposition are carried out by observing the decay, at a given time, by means of a Geiger-Müller counter tube and by comparing the results directly with the decay of a similar standard at the same time. This method avoids corrections for the rate of decay due to lapse of time. Thus, if it is desired to determine the radioactive phosphorus content of the bone of an animal to which an activated phosphate solution has been administered, and hence to determine any exchange in the phosphate of the bone, a known weight of bone ash from the animal is placed under the counter tube and the intensity of electron emission is determined.

The source of phosphatides in egg yolks, the diffusion of phosphate ions into blood corpuscles, the mechanism of enzymatic phosphorylizations as in alcoholic fermentation, and numerous other problems have also been investigated with active phosphorus as an indicator.

The use of radioactive sodium phosphate has been of great help in a study of the formation of goat milk. Samples of blood and milk, taken at intervals after the administration of labeled phosphate, were examined for the activity of the phosphate in the blood and the various phosphate compounds of milk. It was found that after three or four hours the inorganic phosphate of the milk was replaced by the active phosphate of the plasma. It was estimated that the time of formation of casein in the gland cells was about 1 hour. The fact that a few hours after the addition of the labeled phosphate the milk phosphatides were only slightly active as compared with the inorganic phosphate indicated that the latter cannot be produced from the former. This experiment contradicts the view that the fats and inorganic phosphates are produced by the breaking up in the milk gland of the phosphatides of the blood.

If iron is used as a target in the cyclotron and bombarded with high-speed deuterons (Livingood and Seaborg [1938]), about 1 atom in every 10^{12} may be successfully transmuted into radioactive iron (half-life 47 ± 3 days) just as radioactive phosphorus was transformed. This mixture of stable and negative electron-emitting radioactive iron atoms ($_{26}Fe^{59}$) can then be converted chemically to ferrous sulphate. If this ferrous sulphate, containing radioactive iron, is fed to anemic dogs, it will be absorbed and the new red blood cells which are formed will contain hemoglobin made with radioactive iron. Since the radioactive and normal atoms of iron are chemically inseparable, they will retain a constant proportionality to one another. The radioactive atom can thus act as a tracer to locate and follow the progressive use of iron atoms in normal and in anemic animals, as was demonstrated by Hahn, Ross, Bale, and Whipple [1940] and also by Miller and Hahn [1940]. New hemoglobin containing radioactive iron was found by them to be detectable in the blood within about 4 hours. The iron was entirely used up in 4 to 7 days. In this way the breakdown of red blood cells and hemoglobin can be studied quantitatively.

A radioactivated isotope of iodine $_{53}I^{126}$ emitting beta and gamma rays has, according to Tape and Cork [1938], been produced having a half-life of 13.0 ± 0.3 days. Experiments by Herz and Roberts [1941], and Hertz, Roberts, Means, and Evans [1940], have indicated that radioactive iodine is selectively taken up by the thyroid gland from the blood stream within a few minutes after administration.

The thyroid gland plays fundamental roles in the regulation of growth and of body heat. Its hormonal secretions are rich in iodine, and the metabolism of this element, which appears to be of basic importance in the proper functioning of the thyroid, is being studied with the aid of radioactive iodine.

In human beings with toxic goiter, the thyroid gland has been found to take up practically all the administered iodine if the dose is 1 mg or less. Basic studies are in progress on the rate and mechanism of the conversion of the absorbed iodine into various chemical components of the hormonal secretions of the thyroid gland (Hamilton [1941]).

The upward and lateral movement of salts containing potassium, sodium, phosphorus, and bromine has been studied in growing and transpiring willow and geranium plants. Stout and Hoagland [1939] have shown that the path of rapid upward movement of salt is in the wood of the plant rather than in the bark.   They also found a moderately rapid radial transfer from the wood to the bark.

The considerable interest in the metabolism of calcium has been stimulated because radiocalcium (half-life 180 days) has become available for studying this metabolic problem in bone, which is composed largely of calcium in the form of tricalcium phosphate.

Radioactive tracers provide a unique method for investigating a normal animal or plant under equilibrium conditions.   Many problems in physiology and biochemistry are being re-examined with the aid of radioactive tracers.   The new results will probably provide valid evidence for discarding many alternative or conflicting interpretations of old observations.

RADIUM INJURIES AND RADIUM POISONING

The earliest recorded radium injury was acquired by Becquerel, who, in carrying a tube of radium salt in his vest pocket for several hours, discovered several weeks later that he had developed a " radium burn," an inflammation in that part of the skin located underneath the pocket in which he had carried the radium salt.   Curie then repeated the experiment on his own person and conclusively proved that the radiation was capable of effecting an inflammatory reaction in normal skin.   Besnier was probably the first to suggest the use of radium as a therapeutic agent because of his familiarity with the results of roentgentherapy.

Injury from radium may take place when a radioactive substance enters the blood stream by ingestion or injection.   Modes of entrance of radium into the human body include breathing of radioactive gas, drinking of radium water nostrums, and intravenous and other injections of radium salts.   Technicians, chemists, and miners handling radioactive materials are often injured by the radiations and can be poisoned by taking the material by mouth.

As is generally true in any heavy-element poisoning, some radium salts are deposited in the bony tissues.   A small fraction of the total amount of radium taken into the body becomes relatively fixed in the bones, the fixation being considerably higher after intravenous injection than after ingestion of radium.   Retention is diminished by acidosis while on low-calcium diet, as this tends to increase the rate of elimination of calcium and heavy elements from the body.

If radium is taken by mouth or by injection, a fraction of it remains permanently in the body.   According to the individual, from 2 to 35 per cent of the radium received by mouth remains in the system more than 5 days after ingestion, and 55 to 65 per cent received by intravenous injection remains more than 5 days.   By the tenth day after taking radium, the rate of elimination is below 1 per cent of the quantity remaining in the system. Several years later the daily rate of elimination is down to 0.002 to 0.005 per cent per day. At this low rate it would require 45 years to eliminate half the radium in the system.

About 90 per cent of the eliminated radium is excreted in the feces, and the remaining 10 per cent in the urine. No radium is eliminated through the skin. Since radium decays into radon with the emission of an alpha particle, the radon thus formed can be exhaled in the breath. The fraction of the radon expired varies between extreme limits of 2 and 40 per cent of the total amount of radon produced in the body by the decay of radium.

Depending on the resistance of the individual's system from 2 to 10 micrograms of radium, when " fixed " in the system, may be a fatal dose.

The radioactive self-photographs of the bones of deceased victims show a lack of uniformity of distribution of deposited radium. In some individuals two or three small areas have been found to be intensely radioactive, the remainder of the bone displaying only a moderate amount of fairly evenly distributed radiation. This lack of uniformity in the deposition of the radium shows that an analysis of a fragment of bone chosen at random will not be representative of the nature of the deposit.

Radium acts principally to destroy the blood-producing centers and to weaken the bones. Necrosis of the jaw, osteogenic sarcoma, and regenerative anemia are among the most common symptoms of radium poisoning.

An ingenious method has been developed by Evans and Aub [1937] for measuring the gamma radiation from RaC in the patient's body and for determining the absolute amount of RaC from these observations. It involves the use of a very sensitive form of Geiger-Müller counter responding to gamma radiations.

In a victim of chronic radium poisoning, the radium is deposited non-uniformly throughout the bones, the highest concentration being in the vertebrae. The emitted gamma radiation is reduced by absorption and scattering of the tissue. The emerging radiation does not lend itself to computation of the RaC content of the patient, so that calibration observations are resorted to in order to evaluate the radiation.

The effect of non-uniform distribution of radium and of internal absorption and scattering by the patient's body can be completely corrected by making a series of gamma-ray observations in which the patient is placed in definite geometrical relations with respect to the gamma-radiation detector.

The patient lies on a light frame support with his body bent in an arc which has an outside radius of curvature of 1 meter. The gamma-radiation detector is placed at the center of curvature of the arc. Three observations are then made: first, with the ventral aspect of the body away from the counter; second, with the dorsal aspect away from the counter; and, third, with this position retained the total absorption of the body is directly measured by placing small radium standards behind the patient. From proper mathematical combinations of these measurements the absolute amount of RaC in the body can be computed directly.

SAFETY OF PERSONNEL HANDLING RADIOACTIVE MATERIALS

Those persons engaged in handling radioactive preparations must take precautions for their own safety or they will suffer in health. The chief disabilities which may result are:

(a) Damage to the skin which causes warty growths and ulceration, and which may lead to more serious conditions.

(b) Damage to the reproductive organs.

(c) Damage to the blood-forming organs which leads to forms of anemia.

Damage to the skin is usually due to overexposure to beta rays and is more likely to occur during radon plant manipulations than when solid radium salts enclosed in metal tubes are handled.

The fundamental rule for safety is that no radioactive preparation should be handled with bare fingers.

RADIUM STANDARDS

One of the international radium standards is deposited in Paris; it consists of 22.23 mg of anhydrous $RaCl_2$. The second one, at the Vienna Radium Institute, consists of 30.75 mg. Both were prepared in 1934 by Hönigschmid and are composed of pure $RaCl_2$ free from every trace of barium.

The United States Bureau of Standards possesses a secondary standard equal to 15.44 mg of radium element as of 1913.

In a recent number of the *Physical Review* (1940), it is reported that a series of radioactive standards is being prepared for deposit at the National Bureau of Standards in Washington, D. C., to be used as working standards and to be made available to investigators.

The standards under preparation are:

1. Radium standards; 100-cc solutions sealed in 200-cc Pyrex flasks containing 10^{-9} and 10^{-11} gram of radium to be used as emanation standards either directly or by subsolution.

2. Thorium standards: sealed ampules containing sublimed $ThCl_4$.

3. One hundred-grams standard rock samples.

For internal radioactive therapy it is proposed to make calibrated standard beta-ray sources available.

BIBLIOGRAPHY

1921 FAILLA, G., *Am. J. Roentgenol.*, **8**, 215.

1924 ELLIS, C. D., and H. W. B. SKINNER, *Proc. Roy. Soc. London*, **A105**, 185.

1924 EMELEUS, K. G., *Proc. Cambridge Phil. Soc.*, **22**, 400.

1925 GURNEY, R. W., *Proc. Roy. Soc. London*, **A109**, 540.

1927 MADGWICK, M. G., *Proc. Cambridge Phil. Soc.*, **23**, 982.

1928 QUIMBY, E. H., *Radiology*, **14**, 1.

1930 BRAUN, R., *Strahlentherapie*, **38**, 11.

1934 LAWRENCE, E. O., and M. S. LIVINGSTON, *Phys. Rev.*, **45**, 608.

1935 EXNER, F. M., and C. PACKARD, *Radiology*, **25**, 391.

1936 GRAY, L. H., *Proc. Roy. Soc. London*, **A156**, 578; **A159**, 263 (1937).

1936 HENSHAW, P. S., and D. S. FRANCIS, *Radiology*, **27**, 569.

1936 MAYNEORD, W. V., and J. E. ROBERTS, *British J. Radiol.*, **10**, 365.

1936 PACKARD, C., *Radiology*, **27**, 191.

1936 VAN VOORHIS, S. N., *Phys. Rev.*, **49**, 889.

1937 EVANS, R. D., and J. C. AUB, Am. Assoc. Advancement Sci. Occasional Pub., No. 4, p. 227.

1937 FAILLA, G., and L. D. MARINELLI, *Am. J. Roentgenol.*, **38**, 312.

1938 CACCIAPUOTI, B. N., *N. Cimento*, **15**, 213.

1938 LIVINGOOD, J. J., and G. T. SEABORG, *Phys. Rev.*, **54**, 51.

1938 TAPE, G. F., and J. M. CORK, *Phys. Rev.*, **53**, 676.

1939 QUIMBY, E. H., *The Physical Basis of Radiation Therapy*, Syllabus of Lectures, Memorial Hospital, New York, N. Y.

1939 STOUT, P. R., and D. R. HOAGLAND, *Am. J. Bot.*, **26**, 320.

1940 HAHN, P. F., J. F. ROSS, W. F. BALE, and G. H. WHIPPLE, *J. Exptl. Med.*, **71** 731.

1940 HERTZ, S., A. ROBERTS, J. H. MEANS, and R. D. EVANS, *Am. J. Physiol.*, **128**, 565.

1940 LIVINGOOD, J. J., and G. T. SEABORG, "A Table of Induced Radioactivities," *Rev. Modern Phys.*, **12**, 30.

1940 MANN, W. B., "The Cyclotron," *Chemical Publishing Co.*, New York, N. Y.

1940 MILLER, L. L., and P. F. HAHN, *J. Biol. Chem.*, **134**, 585.

1941 HAMILTON, J. G., *J. Applied Phys.*, **12**, 440.

1941 HERTZ, S., and A. ROBERTS, *Endocrinology*, **29**, 82.

Chapter III

BIOPHYSICAL CHARACTERISTICS OF THE EYE

The preceding chapters have discussed the biophysical properties of very high-frequency radiant energy, in the form of x-rays and gamma rays, but man does not possess the necessary sense organs with which to identify such radiations. Comparatively lower frequencies lying in the spectral wavelength band extending from 4000 to 7000 Å, however, can be identified by a unique receptor mechanism, the eye, which is sensitive to changes in frequency and energy of this visible radiation.

The expression " we see " means that we experience a sensation which begins as a photochemical reaction in the retina, provided that the intensity of the radiant energy is adequate and its frequency lies within the limits set by the transmission properties of the ocular media, photosensitivity of the retina, and propagation characteristics of nerve.

A process such as vision in man represents a complicated series of events. As a form of consciousness and its directive function in behavior, vision must be studied by the methods of psychology. As an activity depending on the anatomical structure of the human eye and its nervous mechanism, vision is a physiological problem. So far as the processes involved rest on the physical responses of the ocular media to radiant energy, they relate to phenomena pertaining to the physical sciences.

Merging the last two groups of facts into a single group of interrelated biophysical phenomena permits a better organized approach to the problem of vision.

OPTICAL SYSTEM OF THE EYE

The optical system of the eye consists of those structures which together focus an image of an external object on the retina; they are the cornea, the aqueous humor, the crystalline lens, and the vitreous humor. The media are more or less inhomogeneous, and no satisfactory system of spherical refracting surfaces has been adapted that will replace them exactly. Of the many schematic models suggested, Gullstrand's (Table III–1) seems to possess the most acceptable qualities. Figure III–1 shows such an eye at rest, with its principal focal plane coinciding with the retina and with the refracting surfaces formed so that parallel rays are brought to a focus on the retina.

STRUCTURE OF THE EYEBALL

The human eyeball is an irregular sphere which for simplicity is reduced to an idealized schematic form having an equivalent anterior-posterior diameter of 24.15 mm, with transverse diameter 24.13 mm

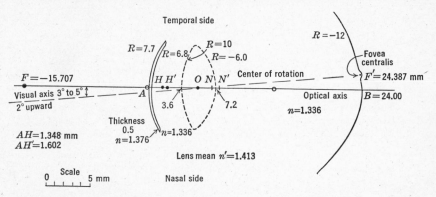

FIG. III–1. Gullstrand's schematic eye. Unaccommodated and simplified. Length, *A* to retina 24.00 mm. All distances on optical axis measured from anterior pole *A* to *B* in millimeters.

and vertical dimension 23.48 mm. In males the dimensions are from 0.5 to 0.6 mm greater than in females. Its mass is about 7 grams, and its volume about 6.5 cc; the average specific gravity is therefore 1.08. Five sixths of its external surface is formed by a firm white membrane called the sclera. Its anterior convex protrusion, the cornea, is transparent and has an area equal to one sixth of the surface area. This corneal area has a horizontal diameter of 12.0 mm and a vertical diameter of 11.0 mm. Abnormal dimensions may arise as indicated in Fig. III–2. Attached to the eyeball behind and slightly to the nasal side is the optic nerve, the function of which is to convey to the brain the nerve impulses initiated in the retina by the light transmitted by the optical system.

CORNEA

The protruding anterior transparent convex structure, called the cornea, is taken in the ideal schematic eye as 0.5 mm in thickness, and with an average index of refraction of 1.376.

The anterior surface of the cornea has a radius of curvature of 7.7 mm. That large departures from this average value may exist is illustrated by the accompanying photographic reproductions, Fig. III–2. The posterior surface of the cornea has a radius of 6.8 mm. The simplified schematic cornea has been taken as having a radius of curvature of 7.8 mm, as shown in Table III–1.

TABLE III–1

GULLSTRAND'S SIMPLIFIED EYE

	Unaccommodated	Maximum Accommodation
Index of refraction of		
Cornea	1.376	1.376
Aqueous humor	1.336	1.336
Vitreous humor	1.336	1.336
Lens	1.413	1.424
Radii of curvature of		
Equivalent cornea	7.8 mm	7.8 mm
Anterior surface of lens	10.0	5.33
Posterior surface of lens	−6.0	−5.33
Optical center of lens (O)	5.85 mm	5.2 mm
Refracting power of eye	+58.64 diopters	+70.57 diopters
Locations on optical axis of		
Anterior vertex of cornea (A)	0.0 mm	0.0 mm
Posterior surface of cornea	0.5	0.5
Anterior pole of lens	3.6	3.2
Posterior pole of lens	7.2	7.2
Fovea centralis	24.01	24.01
Center of rotation	13−14	13−14
Complete optical system of eye		
First principal point	1.348 mm	1.772 mm
Second principal point	1.602	2.086
First (anterior) focal point	−15.707	−12.397
Second (posterior) focal point	+24.387	+21.016
Anterior focal length	+17.055	+14.169
Posterior focal length	−22.785	−18.930
Posterior pole (B)	24.00	24.00
Near point		−102.3

Drugs pass through the cornea by diffusion quite readily; thus atropine placed in the conjunctival sac formed by the lids rapidly reaches the interior of the eye.

AQUEOUS HUMOR

A clear transparent fluid fills the cavity lying between the cornea and the anterior surface of the crystalline lens. It is formed principally by the ciliary bodies. In chemical composition this fluid consists chiefly of water, traces of albumin, globulin, and a reducing sugar. An analysis of the intraocular fluids of the horse as obtained by Duke-Elder [1927] is shown in Table III–2. The intraocular pressure of this fluid varies

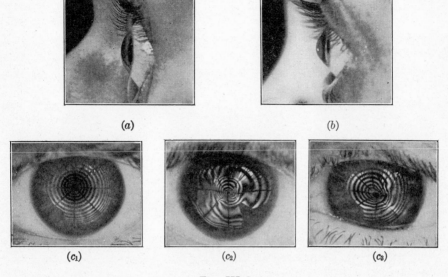

(a) (b)

(c₁) (c₂) (c₃)

FIG. III–2.

(a) Normal cornea. (b) Conical cornea (keratoconus).
Corneal reflections photographed with a keratoscope. (c₁) Normal. (c₂) and (c₃)
irregular astigmatism.
(Photographs by courtesy of A. Marfaing, Institute of Ophthalmology, New York
City.)

TABLE III–2

INTRAOCULAR FLUIDS OF THE HORSE

Quantities in grams per 100 cc

	Aqueous	Vitreous	Serum
Water	99.69	99.68	93.32
Solids	1.08	1.10	9.53

By Courtesy of W. S. Duke-Elder [1927].

between 25 and 30 mm of mercury. Pressure equilibrium is maintained
by drainage through the canal of Schlemm (Fig. III–3, *S*), and through
the crypts in the anterior surface of the iris, or between the suspensory ligaments of the lens into the vitreous humor. Its index of refraction, which may be obtained by means of an Abbe refractometer, is
1.336.

If the temperature of the unclothed head and hence the aqueous
humor is taken as 35° C, and since water at this temperature has an
index of 1.3316, one can appreciate the contribution made by the salts

in solution, for a 1.1068 per cent salt solution at 25° C has an index of refraction 1.3344. The axial thickness of the anterior chamber containing the aqueous humor is about 3.6 mm.

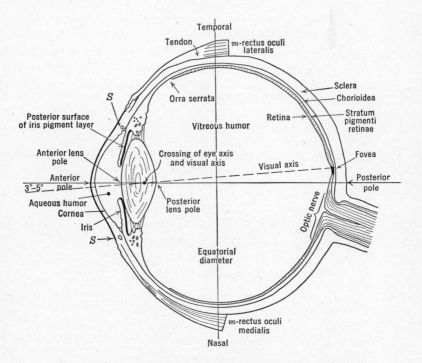

FIG. III–3. Schematic horizontal meridional section of eyeball.

CRYSTALLINE LENS

The contents of the eyeball are partitioned by the iris into two parts. In front of the iris lies the anterior chamber whose outer boundary is the cornea. Behind the iris is the firm, convex crystalline lens.

This lens is a transparent biconvex plastic mass enclosed in an elastic membrane, called the capsule (Fig. III–4). The elastic property of this capsular membrane accounts for the change in shape of the lens. This is shown by the fact that, when the capsule is pierced, the semi-solid lens substance is forced out as a blister; and, if the capsule is removed, the lens does not return to its original shape.

The capsule varies in thickness. It is very thin at the posterior surface near its vertex, but thicker at its anterior pole. It increases in thickness toward the periphery of the lens. The result is that the internal pressure of the lens causes the central section of the capsule to assume a different curvature from its peripheral section.

Histologically the lens is composed of a number of radially arranged fibers each of which is a modified epithelial cell. These fibers are ar-ranged in concentric layers, the more peripheral being soft and nucleated, and of low refractive index, and the fibrous layers between have an intermediate structure and index of refraction.

Gullstrand's schematic eye simulates the above complex structure by substituting for it a crystalline lens having an outer symmetric double convex cover over a core lens of greater index symmetrically placed with respect to the surrounding outer part. This sim-plified equivalent lens has a refractive index 1.413. It has the same size, shape, and focal length as the complex crystal-line lens of the human eye.

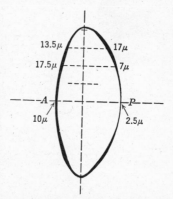

The anterior pole of the human lens lies 3.6 mm behind the vertex of the cornea, and the posterior pole 7.2 mm behind it. Its anterior radius of curvature is 10.0 mm, and its posterior radius is −6.0 mm. When the lens is accommodated for near vision, its anterior pole A (Fig. III–1) moves forward to within 3.2 mm of the cornea pole; its posterior lens sur-face retains its unaccommodated (focused for parallel light) position. The radii of

Fig. III–4. Scale representa-tion of crystalline lens showing changes in thickness of capsule. A, anterior pole. P, posterior pole. (By courtesy of E. F. Fincham [1926].)

curvature change so that its anterior radius of curvature at maxi-mum accommodation is reduced to 5.33 mm and its posterior radius to −5.33 mm. This large posterior change is not universally accepted as representing the complex variations accompanying the rather in-volved change in position of the suspensory ligaments.

When opacities form in the lens (cataract), this structure is removed by a surgical operation. It is then found that a lens of about 10 diop-ters* must be worn by the patient in order that he may see distinctly, and a 4-diopter spherical lens must be added when a glass for reading is prescribed.

The optical center O, of Gullstrand's simplified lens (Fig. III–1), lies 5.85 mm from the vertex of the cornea and 5.2 mm from this vertex when the eye is accommodated for near vision. The first and second

---

* In dealing with spectacle lenses, it is usual to take the unit of length as 1 meter. The reciprocal of the focal length measured in meters is its power in diopters.

nodal points (N, N') lie at 7.08 and 7.33 mm, respectively; hence they are nearly coincident with the posterior pole of the lens.

MECHANISM OF ACCOMMODATION

According to the Helmholtzian theory, the ciliary muscles (Fig. III–5) adjust the lens for near vision by removing the tension from the peripheral suspensory ligaments *S. L.* from which the lens is suspended, and thus allow the lens capsule to expand as the result of its internal hydrostatic pressure.

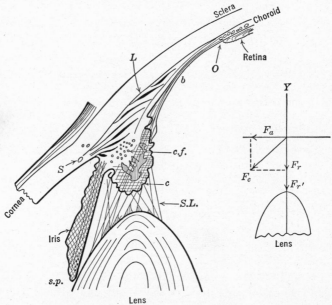

FIG. III–5. A diagrammatic representation of the mechanical interactions of ciliary muscle *L*, suspensory ligaments *S.L.*, and lens. If *L* contracts, the *choroid* is stretched, *b* and *c* move down, removing tension from *S.L.*, the suspensory ligaments of the lens. The vector diagram is supposed to show how the external forces act on the lense. *S*, canal of Schlemm; *s.p.*, *sphincter pupillae*, circular muscle of the iris; *c.f.*, circular fibers of the ciliary muscle; *L*, longitudinal fibers of the ciliary muscle; *c*, ciliary processes; *O*, *ora serrata*, end of retina.

This change in shape of the lens is brought about indirectly through the contraction of the ciliary muscle. The ciliary muscle consists of two separate sets of unstriated muscle fibers: the more superficial set of longitudinal fibers *L*, and the deeper set of bundles of circular fibers *c.f.* The former originate at the sclerocorneal junction near *S* and are attached to the anterior part of the choroid coat behind the ciliary processes below *b*. When these muscles contract they draw the choroid forward. A fundamental objection to Helmholtz's theory, as pointed out by Stilling [1912], is that the choroid cannot move forward when the longitudinal fibers contract.

In Fig. III–5, the ciliary muscle, suspensory ligaments, and lens are shown diagrammatically and a solution is given, on the assumption that the tissue at b is elastic. The longitudinal muscle L is shown sloping at an angle of 45 degrees; the circular fibers (*c.f.*) lie directly below them. Let F_c represent the force of contraction developed by the longitudinal muscles in a coordinate system whose Y axis represents the direction of a radius of the lens passing through the circular fibers above it and perpendicular to the optical axis of the lens. This force may be resolved into two components at right angles to each other, F_a acting along the optical axis of the lens, and F_r acting along a radius of the lens in a direction pointing from the periphery at right angles to the optical axis.

If the radial ciliary muscles contract, lying as they do in the base of the ciliary processes, this contraction causes the apices of the processes to come together and form a smaller circle. In such a circular constriction the forces must again act radially to decrease the circumference of the circle; this latter force is $F_{r'}$ in the diagram. It will be noted that both F_r and $F_{r'}$ act in the same direction, tending to slacken the tension on the suspensory ligaments. The horizontal component of the force F_a which is directed forward tends to slacken the tension in those suspensory ligaments which originate at b and which are attached to the anterior face of the lens. This force does not change the tension on those suspensory ligaments running from the anterior surface of the ciliary process to the posterior side of the lens. These keep the posterior face of the lens under constant tension and do not allow the hydrostatic pressure in the lens to change the radius of curvature of that face. The decreased tension over the anterior surface of the lens allows the lens to bulge in the anterior direction, but not with a uniform change in curvature. The distribution of the suspensory ligaments and the changed thickness of the capsule tend to prevent a uniform change in curvature.

Helmholtz's theory assumes that in a condition of rest the suspensory ligaments which run from the ciliary processes to the capsule of the lens exert a tension upon the capsule which keeps the lens flattened, particularly along its anterior surface, since the ligaments are attached more numerously and more tangentially to this side. The above analysis attributes this greater flattening of the anterior surface of the lens to the increased tension applied to the capsule, to produce the far accommodation, or vision for parallel light, in the normal eye.

AMPLITUDE OF ACCOMMODATION

Objects at a great distance are seen distinctly, as far as their definition permits, without accommodation. This condition is called the *eye at rest*. Practically all objects beyond a distance of 20 to 30 ft (6 to 10 meters) focus on the retina without muscular effort; hence, this distance is usually referred to as the *far point*. The *near point* is that point on the axis which is seen distinctly when the crystalline lens has its greatest refracting power. In youth this may be as little as 10 cm. The *amplitude of accommodation* is defined as the distance of the near point from the far point.

TABLE III-3

LOSS OF ACCOMMODATION WITH ADVANCING YEARS

Age in years	10	15	20	25	30	35	40	45	50	55	60	65	70
Power (F) of accommodation in diopters	14.0	12.6	11.2	9.9	8.5	7.1	5.7	3.7	1.9	1.2	1.0	1.0	1.0

From A. Duane's curves [1912].

The faculty of accommodation is greatest in early life, and diminishes rapidly with advancing years. In this process the near point gradually recedes, but the far point remains practically stationary until the age of 50 years. At 10 years the amplitude or range is from infinity to 7 cm when the maximum accommodation is used. At 20 and 40 years this near point lies at 10 and 22.2 cm, respectively, from the principal point. When the near point has retreated to a distance beyond 25 cm, so that it is no longer possible to read or write conveniently without spectacles, the condition of presbyopia, or old-age vision, has begun to set in. After this it becomes necessary to add a convex lens to the eye so that one may see distinctly at the usual working distance. The decreasing power of accommodation as age increases is expressed conveniently in the number of diopters which may be added to the refractive power* of the eye. Table III-3 shows the results obtained by A. Duane [1912], from a comparative study of 1050 cases, for the mean power of accommodation for different ages. The near point is measured from the anterior focus of the eye, i.e., from a point 15.2 mm in front of the cornea. The gradual reduction in the power of accommodation is attributed to the gradual decrease in elasticity of the lens.

* Reciprocal of the focal length. Units diopters.

VITREOUS HUMOR

The soft jellylike mass which fills the entire cavity of the eye behind the crystalline lens is called the vitreous humor. About 99 per cent of its composition is water. Its index of refraction, readily obtainable with an Abbe refractometer, is 1.336. It is a transparent, rather delicate form of very loose gelatinous connective tissue whose scanty fibers are recognized only with the greatest difficulty. Occasionally a few large cells have been found in it, and small rounded cells somewhat resembling leucocytes are also observed in very limited numbers. These various cells may cast shadows upon the retina within the visual field. Such shadows possess a sort of " flitting " motion when the eyes are moved while looking at a bright light. Frequently one may observe them while looking through a microscope. In advanced age, crystals may form in the vitreous humor, which are observed to settle to the bottom of the eye when the eye is held still.

IRIS

The eye possesses a diaphragm known as the iris. On looking into an eye, one sees the *pupil*, which is the *image of the iris* formed by the interposed cornea and the aqueous humor. From a geometrical optics point of view the iris plays the part of an adjustable stop, through whose aperture the amount of light admitted to the retina is controlled.

The aperture of this stop is controlled by two bands of muscular tissue; the sphincter muscle and the radial muscle. The sphincter muscle forms a circular band under the inner rim of the iris, and its contraction causes the opening in the iris to decrease in size. The contraction of the radial muscle, stretching from the rim to the outer circumference of the iris, causes the opening to increase in size.

Most optical instruments containing lens systems are provided with some means of blocking out such portions of a bundle of rays as are undesirable for one reason or another. This blocking is usually accomplished by interposing in the path of the rays a plane opaque screen set at right angles to the axis, which contains a circular aperture with its center on the axis. The iris is such a perforated screen; it serves as an interior stop or aperture-stop, since it lies within the system. It is placed so as to decrease spherical aberration and thus " sharpen the focus " of the eye and also to control the brightness of the retinal image, which also depends on the size of the stop.

If a rather powerful biconvex reading glass is used as a simple microscope, to examine a sheet of cross-section paper, it will be seen that the central portions of the image and the corners are not focused with equal sharpness, and that the lines also seem curved.   This imperfect focusing results from the fact that this lens reproduces straight lines of a flat object as curved lines concave toward the lens.   A diaphragm placed behind such a lens, leaving only the central area of the lens in use, will block out the peripheral field and allow only the axial rays to pass through the stop to form the image.   These conditions are illustrated

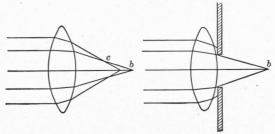

FIG. III–6.

in Fig. III–6, which shows the refracted path of the rays that pass through different zones of the lens.   The outer zones are focused at *c;* the more axial zones are focused further out at *b.*   The *aberration* is measured by the distance *cb.*   A stop placed behind the lens as in Fig. III–6 reduces the aberration and sharpens the focus.

Contraction of the pupil causes a reduction in intensity of the light and limits the beam of light to the central zones of the lens.   The accompanying reduction in axial spherical aberration improves the definition of the image.

SPHERICAL ABERRATION OF THE EYE

Since the cornea and the lens are nearly spherical surfaces, it might be expected that spherical aberration must be present.   The crystalline lens, however, has a structure essentially different from that found in optical instruments.   Owing to the graduated changes of index of refraction, rays passing through the central zone of the lens are refracted to a greater extent than the more peripheral rays, so that the rays marked *b* in Fig. III–6 are more nearly superimposed on the rays *c.*   In addition the more peripheral parts of the lens are flattened; therefore, the lens deviates the rays less than those passing through this area of a spherical lens.

CHROMATIC ABERRATION OF THE EYE

In discussing the simple geometrical formation of images by lenses, it is always assumed that light is monochromatic.   As a matter of fact, when white light is used one must take into consideration not only the deviations but also dispersion.

The convex lens in Fig. III–7 shows how a parallel beam of white light, incident on its left face, is deviated and dispersed. It will be noticed that the violet light is more deviated than the red light; hence the lens has a shorter focal length for violet than for red light. Thus, if a screen is placed at A, we shall get a central white spot surrounded by a violet ring of color surrounded by green and yellow rings with an outside

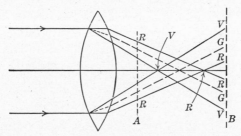

Fig. III–7. Chromatic aberration or chromatic difference of focus of a simple biconvex lens.

border of red; if the screen is placed at B, one may observe a white spot surrounded by a red ring of color surrounded by yellow and green rings with an outside border of violet. This difference of focus for rays of different wavelengths is called *chromatic difference of focus;* it is due to the fact that the *index of refraction of the lens increases with a decrease in wavelength.*

If for the sake of simplicity a simplified eye is adopted consisting of one refracting surface enclosing a single medium composed of water, and giving the single refracting surface a radius of 5.13 mm, the different focal lengths of this eye for red and blue light can be calculated. The indices of refraction of water for red (6536 Å) and blue (4308 Å) light are 1.331 and 1.342, respectively. The focal lengths of the simplified eye are therefore 20.57 and 20.14 mm. If the eye were unaccommodated so that the retina lies at the focus of the yellow rays, approximately halfway between these foci, the focus of the blue ray would be about 0.22 mm behind the retina. Experiments have shown that, when such a series of foci are formed by the eye, the rays of greatest intensity form the most sharply focused image. For maximum brightness, the narrow yellow-green part of the spectrum near 5560 Å is used. For low intensities the focus shifts to the blue-green near 5040 Å. The colors having longer and shorter wavelengths form blurred disks of light of relatively low intensity on top of the sharply focused image. With an increase in the diameter of the pupil, the periphery of the lens is exposed so that the chromatic aberration increases; on the other hand, the diffraction decreases. The two changes, however, practically compensate each other, leaving the definition of the image unchanged, but the depth of focus decreases.

Astigmatism

In an ideal eye the refractive surfaces are sections of true spheres, and, all the meridians being of equal curvature, the refraction along these different meridians is equal. Such an eye with a small pupil will refract a cone of monochromatic light, issuing from a luminous point, to a focal point on the retina and will exclude the disturbing contributions of spherical aberration. If one or all of the refractive surfaces, however, have unequal curvatures along different meridians, then the rays

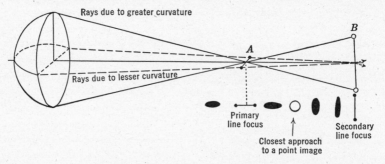

Fig. III–8.   An astigmatic lens, showing the shape of the astigmatic ray bundles.

from a luminous monochromatic point source cannot be brought to a single focal point, since the rays along the meridian of greater curvature will be brought to a focus first and begin to diverge before the rays along the lesser curvature are focused. Such a condition is called *astigmatism* (not a point). The effect can be illustrated by the diagram of Fig. III–8, which represents the refraction of the rays from a luminous point by a cornea whose curvature along the vertical meridian is greater than the curvature along the horizontal meridian. The lower line of figures represents the section of the cone of light, or the images obtained at different distances. The images vary from a horizontal line to a vertical line, but at no place can a point be obtained at which rays along all meridians are focused. At *B* the rays along the vertical meridian are in focus; at *A* the rays along the horizontal meridian are brought to a focus.

Ordinary astigmatism is usually attributed to a defect in the curvature of the cornea. The condition illustrated by Fig. III–8 can be corrected by means of a convex cylindrical lens (+ cylinder), so chosen as to increase the refraction along the meridian in which the cornea has the least curvature; conversely, the refraction along the meridian of greatest curvature can be diminished by means of a concave cylindrical lens (− cylinder).

A simple experiment illustrating astigmatism can be performed by closing the eyelids over a normal eye until only a narrow slit remains, so that the watery fluid bathing the eye forms a concave cylindrical lens which alters the curvature along the vertical meridian. The question is, why is the fluid lens concave? Which meridian is out of focus?

BRIGHTNESS OF LUMINOUS RADIATION

The amount of radiant energy necessary to produce a fixed luminous sensation of brightness varies enormously with the wavelength of the radiation. By *brightness* is meant the luminous flux per unit of emissive area viewed on a plane set perpendicular to the line of sight. It is measured in lumens per square centimeter — a unit called the *lambert*. Thus, when a diffusing surface reflects *all* the light incident upon it, its brightness in lamberts is equal to its illumination in lumens per square centimeter.

The total visible energy emitted by a source per second is called the total luminous flux. The *unit of flux*, the *lumen*, is that flux emitted in unit solid angle by a point source having a luminous intensity of 1 international candle. A uniform point source of 1 *candle intensity* thus emits 4π lumens.

One millilambert equals 0.929 lumen per square foot, or the brightness that would be produced by 0.929 foot-candle on a diffusing surface of 100 per cent reflection factor. Since most of the diffusing surfaces are ordinary " white " surfaces of 80 per cent reflection factor, 1 foot-candle produces a brightness on a white surface of 0.86 millilambert.

Daylight brightness at sunrise and sunset is usually less than 100 millilamberts. The average brightness of an ordinary blue sky is about 500 millilamberts, but a moderate haze increases the brightness of the sky to 1500 millilamberts.

The eye operates normally under intensities comparable to the brightness of white paper in full sunlight (10 lamberts) as an upper limit, and to a threshold of vision of 7×10^{-7} millilambert as a lower limit, or in a range of 20 billion to 1 — a greater range of sensitivity than most physical instruments.

It was found, however, that, when the brightness of a field of constant area varied by a factor of 10 billion, the retinal sensibility varied by a factor of only 10 million. Can this discrepancy be accounted for by a variation in the size of the pupil? The total range in pupillary diameter is from 2 to 8 mm, or a range in area from 1 to 16, the pupil adjusting itself so as to maintain constant light energy on the retina. Apparently, this is not a sufficient variation to account for the discrepancy. A time element, however, is also involved when the retina is exposed to the radiant energy. The time of the exposure, especially at threshold vision, modifies the expected results.

The time element of the retinal exposure can be obtained from some data collected by Reeves [1918], which show that at *low intensities* the product of time and threshold brightness, measured in millilamberts, is only approximately constant. His data were obtained by using a carefully calibrated focal plane shutter for determining the time of exposure, when a 3 cm square test spot was placed at a distance of 35 cm.

This result indicates that, the lower the intensity, the longer must the image remain on the retina to produce a sensation of brightness, and that a *high intensity* lingering for a short period of time does not produce the same brightness effect as a low intensity lingering for a long period of time. Hence the product of threshold by time should be constant if the energy density on the retina is to remain constant. The retina acts as if the radiant energy were integrated in some way to produce the threshold effect. Therefore brightness increases in proportion as either the intensity or the time intervals are increased, and equal brightness near the threshold is obtained if the product time-intensity remains constant. That is, as duration is increased, intensity must be decreased in order that the response remain at threshold value.

This relation ceases to be effective if the time of stimulation is longer than a critical duration of about 0.1 sec, as Reeves' data show in the sudden change in values of threshold × time for values of time greater than 0.160 sec.

This fact is of importance in flashlight signaling. The blinker should remain open for at least 0.1 sec in order to make the greatest possible retinal impression.

ENERGY THRESHOLD

If the energy entering the pupil is E ergs per second, it should be proportional to the square of the radius (r) of the pupil, inversely proportional to the square of the distance (D) of the test spot from the observer, and directly proportional to the area (A) of the test spot measured in square centimeters, to B its brightness in lamberts, and to

M the least mechanical equivalent of light; hence

$$E = \frac{Br^2 AM}{D^2}$$

If M is taken as 151×10^{-5} watt per lumen,* it can be shown that, for a stimulus possessing an area of 2 sq mm viewed at a distance of 35 cm and possessing a brightness of 0.000362 millilambert, the energy entering the eye is as low as 143×10^{-10} erg per sec. The smallest number of photons per second to which the retina will respond can now be calculated.

Let us suppose that the test spot is emitting monochromatic light of wavelength 5560×10^{-8} cm, corresponding with the region of maximum retinal sensitivity. We can then calculate the energy content of 1 photon of this radiant energy incident on the retina. It is $E = h\nu = hc/\lambda$, where h is Planck's constant, of magnitude 6.62×10^{-27} erg sec; c is the velocity of light and equal to 3×10^{10} cm per sec; and λ is the indicated wavelength. Hence $E = 0.036 \times 10^{-10}$ erg.

If the above threshold power value is accepted as 143×10^{-10} erg per sec, then 4000 photons per second of this green radiation is used. If the exposure to produce an experienced sensation occurs in 0.002 sec, it follows that the retina responds to as few as 8 photons — an extraordinary and remarkable sensitivity. Hevesy and Paneth [1938] find that for a practiced eye about 30 photons of the above wavelength suffice for the unaided visual perception of an alpha-particle scintillation Barnes and Czerny [1932] find light flashes of 40 to 90 photons as the minimum sensitivity of the dark-adapted eye.

A solution of visual purple extracted from the retinas of frogs by Dartnall et al. [1938] showed that the number of chromophoric groupings in visual purple destroyed in relation to the number of photons absorbed is nearly equal to unity.

RESPONSE OF THE PUPIL WITH CHANGES IN BRIGHTNESS

It has been found that the pupil has a different diameter for each *brightness level*. This adjustment is due to the fact that the pupil is automatically regulated so as to maintain constant light energy on the retina. In this connection the evidence supplied by Reeves [1920] from his study of the response of the pupil to changing intensities of light is significant. The diameter of the pupil at any given brightness was determined by means of a flashlight and motion-picture camera. The apparent diameters viewed through the cornea and aqueous humor

* H. T. Wensel, *J. Research Natl. Bur. Standards*, **22**, 375, 1939.

TABLE III-4

PUPILLARY DIAMETER CHANGES WITH CHANGES IN BRIGHTNESS

Brightness units B in millilamberts

Pupillary diameters D in millimeters (average of 6 subjects)

B	0	0.00015	0.01	1.0	10	55	100
D	8.0	7.6	7.0	5.0	4.0	3.1	2.8
Area/π	16.0	14.4	12.3	6.25	4.00	2.40	1.96
Log B		−4.17	−2.0	0	1.0	1.74	2.00
Log B × Area					4.00	4.18	3.92

By Courtesy of P. Reeves [1918], and the Eastman Kodak Company.

were photographed and the dimensions were increased 7 per cent so as to obtain the actual dimensions. Under these circumstances the pupillary diameters shown in Table III-4 were obtained. However, we can draw only an approximate conclusion from these results, namely, that the logarithm of the brightness times the pupillary area is nearly constant for brightness greater than 10.0 millilamberts. Reeves' work also shows that the response of the pupil under conditions of artificial lighting is such that at 2000 millilamberts the diameter of the pupil is as small as 2 mm. This contraction of the pupil is comparable to that produced when a 100-watt lamp in a 5-in. diameter globe of good diffusing glass is held near the eye.

SPECTRAL SENSITIVITY OF THE EYE

The quantitative study of the response of the retina to light of various wavelengths originated with R. A. König as early as 1893. His data of *visibility at low intensities* are used in Fig. III-9. The curve of *visibility at high intensities*, as adopted by the Illuminating Engineering Society to represent the composite results of Ives, Kingsbury, Nutting, Coblentz, Emerson, Hyde, Cody, and Forsythe, are also shown for comparison.

The visibility at low intensities was determined by a threshold method, which consists in determining the least amount of energy that is just perceptible at each wavelength. The visibility at high intensities is determined by means of a direct measurement of the relative brightness of equal amounts of energy throughout the spectrum. From these curves it will be observed that the sensitivity of the eye shifts towards the blue end of the spectrum at low levels of illumination. This shift is attributed to a transition from cone to rod vision. Hence, if a red and blue field are matched at a high brightness level and then compared at a low level as in moonlight, the red field appears darker and the blue lighter. This shift to rod vision accounts for the blue appearance of objects as seen by moonlight. (Full moon 0.02 ft-candle.)

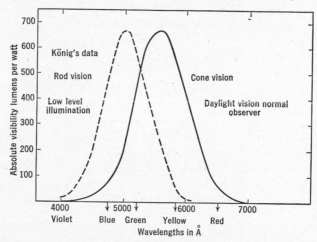

FIG. III–9. The visibility curves of the human eye or the brightness distribution of the visible spectrum. Rod vision attains its maximum visibility at 5040 Å; cone vision, at 5560 Å. The absolute visibility at maximum is 667 lumens per watt.

The curves also show that the amount of radiant energy necessary to produce a desired sensation of brightness varies enormously with the wavelength. It is least in the yellow-green region at 5560 Å, but for low-level illumination this maximum brightness shifts to 5040 Å. If a low-intensity spectrum is viewed and decreased in brightness, a point will be reached at which its violet and yellow ends disappear first, and the blue-green sensation due to 5040 Å disappears last.

In colorimetric methods of analysis as applied to clinical work, reference will again be made to this phenomenon in determining the choice and relative accuracy of colorimetric comparison methods.

TRANSMISSION CHARACTERISTICS OF THE OCULAR MEDIA FOR ULTRAVIOLET RADIATIONS

Extensive experiments on animal eyes have shown that ultraviolet radiation of high intensity and long exposure does not injure the retina since the optical media involved are opaque to these short wavelengths, but that this radiation will produce very painful conjunctivitis.

The cornea is opaque to all wavelengths below 2950 Å, although some evidence exists that the cornea of the rabbit is transparent to shorter wavelengths. The cornea can transmit light of wavelength as small as 3000 Å.

The crystalline lens is opaque to wavelengths below 3200 Å, although young lenses have shown transmissions from 3150 to 3300 Å. With increased age there is some absorption in the spectral region extending from 4000 to 4200 Å. The lens absorbs powerfully the ultraviolet radiations lying between 3000 and 3800 Å roughly; it also fluoresces when this group of rays strikes it. The absorbed radiation is re-emitted as scattered light of longer wavelengths, and is therefore useless for image formation. This scattered light confuses the vision and should be externally absorbed, before entering the cornea, by means of a sheet of Crookes A glass.

The vitreous humor, since it is composed chiefly of water with a slight addition of salts, is comparable to a layer of water 1.46 cm thick, and like water it is transparent to short violet light around 2300 Å. It has, however, an absorption band reaching from 2500 to 2800 Å. But 2800 Å is not transmitted by the cornea or by the lens; hence, the minimum wavelength reaching the retina must be 3500 Å, or longer.

The combined tissues of the " normal eye " probably do not transmit violet light below 4000 Å, a good practical dividing line between the visual spectrum and the ultraviolet.

In the development of artificial sunlight illuminants, Luckiesh [1930] has shown that, when the outer membrane of eyes was exposed to moderate intensities of illumination, even though wavelengths as short as 2800 Å were present in abundance, no conjunctivitis was developed. For instance, reading 3 hours from a book illuminated to an intensity of 300 ft-candles caused no inflammation of the conjunctiva. Intense direct ultraviolet radiations, however, will produce conjunctivitis. Therefore it seems that 3100 Å is a safe lower wavelength limit for inclusion in artificial sunlight, as used for general lighting. A 1-mm soda glass screen is ample protection against the inflammatory radiations emitted by lighting devices.

Infra-Red Transmission

The near-infra-red region extends from about 7000 to 14,000 Å. On a clear day with the sun at zenith and normal atmospheric pressure an intensity of 8540 ft-candles can be recorded. Of this intensity 44 per cent lies between 4000 and 7600 Å and 36 per cent in the short-wave infra-red region. (See chapter on absorption.) The most efficient artificial producers of this radiation are high-temperature solids, as, for instance, the metal filaments in incandescent high-wattage tungsten-filament lamps.

Visible radiation will penetrate great depths of water, but the transmission factor of water falls off rapidly from 7600 Å towards the longer wavelengths, as seen in Fig. III–10. Since the optical system of the eye may be reduced, according to Luckiesh [1921], to an equivalent layer of water 2.28 cm thick, it is possible to predict the transmission of the optical system by analyzing the infra-red transmission curve of water of this thickness. The justification for this water equivalent lies in the fact that the cornea is composed of about 90 per cent water. The cortex of the lens is about 92 per cent water, falling to 84 per cent in the center. It will be noted in Fig. III-10 that the per cent transmission of water falls off rapidly, reaching a very low value for 10,000 Å and dropping to opacity at 14,000 Å.

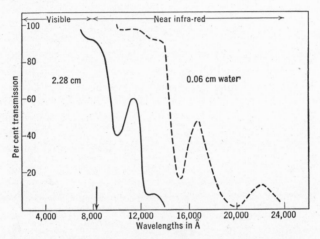

FIG. III–10. The spectral transmission of water in the near infra-red. Retina is sensitive to about 8350 Å. Radiant energy, however, is transmitted up to 12,000 Å. Retina does not respond to region between 8000 and 12,000 Å despite the high transmissivity of the medium. Values of the transmission of water at various thicknesses were obtained from Aschkinass, *Ann. Physik*, **55**, 401 (1895). Values for 2.28 cm reproduced through the courtesy of M. Luckiesh [1921].

The visible limit at the red end of the spectrum under the most favorable conditions has been found to be near 8350 Å; under ordinary circumstances it is difficult to go beyond 8000 Å, although some experimenters place this limit at 7600 Å. At 10,000 Å the media of the eye are about 40 per cent transparent; although the transparency rises to 65 per cent at about 11,000 Å, it rapidly drops to opacity near 12,000 Å. Thus those rays having wavelengths greater than 8000 Å *do not excite a response in the retinal structure.*

The question is often raised as to the efficiency of protection by eyeglasses in the near infra-red. The spectral transmission of glass decreases quite rapidly beyond 30,000 Å, but glasses are fairly transparent in the near infra-red. Even colored glasses have fairly high transmission factors in this region. The clear glasses, including quartz, are almost perfectly transparent to 28,000 Å and quite effectively transmit energy as far as 40,000 Å. Special glasses of the cobalt blue type, however, have marked absorption bands between 5000 and 7000 Å.

A 2.5 per cent solution of crystallized cupric chloride is most effective in absorbing the long infra-red wavelength region. A layer of this fluid 2 cm thick absorbs nearly all the radiation beyond 8000 Å and still transmits rather freely in the visible region.

Very high-temperature furnaces, and the products from such furnaces, immediately after withdrawal as in rolling mills or in glass-blowing establishments, subject the workmen to intense radiations. Goggles must be worn by the operators to protect the eyes against these radiations.

For some operations such as welding, especially arc welding on iron, where the emission is not only rich in infra-red but exceptionally high in ultra-violet radiation, protective goggles must have a high absorption in the visible in addition to a well-nigh complete absorption in both the infra-red and ultraviolet region. For such purposes, special welding glasses are available to meet the specifications drafted by the Federal Government in 1930 and published as " Federal Master Specifications. "

The windows in aviator goggles, which are light green in color, are now being made which possess transmission properties very similar to the daylight visibility curve of the normal eye (Fig. III–9). If the windows in these goggles are 2 mm thick they have a total transmission of approximately 50 per cent in the visible.

CATARACTS OR LENTICULAR OPACITIES

The prevalence of lenticular opacities in the eye of tinplate mill men has been studied by Healy. In all, about 350 men were examined. The men entered the mill at about 18 years of age and developed an opacity about 15 years later. In this group 40 per cent of the men over 35 years of age had lenticular opacities (see Fig. III–11) apparently caused by the manipulation of the red-hot tinplate at distances which vary from 2 to 5 ft from the eyes. A similar affliction, called " bottle-maker's cataract," is attributed by most ophthalmologists to infra-red absorption. In connection with these studies may be mentioned the experiments of Burge [1924], who investigated the cataracts produced in the eyes of fish living in water containing small quantities of calcium chloride or sodium silicate. His conclusions, briefly stated, were that, when excessive salts exist in the humor and the nutritive sources of the lens, the liability to cataractous conditions is increased. The trade cataracts mentioned above are usually attributed to the overheating of the eye as a whole with consequent disturbed nutrition of the lens.

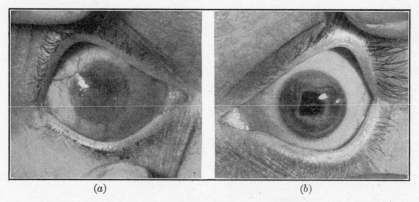

(a)   (b)

Fig. III–11. Correction of a corneal opacity by a transplant from an enucleated eye. (a) Corneal opacity before operation. (b) Transplant 4 mm square taken from an enucleated eye of a stillborn child. Photographs by courtesy of A. Marfaing. For details on keratoplasty see R. Castroviejo, *Am. J. Ophthalmol.*, **17**, 932 (1934); for bibliography, see *Arch. Ophthalmol.*, **22**, 144 (1939).

The near-infra-red rays, though freely transmitted by the cornea, are in large part absorbed by the iris. This excessive local absorption may in turn produce an abnormal stimulus to the processes controlling the secretion of the humor and thus may cause nutritional disturbances in the lens.

RETINA

The retina (*pars optica retinae*) may be said to be formed by the radial expansion of the fibers of the optic nerve which enter the eye at the inner side of its posterior pole, pierce the sclera and choroid, and spread out over the inner surface of the eyeball. The retina is considered to extend forward from the entrance of the optic nerve (optic disk) as far as the posterior margin of the ciliary body, where it apparently ends abruptly with an indented border, the *ora serrata*. During life the retina is perfectly transparent, despite its complex cell structure, with the exception of its pigment layer. It presents on its inner surface a slightly elevated yellow spot, the *macula lutea*, which is located at the posterior pole of the visual axis. The *fovea centralis*, a slight depression in the center of the yellow spot, is the result of an apparent thinning of the retinal layers at this point.

The retina, if considered in detail, is made up of ten layers (Fig.

III–12). The radiant energy passes through them in the following order to reach the photoreceptor layer of rods and cones bounded on the external side by the pigment epithelium lying adjacent to the choroid: (1) the internal limiting membrane, (2) the optic nerve fiber layer, (3) the ganglion cell layer, (4) the inner plexiform layer, (5) the inner nuclear (bipolar cells) layer, (6) the external plexiform layer, (7) the outer nuclear layer, (8) the external limiting membrane, (9) the photoreceptor layer, and (10) the pigment layer. The first six layers are grouped as contained in the cerebral portion and the last four in the neuroephithelial portion of the structure.

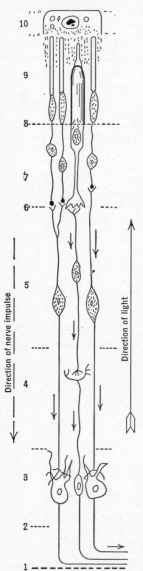

From a biophysical point of view the chief interest centers on the visual cells (9) and pigmented epithelium (10) as the basic elements concerned with the interception of the radiant energy and the use of the absorbed energy to excite the nerve impulses that are propagated along the nerve fibers.

RETINAL RECEPTOR MECHANISM

The rod and cone visual cells are radially packed in a shell lying between the external limiting membrane and the pigmentary epithelium (10). Their photosensitive segments are turned radially outward with

FIG. III–12. Grouping of the neurons in the human retina into functional systems. The incident light passes through the following layers: 1. Internal limiting membrane next to the vitreous humor. 2. Layer of optic never fibers. 3. Layer of ganglion cells which receive the nerve impulses from the bipolar cells above them. 4. Inner plexiform layer. 5. Inner nuclear or bipolar cell layer. 6. External plexiform layer. 7. Outer nuclear layer. 8. External limiting membrane. 9. Photoreceptor layer. Cones and rods mixed. Cones resemble flasks with narrow necks. They are about one-sixth shorter than the slender, nearly cylindrical rods. Rods about 2 microns thick and 60 microns long. The nerve impulses are supposed to originate in them as a result of the absorption of the incident radiant energy. 10. Pigment layer. Single pigmented cell, vertical section, hexagonally packed. Color, dark brown.

their outer segments pointing to the pigment cell layer. Protruding beyond the external limiting membrane (8) is a rod or filament-like structure divided into three segments: inner segment, fiber apparatus, and outer segment. If the structure is a cone, it is also divided into three sections: inner segment, lentiform body, and outer segment. The rod and cone elements are regarded as specialized neuroepithelial cells and not as nerve cells. It has been suggested that the rods and cones are not distinct elements because various characteristics of the one are found in the other. Since in man the cones in the fovea resemble the rods at the periphery of the retina, it might be concluded that the cones have become specialized in one direction and the rods in the opposite direction, having a common relatively neutral ancestor.

The distribution of rods and cones is not uniform throughout the retina. At the entrance of the optic nerve (optic disk), rods and cones are absent; hence light incident upon this area (blind spot) gives no visual sensation. The *fovea centralis* contains no rods. In the *macula lutea*, and in a widening circle around the fovea, rods and cones are present in approximately equal proportions. Towards the periphery the cones decrease in number until at the very margin only rods remain.

The mosaic of rods and cones is very regular. Near the *macula* the cones are separated from each other by a single circle of rods; a short distance from the *macula* each cone is surrounded by series of three rows of rods, then four, and this pattern of increasing number of rods continues even close to the *ora serrata*, where only rods are found.

The *macula lutea* is about 0.6 mm in diameter, and in this minute area a real image must be projected to produce distinct vision. The inference is that the cone structure is identified with perception of detail. The threshold for stimulation in this region is rather high and it is not appreciably increased by dark adaptation. The cones, therefore, are not particularly adapted to perception of low intensities of illumination. This fact can be verified experimentally by looking at a night sky; the stars located at the border of the visual field appear much brighter than those lying at the center.

In the most peripheral zones of the retina, where only rods are present, the threshold for vision is much less and can be decreased still more by dark adaptation; hence, the inference is that the rods respond best in dim illumination, and it has been found that they are particularly capable of detecting movements of retinal images of low intensity.

Color perception, being associated with the cones, is most highly developed at the fovea. Here the inner layers of the retina become very much thinned, until near the center the transparent nerve tissues are represented merely by scattered cells of the inner nuclear and ganglion cell layers. The inner segments of the cones in the fovea are closely packed into a hexagonal pattern. This close-packed small elliptical depression, whose horizontal and vertical diameters are about 0.3 and 0.2 mm respectively, is also the seat of most distinct vision. The cones

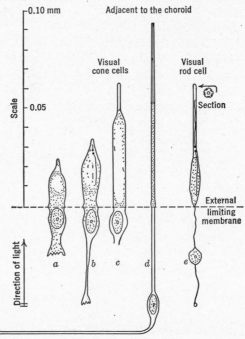

Fig. III–13. Visual cone and rod cells of man. Cone cells: *a*, from the *ora serrata*; *b*, from *fundus* outside of *macula lutea* (yellow spot); *c*, from the margin of the *macula lutea*; *d*, from *fovea centralis*. Rod cell *e* contains visual purple.

in this depression are very much longer, as illustrated by *d* in Fig. III–13. They have the appearance of elongated rods. The number of cones in the fovea is about 4000. The number rods in the human retina totals about 130 million, the cones 7 million.

VISUAL ACUITY

Acuity of vision is the ability to perceive the interspace between two very close objects. It is defined as the reciprocal of the just resolvable visual angle measured in minutes of arc. For the purpose of measurement a test object, in the form of an equally spaced ruled grating, a pair of parallel bars, or an incomplete circle or C-shaped figure, is employed.

Experiments show that the interspace between two parallel bars must be increased as their distance from the eye is increased, and that the angle at the eye, subtended by the interspace, must be greater than a certain minimum value. This angle is very close to 1 minute of arc, although values as low as 30 seconds have been obtained for persons of exceptionally good vision. Taking the posterior nodal point of the lens as 16.7 mm from the retina, 1 minute of arc corresponds with a distance of 0.0048 mm between the images at the retina. The diameter of the outer segment of a cone in the fovea is 0.002 mm, and its inner segment, which is a close-packed hexagonal mosaic, has a diameter of 0.003 mm; it follows that two points on an image can straddle a single cone and still be 0.0048 mm apart. Two point images can, therefore, be resolved by the mosaic of the fovea if one unilluminated cone lies between them.

E. Hering in 1900 advanced the following interpretation in support of the mosaic-pattern-structure theory. Figure III–14 shows a scale drawing of the retinal mosaic on which an image with a broken line of separation between light and dark portions is indicated. It is assumed that a change in stimulation of a single cone or column of cones is necessary to perceive the displacement of a retinal image. In image *a* the upper half of the cells in column *c* is stimulated, but in the lower section no cell of this column is stimulated. Hence a break in the edge of the image should be perceived. In *b* the image is shown slightly displaced to the right. No discontinuity can be perceived in its edge because all the cells in column *d* are stimulated.

The upper diagram in Fig. III–14 indicates that the horizontal displacement of the broken edge of the image can be as small as *x* and still excite two parallel columns of cells. If *x* is as small as 0.00087 mm for the hexagonal close-packed cone system in the retina, then *x* sub-tends an arc of 12 seconds at the nodal points of the eye, which are at an average distance of 16.8 mm from the retinal image. The results are supported by the experimental evidence. It has been shown experimentally that the minimum separation of a break in a line detectable by unaided vision is as low as 12 ± 4 seconds of arc.

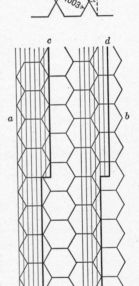

Fig. III–14. Hering's mosaic pattern of the retina.

The conclusion is, therefore, that visual acuity for the positions and movements of contours is about five times greater than it is for resolution of double points and lines. Therefore, where interpolation methods of measurement are used, as in the estimation of the position of a slide rule, or of a meniscus of a barometer or chemical burette, the observations are much less accurate than those obtained by a coincidence method as is used in mensuration.

VARIATION OF ACUITY WITH DISTANCE FROM FOVEA

The acuity of vision rapidly decreases as the image moves away from the fovea. Figure III–15 shows this decrease in visual acuity and its variation with angular departure from perpendicular incidence on the

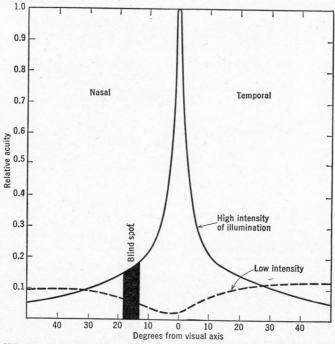

FIG. III–15. Variation of acuity with distance from the *fovea centralis* in direct vision. Composite curve after Helmholtz, *Handbuch der physiologischen Optik.*

fovea. At 5° from the fovea it falls to one third of its maximum. The broken line represents the visual acuity under very low intensities of illumination. On the other hand, when the eyes are used for fine work at high-level brightness, the visual acuity is very high at the center of the fovea. The drop in visual acuity across the fovea at low intensities, apparent in the depression of the dotted curve, indicates why we see a faint star in the night sky better near the rim of vision than when it is focused on the fovea. The crossing of the blind spot is shown by the gap in the two lines at the nasal side of the axis.

MEASURES OF ACUITY OF VISION

From the theoretical standpoint the simplest measure of acuity or "sharpness" of vision is the minimum angular separation which permits of resolution for two point objects. As mentioned above, this value for the normal eye is taken as 1 minute of arc. Hooke first pointed out in 1671 that the resolving power of the normal eye for such an object as a double star is about 1 minute of arc. The double star,

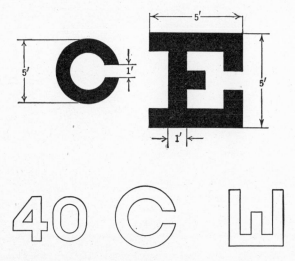

FIG. III–16. The upper letter E should be read by a normal eye at 50 ft. The lower line and upper letter C should be read at 40 ft.

imaged on the fovea of the retina, can be perceived as two point sources if a relatively unstimulated cone lies between two others on which more energy is received.

Vision is usually tested at 6 meters or about 20 feet. For this purpose a "page of type" is usually employed as a test object. In 1862 Snellen published a chart of test letters based on the assumption that 1 minute of arc is characteristic of the *minimum separable*. Figure III–16 illustrates the principle of construction of a typical test-chart letter. Each letter in one row has a diameter subtending 5 minutes of arc at a distance marked on the chart against the row, and the stroke of the letter has a width subtending 1 minute of arc. A person with normal vision should be able to read the letters of any row at the distance indicated by the numerals set at the end of the row. The types are printed for distances from 20 to 200 feet. The illumination should be above 50 ft-candles, and glare must be avoided.

The " broken ring " of Landolt [1876] aims at providing a test less variable than that of the letters.   The ring has a diameter which subtends 5 minutes of arc at the standard distance, while its width and a gap in the ring each subtend 1 minute of arc.   The observer must be able to recognize the position of the gap in any relative position of the letter.   Although the measurement of acuity by such a broken ring may be rendered more difficult in the presence of uncorrected visual astigmatism, a greater consistency can be claimed in tests with this type of standardized object.

Color Variables

Color is an experienced sensation.   The color variables are brightness, hue, and saturation.

At ordinary levels of illumination intensity or of brightness, one can see about the same brightness-difference of colored surfaces as of colorless ones.   Between a perfect white and a perfect black one perceives about 60 perceptible shades of neutral grays for an intensity of illumination of about 50 ft-candles.   Thus, one can distinguish about 125 hues in the spectrum of sunlight.   Hue is a property of color which varies with changes in the frequency of the stimulating light.   The ability to detect a difference in saturation (tint) is not very well developed. It is estimated that 20 different degrees of saturation represent the average number of tints of a color actually distinguishable.

Therefore, multiplying the number of distinguishable hues (125) by the distinguishable shades (30) under a given high intensity of illumination by the distinguishable tints (20) gives 75,000 as the approximate number of different color sensations.   If, in addition, the intensity of illumination is changed so as to introduce a range of brightness, it is seen that the number of distinctly different visual sensations which one can experience, excluding those of form, runs into the millions.

The Fundamental Colors

It can be shown experimentally that three frequencies may be selected from a continuous spectrum — one from the red end at about 6800 Å, one from the blue end at about 4500 Å, and one from the middle at about 5560 Å — whose combinations in different proportions will give a sensation of white, any of the intermediate shades, or purple.   Considered physically, these three frequencies may be designated as fundamental color arousers, but it is to be remembered that color is a term used to indicate a reaction in consciousness, and it is therefore not strictly applicable to the physical stimuli.

The fundamental color sensations according to some theories are red, green, and blue; according to others, they are red, yellow, green, and blue.

Theories of Color Vision

It is doubtful that any subject in science has given rise to so much speculation as the cause of color vision. The earliest historical period of speculation on how color is experienced, 640 B.C. to A.D. 1671, contains such great names as Pythagoras, Epicurus, Aristotle. The second great period, 1671 to 1801, of color theory was dominated by Newton's corpuscular theories. During the third period, 1801 to 1874, the contributions of the great minds of Young, Helmholtz, and Maxwell were added. The fourth period, which began with Hering's outstanding contribution, extended from 1874 to the early nineteen hundreds and culminated in the quantum interpretation of the photoelectric effect and applications of the quantum theory to photo-chemistry of the photoreceptor processes in the retina.

The Young-Helmholtz theory, as Troland [1920] points out, is preferred by physicists because it lays emphasis primarily upon the stimuli to vision, while the Hering theory receives more attention from the psychologists because its fundamental conceptions are derived from introspective analysis.

These theories postulate the existence in the photoreceptors of the retina of a number of specific chemical substances which are acted upon by light. According to the Young-Helmholtz theory, there are three of these substances which are decomposed at a maximum rate by red, green, and blue light, respectively, and less so by the remainder of the visual spectrum. The rates of photochemical decomposition of these three chemical substances are supposed to be reported individually to the brain via the optic nerve, and the ratio between the three decomposition products determines the nature of the sensation. This ratio accounts satisfactorily for the laws of " color mixture " for normal, and also for some forms of color-defective vision, but it does very little more than this. It fails completely to explain the changes in the nature of the colors when the combination of red and green forms yellow, or when the combination of yellow and blue forms white.

The theory of Hering also postulates the presence in the entire retinocerebral apparatus of three substances. One of these substances is decomposed by light of all frequencies, although to the greatest extent by yellow-green light. This substance is then supposed to accumulate during the absence of light, owing to a reversible chemical reaction.

The other two substances are supposed to be decomposed at a maximum rate by red and yellow lights, and recomposed by green and blue lights.

TABLE III-5

PHOTOCHEMICAL SUBSTANCE	RETINAL PROCESS	SENSATION
A. Red-green	Disassimilation	Red
	Assimilation	Green
B. Yellow-blue	Disassimilation	Yellow
	Assimilation	Blue
C. White-black	Disassimilation	White
	Assimilation	Black

The six psychological primary colors, red, green, yellow, blue, white, and black, are correlated directly with six distinctive rates of change in the three basic photochemical substances, as shown in Table III-5.

This system of relationships satisfactorily explains the manner in which the psychological primaries combine with one another, and accounts especially for the " antagonistic " behavior of red and green, and yellow and blue.   Troland [1920] points out that the three weakest points in this theory are: (1) the failure of opposite processes in the black-white substance actually to cancel each other while those in the other two substances always leave a residual gray; (2) the fact that psychologically primary red and green do not in fact combine to produce gray, but rather a yellow; and (3) the failure of continuous stimulation of a single region of the retina to reduce the sensory effects of all stimuli to a neutral mid-gray.

Apparently, therefore, the essentially antagonistic natures of the processes underlying respective members of the three pairs of primary colors are not supported by the experimental facts.

To meet these and other criticisms, Mrs. Ladd-Franklin [1892] proposed a theory based essentially on the existence of a single light-sensitive substance located in the retina.   She also assumed a gradual evolution of the color sense of the retina from a primitive condition of colorless vision such as still exists in the periphery of the retina to a high degree of specialization by the fovea to reactions of color.   Thus the retina is supposed to preserve a complete record of the historical changes of the anatomical development of rods into cones and also a comparable development of the rod-pigment sensitizer.   In man only is there an additional intermediate cleavage stage, the visual yellow.

According to the Ladd-Franklin theory a hypothetical light-sensitive substance must be assumed to break down in three stages.   In stage I its decomposition by light leads to the initiation of nerve impulses in such a manner as to produce various gradations of achromatic luminosity in the visual sensation ranging from black, which is associated with the absence of excitation, to a white associated with the maximum rate of decomposition. In stage II of differentiation, the substance presents to the action of light two separate parts, corresponding, for example, " with two different radicals involved in the constitution of its original complex molecules." One of these parts is decomposed at a maximum rate by yellow light, and the other by blue light. The products of decomposition act upon the optic nerve to produce the colors yellow and blue in consciousness. Simultaneous and equivalent decomposition of the two parts of the substance, however, generates a gray in consciousness. Stage III of evolution of the substance involves a differentiation of the yellow-sensitive component into red-sensitive and green-sensitive constituents. When these are acted upon separately, they produce a psychologically primary red and green in consciousness, but when simultaneously and equally decomposed they yield the original value.

Hecht [1928] objects to the assumption that the sensations yellow and white are unique. He points out that if Young's idea is correct then yellow is a phenomenon which is produced where red and green receptor substances respond simultaneously. Similarly, white is identified when all three — red, green, and blue — receptor substances respond simultaneously. Both Hering and Ladd-Franklin have devised theories that assume the existence of separate receptor substances for yellow and for white.

Hecht raised the question as to which of these two conceptions of yellow and white is correct. His answer was obtained by means of a simple experiment of binocular color mixing. He placed a red filter (Wratten 29) in front of one eye and a green filter (Wratten 58) in front of the other eye, and then viewed a brightly illuminated white surface about 20 cm square placed on a black background. He found that with one eye open the surface appears red; with the other open, it appears green; with both eyes open, the surface appears yellow. In this experiment red light falls on a part of the retina of one eye and green light falls on the corresponding portion of the retina of the other eye, and the result is a yellow sensation; hence, Hecht concludes that only Young's theory is tenable. If the green and red Wratten filters are replaced by yellow (16) and blue (44A), a reasonably good white is produced binocularly.

The binocular formation of yellow and white shows that theories which require special sensitive substances in the retina for yellow and white are untenable.

One must, therefore, conclude that no theory of color sensation is deserving of consideration which is not built on the fact discovered by Thomas Young, and confirmed by Helmholtz, that three radiant-energy stimuli are sufficient as a physical cause to start the retinal photochemical processes, which probably initiate the nerve impulses transmitted along the optic nerve to the brain, and the result is an experienced sensation called color vision.

BIBLIOGRAPHY

1876 LANDOLT, E., *Ann. d'Ocul.*, **75**, 207.

1892 LADD-FRANKLIN, C. For summary see *Science*, **60**, 555 (1922).

1909 Gullstrand's Schematic Eye. For complete data see H. VON HELMHOLTZ, *Handbuch der physiologischen Optik*, 3rd Ed., Vol. 1, p. 335.

1912 STILLING, J., *Ophthalmoscope*, **10**, 519; see also SOUTHALL [1937].

1912 DUANE, A., *Ophthalmoscope*, **10**, 486.

1918 REEVES, P., *Astrophys. J.*, **47**, 141.

1920 NUTTING, P. G., *J. Optical Soc. Am.*, **4**, 55.

1920 REEVES, P., *J. Optical Soc. Am.*, **4**, 35.

1920 TROLAND, L. T., *Am. J. Physiol. Optics*, **1**, 317.

1921 LUCKIESH, M., A. H. TAYLOR, and R. H. SINDEN, *J. Franklin Inst.*, **192**, 757.

1921 LUCKIESH, M., *Am. J. Physiol. Optics*, **2**, 3.

1924 BURGE, W. E., *Am. J. Physiol. Optics*, **5**, 231. (Referred to by SHEARD [1924].)

1924 SHEARD, C., *Am. J. Physiol. Opics*, **5**, 214.

1926 FINCHAM, E. F., *Am. J. Physiol. Optics*, **7**, 469.

1927 DUKE-ELDER, W. S., *J. Physiol.*, **62**, 315.

1928 HECHT, S., *Proc. Natl. Acad. Sci.*, **14**, 237.

1930 LUCKIESH, M., *Artificial Sunlight*, D. Van Nostrand Company, New York.

1932 BARNES, R. B., and M. CZERNY, *Z. Physik*, **79**, 436.

1935 HARTLINE, H. K., *Cold Spring Harbor Symposia Quant. Biol.*, **3**, 245; also H. K. HARTLINE and C. H. GRAHAM, *J. Gen. Physiol.*, **18**, 917.

1935 HECHT, S., " The Nature of the Photoreceptor Process," MURCHISON'S *Handbook of General Experimental Psychology*, Clark University Press, Worcester, Mass.

1937 SOUTHALL, J. P. C., *Introduction to Physiological Optics*, Oxford University Press.

1938 DARTNALL, H. J. A., C. F. GOODEVE, and R. J. LYTHGOE, *Proc. Roy. Soc. London*, **A164**, 216.

1938 HECHT, S., " A Review of The Photochemical Basis of Vision," *J. Applied Phys.*, **9**, 156.

1938 HECHT, S., " The Nature of the visual Process," *The Harvey Lectures*, New York Acad. Med., Series XXXIII.

1938 HEVESY, G., and F. A. PANETH, *Radioactivity*, p. 30, Oxford University Press.

1941 BARTLEY, S. H., *Vision. A Study of its basis*, D. Van Nostrand Company, New York.

1941 GRANIT, R., *Ann. Rev. Physiol.*, III, 461 Part II, " Visual Receptors."

1941 POLYAK, S. L., *The Retina*, University of Chicago Press.

Chapter IV

EMISSION AND ABSORPTION OF BIOPHYSICALLY ACTIVE LIGHT

Statistics yield much evidence that sunlight is of direct benefit to human beings. During the winter the sun is at lower altitudes and the maximum possible duration of sunshine is much less than in summer. Furthermore, the solar radiation must pass through a greater air mass since it reaches the earth more obliquely. As a consequence, the photobiologic radiations in sunlight are greatly weakened in winter.

There is some evidence that sunlight increases the resistance to infection. Sunlight tends continually to sterilize earth and water because of the resulting photochemical activity. Perhaps the most outstanding importance of sunlight, or its artificial equivalent, is in its relation to the prevention and cure of rickets. Rickets occurs with marked frequency during the winter and spring and almost disappears in midsummer. Sunlight or its equivalent is also known to promote calcium anabolism, and the most important function of all is that chlorophyll, the green coloring matter in the leaves of the plants, makes use of certain wavelengths in fixing the carbon from carbon dioxide gas in plant structure.

SPECTRAL TRANSMISSION OF THE ATMOSPHERE

The atmosphere serves as a gigantic filter for the sun's radiant energy. The short-wave ultraviolet energy is absorbed by the ozone in the upper strata, and smoke, water vapor, and the dense gases near the earth's surface all act as scattering agents of light. The visual proof is the clear blue color and the brightness of the sky. Without this scattering, the sky would be as dark as it is at night.

As a result of absorption of solar radiation by the atmosphere, the spectral nature and the intensity of the sunlight vary with the altitude of the sun.

In order to give an idea of the spectral distribution of direct solar radiation, curve A, Fig. IV-1, has been plotted from Abbot's data, which clearly shows the prominent atmospheric absorption bands appearing as depressions in the curve. Their depths indicate to what degree the atmosphere is opaque to these wavelengths. Those in the infra-red are due chiefly to water vapor which was slightly above average when these data were obtained. There is a rapid decrease between

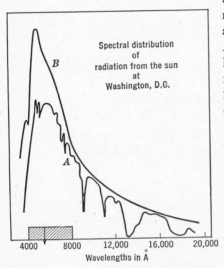

5000 and 4000 Å, indicating a rapid increase in opacity of the atmosphere in this violet region. Although the short-wavelength limit of the solar spectrum as recorded on earth is set close to 2885 Å, for all practical purposes, owing to smoke, it is usually accepted as 2950 Å in summer and 3100 Å in winter. In order to appreciate the absorption effect of the atmosphere, curve B in Fig. IV-1 has been introduced to show the relatively greater intensity of the energy at very high altitudes where absorption is a negligible factor.

FIG. IV-1. The spectral distribution of radiation from the sun. *A*, as measured at Washington, D. C., with 1.37 cm water vapor in the atmosphere, for the sun at zenith. *B*, similar measurements made at altitudes so great that absorbing atmosphere is negligible. Shaded area shows visible spectral region with maximum visibility at 5560 Å. (By courtesy of J. H. Clark [1931].)

Figure IV-2 shows the fluctuations of the ultraviolet content of sunlight during a typical clear day at different times of the year. It was found that the ultraviolet content of sunlight rises more sharply to a maximum and then decreases more rapidly than the total radiation. This difference is due to the relatively greater atmospheric

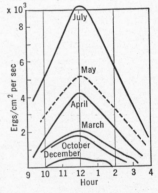

FIG. IV-2. Ultraviolet content of sunlight on a typical clear day in the months indicated. (By courtesy of J. H. Clark [1931].)

absorption for the ultraviolet radiation. The predominance of the ultraviolet content between 11 A.M. and 1 P.M., especially during the summer, is apparent from these curves.

DEGREE OF ERYTHEMA

Using the homogeneous emission line of mercury at 2967 Å as a source, a minimum perceptible erythema is defined as that produced by 180,000 ergs per square centimeter. For an exposure of 15 minutes a radiant flux intensity of 20 microwatts per square centimeter would be required (Council on Physical Therapy [1932], [1934]).

Medical authorities usually recognize four stages of erythema. From the viewpoint of therapy the first three stages may be beneficial, depending upon the objective sought. The final blistering stage may even be curative locally; it is, however, in general pathological. The first three vary visually from a faint redness to a vivid redness which is the more lasting. For midsummer sunlight the relative exposure times, for an assumed average untanned skin, are as follows:

Degree 1, minimum perceptible erythema	1.0
Degree 2, vivid, producing moderate tan	2.5
Degree 3, painful " burn "	5.0
Degree 4, blistering	10.0

From this point of view the minimum perceptible erythema is one that disappears in 24 hours. These relative values are only approximate and are modified by the degree of pigmentation, but in general they represent a good working range for time of exposure and erythema produced. In order to save time of exposure ultraviolet-ray therapy has been generally investigated and practiced with high-intensity sources of ultraviolet radiations in which exposures of a few minutes are usually resorted to. The conclusions gained from high-energy exposures for short periods of time, however, cannot be applied to the production of erythema by moderately intense sources over longer periods of time.

TABLE IV-1

ERYTHEMAL EFFECTIVENESS OF RADIATION IN RANGE
2400 TO 3300 Å, 2967 Å TAKEN AS UNITY

Wavelengths Å	Relative Effectiveness	Wavelengths Å	Relative Effectiveness
2400	56	2967	100
2500	57	3000	83
2600	42	3050	33
2700	14	3100	11
2800	6	3150	1
2900	31	3200	0.5
2950	98	3250	0.3
		3300	0.0

TABLE IV-2

MINUTES REQUIRED FOR THE PRODUCTION OF ERYTHEMA FROM ARTIFICIAL SOURCES

Artificial Sources 76 cm from Skin	Degree of Erythema	
	Minimum Perceptible	Vivid
Sunlight and skylight (noon, midsummer)	20	50
Quartz mercury arc (3.5 amperes, 110 volts)	7	17
Sunlight lamp (Type S-1), Corex D bulb (400-watt tungsten mercury arc)	8.5	21
Bare carbon arc (1000-watt) 8 mm, "Sunshine carbons"	16	40

By courtesy of M. Luckiesh.

It should be kept in mind that a value of erythemal effectiveness (Table IV-1) expressed in watts per square centimeter remains unchanged only as long as the physical characteristics of the radiation do not change. For example, such a factor established for a bare source of radiation ceases to hold when the source is placed in a reflector which does not reflect the ultraviolet rays as well as the visible rays. In Table IV-2 is indicated the exposure time required to produce two degrees of erythema, with common commercial artificial sources placed at a distance of 76 cm (30 in.) from average untanned skin.

Erythemal measurements are semiquantitative and uncertain, since the untanned skins of individuals vary over a wide range, and it is essential to recognize a skin of approximately average sensibility. An approach to a quantitative method of detecting " degree of erythema " is attained by means of a strip of tape in which is punched a series of holes $\frac{1}{4}$ to $\frac{1}{2}$ in. in diameter. This is attached to the untanned skin of the back, chest, or abdomen. The source is placed at a measured distance from the skin and then the effect of the incident energy is observed at a given skin distance. As the time passes, the holes are successively covered; the result is a series of exposures of various durations. For accurate work a second series of holes should be used adjacent to the first as a check. The intensity of illumination is varied according to the inverse square law, and the minimum perceptible erythema is fairly easy to establish.

Luckiesh, during an extensive study of the reciprocity law over a range of 25 to 400 ft-candles with the " Sunlight (Type S-1) Lamp " (Fig. IV-3), found that the equality of products of exposure time and ft-candles holds very well for this type of mercury-arc radiation, and that the minimum perceptible degree is very definite. The second degree is described as " vivid," but a moderate tan results from it and the relative time of exposure is about 2.5 times that of degree 1.

TANNING

The color of normal human skin depends upon its pigment content and the back-scatter of that part of the incident energy which has succeeded in penetrating without absorption (Edwards and Duntley [1939]). Below the external horny layer (*corneum*) is found the basal cell layer in which the principal concentration of photoactive pigments is located. A network of blood vessels is found in the layers

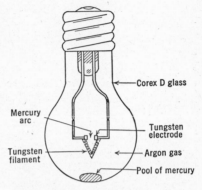

Fig. IV–3. " Sunlight Lamp " (Type S–1) General Electric Company. (By courtesy of Forsythe, Barnes, and Easley [1931].)

below these basal cells. The next deeper layer is called the *derma*, below which lie the subcutaneous tissues.

It has been suggested that the tanning mechanism is probably a photodynamic action in the presence of oxygen and is due to the oxidation of pigments already present in a colorless reduced state. The bleaching of tanned skin shows it to be a reversible process quite independent of the formation of new pigment.

The major pigments are found to be melanin and an allied diffuse substance melanoid. Carotene was also found in the subcutaneous tissues. In different races the melanin content of the skin is found to increase in the following order: Japanese, Hindu, mulatto, and negro. Albino skins apparently do not have the ability to produce pigmentation even with the aid of long-wave ultraviolet light.

Irradiation of the normal skin with long-wave ultraviolet light from the spectral region extending from 3000 to 4500 Å produces a darkening of the pigment found in the skin. The maximal effect is obtained from the narrow band of energy lying near 3400 Å, according to Henschke and Schulze [1939], or at 3850 Å according to Hausser [1938].

It is doubtful that an erythema accompanies the tanning when this spectral range is used conservatively. Owing to the filter action of the cumulative darkening pigment, it seems reasonable to expect that the erythema threshold accompanying tanning is very much greater. It was found, for instance, that if a normal skin was irradiated with 3850 Å it took 18×10^7 ergs/cm^2 or 3.4×10^{19} photons/cm^2 of skin to produce the erythema threshold; if irradiated with 2967 Å, it took 34×10^4 ergs/ cm², or 5.1×10^{16} photons/cm². Apparently the erythema accompanying gradual tanning by long-wave ultraviolet light is a negligible factor if no 2967 Å radiation is present.

If the intensities of these two radiations are so chosen that the same final degree of erythema is developed, that at 3850 Å reaches its maximum in 2 to 3 hours, but that at 2967 Å is just becoming visible at the end of this period of time.   Twelve hours after irradiation each shows its maximal reddening; the former has developed into a brown red, the latter into a pronounced carmine red color.   After 48 hours the former is still maximal red and the latter is strongly brown.   After 5 weeks the erythema has subsided; the 2967 Å exposure is slightly pigmented, and the 3850 Å exposure has developed into a deep brown pigmentation.

As yet the photochemical reactions involved in these biophysical activities are only slightly understood.   The trend of the evidence (Blum [1941]) seems to indicate that an active substance is liberated which is responsible for the erythemal response as an indirect capillary reaction. Apart from the vasodilatation, which appears after a latent period, the structural injuries are limited almost entirely to the first 0.1 mm when wavelength 3000 Å was used.   Penetration by 7500 Å is only about 2.5 mm, although a wavelength of about 11,500 Å can penetrate to a depth of 5 mm.

ARTIFICIAL SOURCES OF ULTRAVIOLET RADIATION

A typical mercury-vapor arc is illustrated in Fig. IV–4.   This is a Cooper Hewitt quartz-enclosed mercury-vapor arc.   The luminous tube of the burner is made of clear fused quartz of high ultraviolet trans-

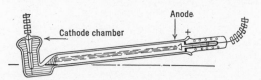

FIG. IV–4.   Sectional view of a " Cooper Hewitt " quartz mercury arc.   110-volt burner.   Length 6⅜ in.   Luminous tube diameter ⅝ in.

mission.   The leads are flexible stranded wire insulated with porcelain beads because of the high temperature attained by the terminals.   The anode, or positive electrode, of the burner consists of a tungsten wire coiled into a target.   In operation it is heated white hot by the arc which extends from it to the surface of the mercury cathode, or negative electrode.   The cathode chamber serves to keep the mercury at the proper temperature and to store up the mercury used in starting the burner to arc.

The arc is started by tilting the burner so that a series of mercury globules runs from the cathode to the anode and back to the cathode chamber. The arc first strikes between these globules, and when the device is operating with sufficient resistance in series (it is a low-pressure

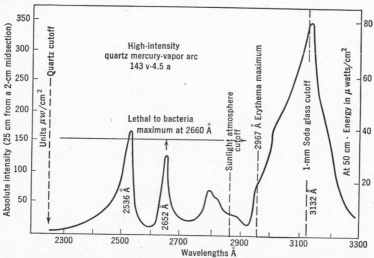

Fig. IV–5. Distribution of the energy among the wavelengths emitted by a quartz mercury-vapor arc. The right-hand axis shows the relative erythemal effectiveness of the various wavelengths at 50 cm from the arc.

arc) the light column appears to fill the whole arc tube uniformly. In this condition its spectrum shows only the strongest mercury lines and no continuous spectrum is visible. When the arc is adjusted for operation at high intensity, it starts as a low-pressure arc but, as it heats, changes to the high-pressure condition. In this state, indicated by an apparent concentration of the light into a narrow thread of great intensity in the axis of the arc tube, a continuous spectrum is superimposed upon the mercury line spectrum, several additional mercury lines become visible, and the ultraviolet radiation is greatly intensified.

The quartz mercury arc from which the data for Fig. IV–5 were obtained was rated and operated at 143 volts and 4.5 amperes. It radiated considerable energy shorter than 2537 Å, and, notwithstanding the low intensity of these short wavelengths, considerable erythema can be produced by them. In substituting this arc for ultraviolet sunlight, the radiations shorter than 3150 Å are of primary importance. The quartz mercury arc radiates strongly in the following groups of wavelengths: 2536, 2652, 2894, 2967, 3021, and 3130 Å; less strongly at 2752 and 2804 Å; and weakly at 2378, 2399, 2482, and 2698 Å. The newer high-potential ".SC-2537 Hanovia" mercury-vapor arc has as much as 85 per cent or more of its energy of emission concentrated at 2537 Å.

"STERILAMP"

This lamp was designed and constructed by the Westinghouse Lamp Company to emit its predominant radiations at wavelengths having the highest bactericidal properties and the least erythemal effect. Radiations from these lamps produce a mercury spectrum with the greater portion of the radiant energy in the region of 2537 Å. There is also some radiation in the region of 1849 to 1960 Å. The shortest radiations are readily absorbed by the surrounding air but are very strong in bactericidal action.

These lamps are tubular and are made in various lengths. A typical example has an overall length of 14 in. and a $\frac{7}{8}$-in. diameter. Its starting potential is 400 volts alternating current, operating, however, at 275 volts with a current of about 0.03 amp. They have two terminals, one at each end, and burn in any position when connected to the 110-volt a-c circuit with proper transformers. Hart and Gardner [1937] and others have used this type of lamp for sterilization of the air in the surgical operative region.

"SUNLIGHT LAMP"

Of the number of tungsten-mercury arcs that have been patented, the only one which has been commercialized is the sunlight (Type S–1) lamp, developed by the General Electric Company. It consists of two tungsten button electrodes at the terminals of a tungsten filament support, as shown in Fig. IV–3, a pool of mercury, and an argon-filled "Corex D Glass" globe. The lamp starts in any position. When the proper voltage is applied, the filament heats and the arc strikes between the button terminals. The biologically active radiation becomes more intensive as the bulb increases in temperature. It is essentially a low-voltage lamp, and the attached transformer must deliver 9.5 amp at approximately 30 volts in order to heat the filament. When the arc is completed, the current rises to 30 amp and the voltage drops to about 11 volts. The lamp consists of two primary sources of energy, incandescent tungsten and mercury vapor. The emitted radiant energy of the former consists of a continuous spectrum of all wavelengths extending from the long-wave infra-red to about 3500 Å in the violet region. The mercury vapor emits energy of only the characteristic wavelengths of mercury, comparable to those shown in Fig. IV–6.

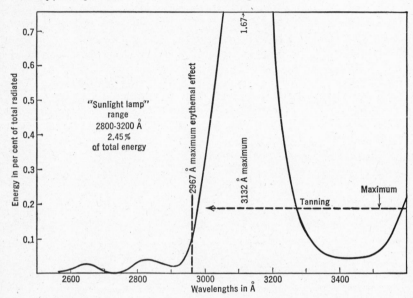

FIG. IV–6. Distribution of energy curve of the " Sunlight Lamp " from data by A. H. Taylor [1931].

The following average values for the ultraviolet output are obtainable when the arc strikes in a mixture of mercury vapor and argon gas enclosed by a Corex D bulb of about 1-mm thickness:

RELATIVE ULTRAVIOLET OUTPUT

Wavelength	3657	3130	3024	2967 Å
Output	198	100	28	17

If a shallow oxidized aluminum reflector, about 13 in. in diameter, is used over the bulb, then at 30 in. a minimum perceptible erythema is produced on average untanned skin by exposures of 8 to 10 minutes. At a distance of 1 meter this type of lamp emits an energy flux one third as great as midday summer sunlight in the spectral range 2800 to 3100 Å. The Corex D glass transmits about 59 per cent of the 3000-Å wavelength.

THE ELECTRIC ARC

Carbon arcs produce the highest available artificial temperatures, 4000° K being obtainable. The positive crater of a direct-current arc is used as a source of continuous radiation. By introducing salts into the core of the carbon, selective emission in the hot gases may be utilized to enrich different parts of the spectrum. If the lower terminal of such an arc, set in a vertical position, is made of a large cylinder of iron with a shallow depression in its center, the arc is termed an " iron arc " and is extraordinarily rich in ultraviolet radiations. In the commercial types of carbon arc the amount of ultraviolet radiation between 2800 and 3100 Å varies considerably. For example, the energy distribution

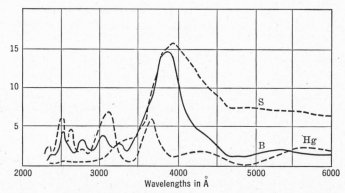

Fig. IV–7. Emission of " Sunshine S " carbon and " Therapeutic B " carbon arcs as compared with quartz mercury arc. S and B, bare arc without reflector, 30 amp, alternating current, 50 volts across arc. Hg, quartz tube mercury arc, no reflector, average voltage 140 and 170, alternating current, and 4 amp. Each square represents 250 microwatts of radiant flux per square centimeter at 1-meter distance from the arcs. (Data by courtesy of the National Carbon Company.)

of the radiation obtained from the " therapeutic carbons " of the National Carbon Company as determined by Greider and Downes are shown in Fig. IV–7. The " Eveready therapeutic B carbons " and the " Sunshine carbons " are marked B and S, respectively. The B carbon supplies more biologically active radiation than the S carbon. The B carbon contains iron. It gives light with a slightly bluish tinge but in the visible range has a candlepower less than one fourth that of the S carbon.

The spectrum of B carbon is characterized by many lines that extend from the visible through the ultraviolet region to 2300 Å or shorter. It is very intense in the long-ultraviolet region. In order to avoid conjunctivitis during exposure with this type of carbon arc it is necessary to protect the eyes with glass goggles.

FINSEN UNIT

Inasmuch as interest in the biological effectiveness of ultraviolet radiation arose first in therapy, powerful sources of ultraviolet radiation have been studied and exploited primarily for their therapeutic effectiveness. It must be emphasized, however, that there is no necessary relation between erythemal effectiveness and therapeutic value. As a result, the establishment of a system of units based on erythemal effectiveness must not be viewed as a solution to the problem of measurement of energy in the ultraviolet region for general biological application.

The practical necessity of establishing some criterion for the comparative evaluation of different types of ultraviolet sources for medical purposes cannot be escaped. This has led to the adoption of certain standard units.

The Council on Physical Therapy [1934] has tentatively adopted the Finsen unit (F.U.) as a beam of homogeneous radiation of wavelength 2967 Å with flux density of 10 μw/cm^2.

It has been observed that 2 F.U. for 15 minutes is a representative requirement for minumum perceptible erythema. Therefore it has been proposed that 1 erythemal unit be defined as 2 F.U., or 20 μw/cm^2 for 15 minutes of homogeneous radiation of wavelength 2967 Å.

In the use of such a unit it must be borne in mind that even small changes in operating conditions of a source will change the energy-wavelength output and hence the radiation erythemal equivalents.

ABSORPTION OF RADIANT ENERGY

The transmission of radiant energy through a medium is always accompanied by a certain amount of absorption, regardless of the wavelength incident on the medium. Media which are commonly referred to as transparent, if not employed in too great thickness, transmit without appreciable absorption the range of wavelengths comprised within the region of the visible spectrum.

In general, however, they show powerful absorption in the infra-red and ultraviolet regions, and if a sufficiently great thickness is employed absorption will be found present even in the range of visible radiations. Pure water, which is one of the most transparent of the common substances, appears distinctly blue in long columns, showing that it absorbs more or less completely the red end of the spectrum.

It is conventional to distinguish between two types of absorption: *general*, in which the absorbing power is very nearly the same for all wavelengths; and *selective*, in which the absorption is more or less limited to a narrow spectral region. Lampblack, developed photographic films, neutral filters, and some forms of close-meshed rocking wire screens represent the first type. Analine dyes, inorganic colored salts, blood, bile, and generally all colored media represent the second type, in which certain wavelengths are freely transmitted while others are strongly absorbed.

LAW OF GENERAL ABSORPTION

When radiant energy passes through a homogeneous medium, the medium absorbs part of the energy and the amount of this absorption is generally different for various wavelengths.

If a monochromatic beam of light has its intensity (the energy per square centimeter per second of a plane parallel beam of monochromatic light) decreased by an amount dI in passing through a distance dx in the material, and if the loss is the same at all depths, then $dI \sim dx$. If at the same time the decrease in intensity is proportional to the intensity itself $(dI \sim I)$, then

$$dI = -aI\,dx$$

On integration this becomes

$$I = \text{constant } e^{-ax}$$

where a is the constant of proportionality whose magnitude depends on the material and wavelength of the beam of radiant energy. The negative sign is used to indicate that the change in I is a decrease.

If I_0 denotes the constant intensity of the beam which enters the surface of a slab of absorbing material, where $x = 0$, then the constant in the above relation is the intensity of the incident energy, I_0. It follows that the intensity of the beam after passing through a thickness $x = d$ has an intensity I_d given by the relation

$$I_d = I_0 e^{-ad}$$

where a is known as the *coefficient of absorption*. This law implies that the absorption increases in geometrical progression as the thickness increases in arithmetical progression.

To illustrate the law, let us consider the slab d composed of five layers, each of unit thickness, and made of a material having an absorption coefficient equal to $\frac{1}{10}$. Let the incident energy $I_0 = 100$ units. In traversing the first layer, this value is reduced $\frac{1}{10}$ by absorption so that 90 units leave the first and enter the next layer. The 90 units lose $\frac{1}{10}$ of their magnitude in the second layer, so that 81 units are incident on layer three. Then layer three absorbs 8.1 units, leaving 72.9 units, etc. The energy leaving the final surface of the fifth layer is only 59.0 units. Hence the total energy loss through absorption is 41 units. The per cent transmission or transmissivity for wavelength λ is

$$T_\lambda = 100\,\frac{I_d}{I_0}$$

BEER'S LAW OF ABSORPTION

The absorption law is used in various forms. Beer (1852) used it for solutions to describe the absorption of monochromatic light in which the solvent contributed nothing to the absorption. If we consider the absorbing layers as having molecular structure, and if we can say that each molecule absorbs an equal fraction of the energy which passes over it, then Beer's law expresses the absorptions in terms of concentrations of the absorbing layers.

Let c be the concentration of a solution; then, if I_0 is the entering intensity and I_d the reduced intensity upon leaving an absorbing layer of thickness d, Beer's law states that

$$I_d = I_0 e^{-\alpha c d}$$

where α is called the *absorption coefficient*. Beer's law holds only when the absorbing property of a molecule is not influenced by the proximity of its neighbors, which condition is not always true.

It must be emphasized that the laws of absorption apply only to monochromatic radiation and cannot be rigorously applied to the absorption of narrow bands of spectral wavelengths or to the absorption of extended spectral regions.

EXTINCTION COEFFICIENT

A common practice (after Bunsen and Roscoe) is to express the absorption as the reciprocal of the thickness which is necessary to weaken the light to one tenth of its incident value. This definition gives

$$I_d = I_0 10^{-kd} \quad \text{and} \quad I_d = I_0 10^{-\epsilon C d}$$

or

$$\log_{10} \frac{I_0}{I_d} = kd \quad \text{and} \quad \log_{10} \frac{I_0}{I_d} = \epsilon C d$$

where k is called the *extinction coefficient*, and ϵ is the *molecular extinction coefficient*. The extinction coefficient (k) is used when the molecular weight of the absorbing material is not known. The concentration C is expressed in moles per liter.

PRESENTATION OF DATA

Figure IV–8 illustrates the use of transmissivity (I_d/I_0) in presenting data. Graph 1 in this figure shows how the transparency of an 0.08-mm thickness of human epidermis varies with the incident energy at the wavelengths designated (Lucas [1931]). Superimposed is graph 2,

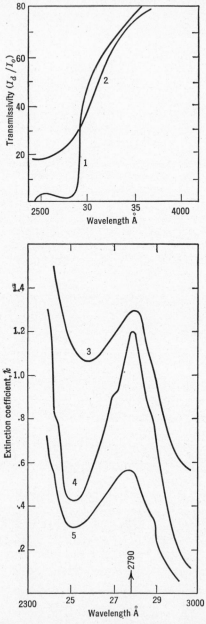

FIG. IV–8. Curve 1 shows how the transmissivity of an 0.08-mm layer of human epidermis varies with wavelength. Note its rapid rise in transparency near 3000 Å. Curve 2 shows the relative greater transparency of human sweat, 1 mm thick, in the ultraviolet. The lower curves show how the extinction coefficient k can be used to compare the absorption of (3) egg albumin, pH 1.65 (L. E. Arnow [1935]), with (4) serum pseudoglobulin, and (5) serum albumin. Note characteristic absorption band at 2790 Å. (F. C. Smith [1929].)

showing the comparable transmissivity of human sweat about 1 mm thick (Crew and Whittle [1938]).

The lower series of graphs illustrates how the extinction coefficient k can be used to show the relative absorption of (3) egg albumin, (4) serum pseudoglobulin, and (5) serum albumin. Note that they all have a pronounced absorption band at 2790 Å, which is common to proteins, and are rather transparent to radiation around 2500 Å.

Figure IV–9 illustrates the use of the molecular extinction coefficient to show that the combined absorption of several constituent molecular groups is equal to the absorption of the composite molecule. The broken graph shows how closely the sums of the extinction coefficients of the products of hydrolysis of thymus nucleic acid [purine (guanine and adenine), and pyrimidine constituents (thymine and cytosine)]

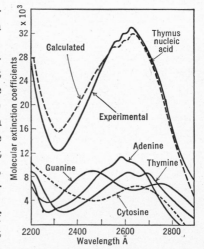

FIG. IV–9. The ultraviolet absorption spectrum of thymus nucleic acid as compared with the absorption spectra of its purine and pyrimidine constituents. The graphical sum of the absorbing constituents is the upper broken curve. Note how closely it approximates the experimental value. (By courtesy of J. R. Loofbourow 1940].)

resemble the experimental values obtained from the composite molecule, thymus nucleic acid.

ABSORPTION SPECTROPHOTOMETRY

The essential pieces of apparatus for absorption spectrophotometry are: (1) a constant source of radiation, (2) an optical instrument for resolving the radiation into a spectrum, and (3) a means of evaluating the relative intensities of the incident and transmitted energy passing through an absorption cell.

When absorption measurements in the visible spectral regions are made, incandescent linear-filament lamps are used. For the ultraviolet, the condensed under-water spark between molybdenum terminals gives a nearly continuous strong spectrum containing wavelengths as low as 2000 Å. Figure IV–20 shows the limits of transmission set by very pure water. Recently developed high-pressure mercury arcs (Buttolph [1939]) emit a practically continuous spectrum in the long-wave ultraviolet.

A prism monochromator or prism spectrograph is preferably used to resolve the visible beam of light into its spectrum. For exploring the ultraviolet, the above instruments are provided with quartz lenses and prisms.

A means of evaluating the relative intensities of the various wavelengths before and after they have passed through the absorption cell constitutes the photometric phase of the absorption measurements. A photoelectric cell or a linear thermocouple may be used for this purpose in connection with a monochromator. The intensities are evaluated from a developed photographic plate when a spectrograph is used.

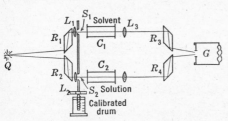

FIG. IV–10. Diagram of a "Spekker" photometer placed in front of the spectrograph slit G.

One of the simpler precision absorption instruments now much in use is the split beam "Spekker" absorption photometer (Twyman and Allsopp [1934]), illustrated in Fig. IV–10. The light source Q, and the "Spekker" photometer containing the absorption cells C_1 and C_2, are adjusted so that the two emerging beams are focused one above the other on the slit of the spectrograph G. The spectrograph resolves these two sources and focuses them as two contacting spectral images on the photographic plate.

The light from source Q is internally reflected from the faces of the two rhombs R_1 and R_2. Thus two beams of equal intensity are produced. One beam is diverted upward, and the other downward; both are reflected forward through the lenses L_1 and L_2. The upper beam passes through a precision slit S_1 and an absorption cell C_1 containing the solvent, and thence through the lens L_3 via the rhomb R_3 into the upper half of the spectrograph slit G. An identical optical path is traced by the downard deflected beam in passing through the absorption cell C_2 containing the solution. The image of the adjustable slit S_2 falls below that of S_1 on the spectrograph slit. The slits S_1 and S_2 control the intensity of the two beams. The slit S_2 is variable in size by means of a precision micrometer push screw. By proper adjustment of the light energy passing through S_2 the photographed spectrum of this beam may be matched for intensity at any desired wavelength with a similar wavelength in the spectrum photographed just above it by means of the light passing through S_1.

Slits S_1 and S_2 are illuminated with equal fluxes of uniform radiation, which may be represented by I_0 (per unit area). Let A_1 and A_2 be the areas of the apertures of the slits S_1 and S_2 when an intensity match for a given wavelength is produced on the photographic plate. The quantities of radiation transmitted by the apertures and incident on the absorption cells C_1 and C_2 are A_1I_0 and A_2I_0, respectively. After transmission through the absorption cells, both these quantities are reduced to I_d. The matched intensities for a given wavelength are given in the Bunsen-Roscoe notation

$$I_d = A_1I_010^{-k_1d} = A_2I_010^{-k_2d}$$

where d is the length of the matched absorption cells. Then

$$\log_{10} \frac{A_2}{A_1} = (k_2 - k_1)d$$

The screw regulating the size of the slit S_2, if calibrated to read log (A_2/A_1) for a fixed value of A_1 and d, will give the optical density of the absorbing substance with reference to that of the comparison liquid (the solvent) for a given wavelength. If the extinction coefficient of the solvent is known, the extinction coefficient of the solution may be obtained.

COLORIMETER FOR MONOCHROMATIC LIGHT

Colorimetric methods of analysis consist of treating a solution of a substance whose absorption characteristics are desired with a reagent so as to produce a color which is proportional in intensity to the amount of the substance present in the solution. If Beer's law is applicable, then the concentration must be directly proportional to the logarithm of the transmitted light intensity (Fig. IV–11). In the usual colorimetric analysis it is desirable to determine the amount of colored material in the sample as compared with a standard. The amount of material present is measured by the amount of light absorbed. Accurate measurements can be made only by a spectrophotometric determination at that wavelength which corresponds with the maximum of its absorption band. A very good first approximation can be attained if one uses a narrow band of wavelengths as a source coinciding with the maximum absorption in the absorption band of the colored solution. Figure IV–12 shows a simple way in which this analysis may be accomplished.

The basic design developed by Moll [1919] uses a nearly monochromatic illumination obtained by means of a direct-vision spectroscope or Amici prism. A straight horizontal-filament lamp L is placed in the focal plane of an achromatic objective O_1. The beam of parallel light passes through an Amici prism train from which it emerges as a con-

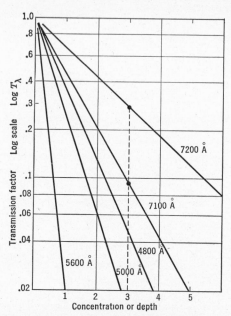

Fig. IV-11. Relation between spectral transmission-factor and depth or concentration of a solution of methyl green. (From data by M. Luckiesh [1917].)

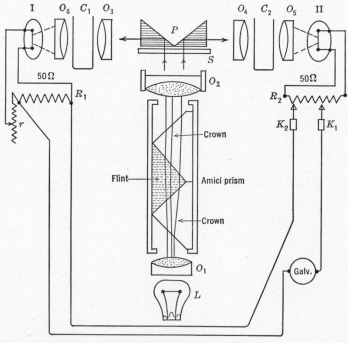

Fig. IV-12. Optical system of a colorimeter or nethelometer for monochromatic light. (By courtesy of Kipp and Zonen.)

tinuous spectrum, which is focused by the second objective O_2 on the horizontal slit S. The filament acts as a primary slit of the monochromator. A selected narrow part of the spectrum, after passing through the slit, is reflected by two rectangular prisms (P), one half to the right and the other half to the left. These two beams are now made parallel by the objectives O_3 and O_4. Identical beams therefore pass through absorption cells C_1 and C_2. The transmitted beams are focused by means of objectives O_5 and O_6 on the vacuum thermocouples I and II. The thermocouples are connected in opposition through the resistances to the galvanometer. The resistances are adjusted so that the galvanometer reads zero. Now if a semitransparent solution is introduced in absorption cell C_1 and the solvent into C_2, the current generated by the thermocouple I decreases and the galvanometer deflects. The equilibrium is restored by reducing the current in circuit II in the following manner. Each thermocouple is shunted with a 50-ohm resistance. The shunt of II is a variable-resistance box R_2 connected in such a way that a known fraction of the drop in potential across R_2 can be removed from the galvanometer circuit. This fraction is adjusted so as to balance the current through the galvanometer to read zero. The resistance between the two keys K_1 and K_2 then indicates the percentage of the drop in potential which has been made inoperative. This number is thus equal to the percentage extinction caused by the absorbing solute for the wavelength under examination. The accuracy obtainable is claimed to be of the order of 0.01 per cent.

The sensitivity of such an instrument is dependent largely on the spectral region used. For the shorter wavelengths, the radiant energy emitted by an incandescent lamp burning at its normal voltage is small. The dispersive power of the Amici prism, however, is higher in the blue than in the red. Since the slit width per 100 Å is smaller in the red than in the blue, a wider slit may be used in the blue than in the red end of the spectrum.

To test the applicability of Beer's law to any solution, a preliminary test (Fig. IV–11) should be made to show that the logarithm of the transmissivity for a given wavelength (log T_λ) is proportional to C. For this test a cell of known thickness is filled with the solution, and a spectral absorption analysis is obtained. If a sufficiently thin cell is chosen, most wavelengths available will be appreciably transmitted. On coordinate paper having a logarithmic scale ruled along the vertical axis and a uniform scale of concentration on the horizontal axis, as in Fig. IV–11, a plot of log T_λ is made for a given wavelength with change in concentration. Unity on the log scale is chosen as 100 per cent transmission. Straight lines are drawn through the data. Any variations from a linear relation show departures from Beer's law. If corrections have been made for surface reflections in the cell, the extrapolated line will pass through transmission factor 1.0 at zero concentration. If this correction has not been made, the common point will be near 0.92 on the " transmission axis " (Luckiesh [1917]) if two surface reflections must be accounted for. Each straight line represents the relation of log T_λ and concentration or depth for the wavelength used. By extending these lines to intersect the concentration axis the spectral characteristic of any depth or concentration may be read from the graph. Some lines are very steep; the larger the absorption coefficient the steeper (greater slope) the transmission curves for a particular wavelength of the incident energy.

Dichromatism

It will be seen from Fig. IV–11 that the slopes of the lines labeled 4800 Å, 5000 Å, and 5600 Å increase, while those labeled 7100 Å and 7200 Å decrease with increase in wavelength. This change indicates that the dye is *dichroic*.

This means that the color of a solution is composed of two or more maxima of transparency, and, if the rate of change of these maxima is not the same, dichromatism occurs with change in concentration. Suppose that in a solution the transmission color of the molecule is yellow and the ion blue. The color of the solution with decrease in concentration would vary from yellow through green to blue. Comparison of sample and standard at concentrations differing to any considerable extent would be impossible since a deep column of dilute solution would be blue and a shallow column of a more concentrated solution would be green.

From the figure it may be seen that methyl green dye in solutions of high concentration or of great depth will be not green but red. This change in color is indicated by the large transmission factor of wavelength 7200 Å (red) at concentration 3 on the graph as compared with the very low transmission of 5000 Å (green), indicating that the solution has an absorptive band between 5600 and 7100 Å. It follows that comparison of sample and standard at concentrations differing by any considerable extent would be impossible.

Duboscq Colorimeter

The Duboscq colorimeter is designed so that light from an even source of illumination R, Fig. IV–13, is reflected from a fine ground-glass surface. The two glass cups G are inserted in the beam of reflected light; they contain the solutions to be tested. Two solid cylindrical plungers of optical glass, matched for color and with optically plane and parallel ends, are lowered to various depths into the cups. These plungers can be set independently so that various depths of liquid may be examined. The two beams of light which pass through the glass

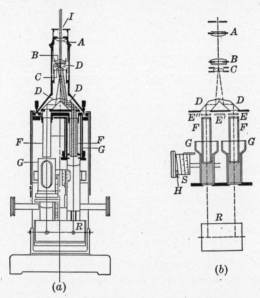

Fig. IV–13. (*a*) Path of light rays through a Duboscq colorimeter. (*b*) Path of light rays through a hemoglobinometer. (By courtesy of Bausch and Lomb Optical Company.)

plungers are brought to a common axis by means of the rhombohedral prisms *D*. The biprism refracting system *C* places the two images side by side so that the light from each cup illuminates half the field. The eyepiece *BA* by which the observer sees both fields with one eye is focused on the line of separation of the two fields.

The depth of the two columns of liquid may thus be altered by moving the plungers independently in their respective cups until the two halves of the field are identical in brightness. When these conditions are fulfilled, the concentrations of the two solutions are inversely proportional to the depths, which are read on the scales of the instrument. Such a subjective setting is good to 1 per cent.

For best results the source must not vary in intensity or color-temperature. Artificial illumination is therefore recommended.

To increase the sensitivity of color match in working with a blue field, a yellow filter is added over the eye lens, so as to work with a neutral green. Under these circumstances, should the layer of the variable thickness be too thin, it will appear not only brighter but more yellow-green.   If too thick, it will appear darker and more blue-green.

In a similar way one may use a red filter that produces a neutral violet.

HEMOGLOBINOMETER

The hemoglobinometer is a colorimeter with which the amount of hemoglobin in a sample of arterial blood is determined without resorting to chemical analyses.

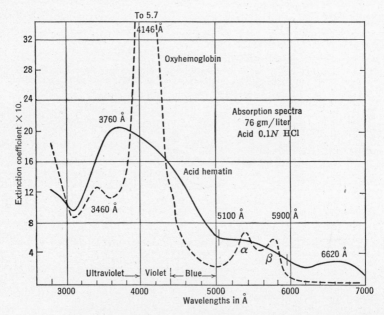

FIG. IV–14. Absorption spectrum of oxyhemoglobin with α and β band indicated. The β band disappears first on dilution.   (From data by Newcomer [1919].)

Whole blood, as well as its various chemical modifications, shows marked spectral absorption bands which cannot be matched by using any single filter.   A good match may be obtained, however, by converting the hemoglobin to acid hematin, in which the absorption bands are less prominent, and choosing a yellow glass filter, placed below the cups, whose absorption curve runs as a mean through that of the acid hematin.

Acid hematin (globin hemochromogen) has, according to Newcomer [1919], an absorption band near 6620 Å and two weak bands extending from 5100 Å to 5900 Å (Fig. IV–14).   A " blue " filter can be inserted to absorb most of the light having wavelengths greater than 5000 Å.

This filter transmits 60 per cent at 4500 Å and 70 at 4250 Å, so that the brightness match is made in terms of the blue transmitted light.

The number of grams of hemoglobin per 100 cc of blood may be read directly off a scale to 0.5 gram and estimated to 0.1 gram. The filter should transmit those wavelengths corresponding as nearly as possible to the absorption maximum of the solution.

PHOTOELECTRIC COLORIMETERS

In the design of modern colorimeters the aim is to embody rigorous physical principles and to avoid all empirical procedures. The photoelectric method of measuring light intensities can be used to give quantitative results under the requirements laid down by Beer's law.

Since Beer's law requires that the log T_λ be proportional to the thickness d and the concentration C, for a constant incident intensity, it follows that for a fixed thickness of solution the

$$\log T_\lambda \sim C$$

There are two ways of approaching the design of a colorimeter which uses a photoelectric cell and a galvanometer as an indicator of the transmissivity. The deflections may be observed on a logarithmic scale with the inevitable crowding of the engraved divisions at large-scale deflection, or else the electrical instrument may be a logarithmic device with its deflections observed on an equally spaced or linear scale.

THE BARRIER-LAYER PHOTOELECTRIC CELL

The barrier-layer photoelectric cell is of the photoemissive type requiring no vacuum-tube amplification. In the trade these types are called " photronic cells." A photronic cell consists of a metal supporting disk upon which has been deposited a layer of photosensitive material. Upon this is placed a special kind of metallic grid acting at once as electrode and as collector for the current set up by the electrons freed from the light-sensitive material. The light reaches this material through the grid itself.

Figure IV–15 shows the construction of a Weston Photronic Cell, and Fig. IV–16 indicates the relative sensitivity to various wavelengths of light as compared with the visibility curve of the eye. Under full sunlight such a cell may deliver as much as 10 milliamperes current. The response is linear, i.e., 100 ft-candles generates 100 times as much as 1 ft-candle when a current-indicating instrument having a resistance of about 100 ohms or less is used to measure the current.

A typical sensitivity curve of the average photronic cell indicates that the cell is most sensitive to yellow light of wavelength 5800 Å, while the eye's sensitivity as shown by the dotted curve is in the yellow-green at 5560 Å. Note, however, how much more sensitive it is in the blue than the eye.

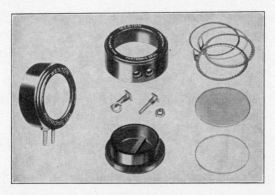

FIG. IV-15. Weston photronic photoelectric cell and its component parts, Model 594. (By courtesy of Weston Electrical Instrument Corporation.)

Should it be desirable to use such a cell to simulate the human eye, it will be necessary to place a special filter, made for this purpose, over the cell so as to absorb the radiant energy represented by the area between the visibility curve and sensitivity curve of the cell.

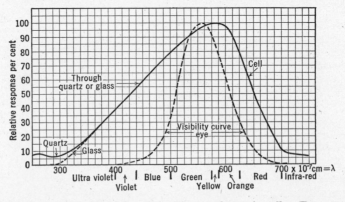

FIG. IV-16. Spectral sensitivity of the Weston photronic cell. (By courtesy of Weston Electrical Instrument Corporation.)

A typical example of the use of a photronic cell in a colorimeter is found in the instruments designed by Armstrong and Kuder [1935], or that of Evelyn [1936]. The so-called Kuder Photoelectric Model (Fisher Scientific Company) is a colorimeter operating with a direct-reading scale. The operator can plot his own transmissivity concentration curve on the attached scale, graduated from 0 to 100 arbitrary units.

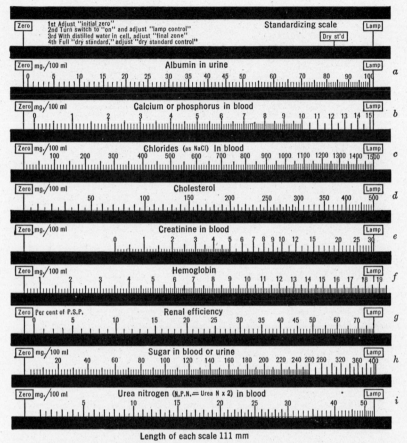

Length of each scale 111 mm

A brief statement of the technique used for each scale

a Accurate quantitative albumin determinations using a modified Exton's Reagent.
b Calcium by Brigg's method, modified by Roe and Kahn. Phosphorus by Benedict's method.
c Turbidimetric test using silver nitrate. Rapid and accurate.
d Cholesterol determination by the modified Bloor or Leiboff methods.
e Creatinine determination by the commonly accepted Folin and Wu method.
f Employs acid hematin method. Scale standardized by Van Slyke oxygen capacity method.
g Determination by the well known phenolsulphonphthalein method.
h Sugar determinations by the commonly accepted Folin and Wu method.
i Urea nitrogen or non-protein nitrogen determinations by Folin and Wu method.

FIG. IV–17. A set of nine colorimetric calibration scales, for clinical laboratory determinations. (By courtesy of Fisher Scientific Company, Pittsburgh, Pa.)

In this instrument, other scales which are engraved by the maker to read directly the concentrations in milligrams per 100 ml may also be used. Examples of such scales used in clinical work are shown in Fig. IV–17.

PHOTRONIC CELL COLORIMETERS

A photronic cell colorimeter of very simple design as suggested by Evelyn [1936] is shown in Fig. IV–18.

Since the light transmitted by the absorption cells is a logarithmic function of the concentration, one may obtain linear readings by using a circuit which reacts with a logarithmic response to the transmitted light. A device of this kind is the logarithmic response vacuum-tube voltmeter used by Müller and Kinney [1925] in their design of a photoelectric colorimeter.

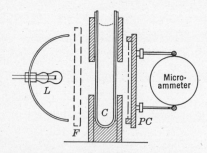

FIG. IV–18. Colorimeter design after Evelyn [1936] showing use of a photronic cell. Source of light *L*, with reflector, produces near parallel beam through filter *F*. Light beam limited by external stops in opaque cover over a 6-cc parallel fused absorption cell *C*. Energy incident on photronic cell (*PC*) directly connected to microammeter, of less than 50 ohms resistance, which reads current developed by *PC*.

ABSORPTION OF ULTRAVIOLET RADIATION BY PROTEINS

The absorption of ultraviolet radiation by serum proteins was investigated as early as 1922 by Judd Lewis. Improvements in design of the rotating sector quartz spectrophotometer made it possible for F. C. Smith [1929] to obtain the absorption spectrum of horse and human serum proteins with a great degree of precision. These results are shown in Fig. IV–8. It will be noticed that as the wavelength decreases from 3000 Å to 2790 Å the extinction coefficient rises very rapidly, indicating the approach to a sharp opacity at 2790 Å. Then, with decreasing wavelength, the material becomes more transparent, and reaches a relatively high transparency at 2500 Å, from which minimum it rises very rapidly to high absorption values at 2000 Å. These graphs indicate that the absorption spectra of these proteins are the same, except that the extinction coefficient for globulin at 2790 Å is nearly double that of albumin.

It is possible by means of such absorption measurements to determine the ratio of albumin to globulin in small amounts of cerebrospinal fluid. This type of curve may also be used to indicate the purity of a given sample of protein by comparing the values obtained for *k* at 2790 Å with those at 2500 Å.

Notice the striking resemblance between the absorption of serum albumin and egg albumin. An analogous absorption curve was obtained by Gates [1934] for pepsin of pH 2.06. These data place the maximum absorption at 2775 Å.

The energy required to *inactivate* 50 per cent of pepsin, for the wavelength band between 2640 and 2820 Å, is 230,000 ergs/mm^2, and between 2425 and 2570 Å is 305,000 ergs/mm^2; between 2300 and 2400 Å it falls to 77,500 ergs/mm^2.

The most striking and important change produced by absorbed ultraviolet light in all proteins, whether globulins or albumins, and whether positively or negatively charged, is a change in solubility or *denaturation*. It should follow that the wavelengths from 2650 to 2900 Å, which include the absorption maximum at 2790 Å, are highly efficient denaturating agents.

The absorption band of blood serum around 2800 Å is apparently due to the proteins present, and the tyrosin and tryptophan constituents of the proteins are mainly responsible for this band.

In conclusion some relations between the absorption of proteins and some of the amino acids should be pointed out which support the theory that the ultraviolet absorptions of the proteins in the 2800 Å region are due to the aromatic acids.

An extensive analysis by Coulter, Stone, and Kabat [1935] shows that all the narrow absorption bands between 2530 and 2690 Å found in all protein may be assigned to phenylalanine, while the bands at 2700, and 2850 to 2900 Å, may be attributed to tryptophan and tyrosin, respectively. Their conclusions were drawn from an examination of serum albumin, egg albumin, thyroglobulin, englobulin, pseudoglobulin, pneumococci antibody, gelatin, insulin, tyrosin, tryptophan, and phenylalanine.

The general evidence suggests that ultraviolet radiation and soft x-rays cause liberation of material of low molecular weight which with albumin residues undergo photo-oxidation reactions, due to the absorption of ultraviolet energy.

In order to illustrate what a powerful tool the spectroscopist has made available to the biochemist attention is called to the work of Wald [1934], who demonstrated the presence of vitamin A in ox and pig retina, in sheep pigment-choroid, and in sheep retina by means of the ultraviolet absorption band of vitamin A with maximum at 3280 Å. The standard method of determining the vitamin-A content of cod-liver oil is by the extinction coefficient of its absorption spectrum band at 3280 Å.

TABLE IV-3

Author	Maximum Lethal Effect at Wavelength	Bacteria
Gates, F. L. [1929] [1930]	2600 to 2700 Å	*S. aureus*
Ehrismann and	2510	*Eresch. coli (B. coli)*
Noethling [1931]	2810	*Serratia marcescens* (*B. prodigiosus*)
	2650	*Pseudomonas aeruginosa* (*B. pyocyaneus*)
	2650	*Micrococcus candidus*
	2650	*S. aureus*
	2696	*Vibrio* Finkler
Wyckoff [1931]	2696	*S. aureus*
	2652	*Eresch. coli (B. coli)*
	2652	*Salmonella aertrycke* (*B. aertrycke*)
Hollaender and Clauss [1935]	2600	*Eresch. coli (B. coli)*
Landen and Uber [1939]	2650	*Sacc. ellipsoideus*
Burge [1915]	2650	Coagulates egg albumin

EFFECT OF ULTRAVIOLET RADIATION ON BACTERIA

Finsen and Dreyer (1903) were probably the first to show that light of short wavelengths is virucidal. Except in the more recent investigations in this field, monochromatic radiation has not been used, nor has the amount of energy which is associated with the lethal wavelengths been determined. In a study of the ultraviolet effect upon vaccine virus by Rivers and Gates [1928], a series of experiments showed that the effect of monochromatic ultraviolet radiation in terms of the incident energy required to inactivate all of a given specimen of vaccine virus is a maximum at about 2650 Å. More significant than the involved absolute energies is the general shape of these lethal curves. They exhibit a rapid drop in the required lethal energy between 3000 and 2800 Å, a minimum at 2650, and a rise towards 2250 Å corresponding closely to the curve representing the absorption of ultraviolet energy by protein substances. In an attempt to narrow the energy band that is required for a lethal exposure the results obtained by others as shown in Table IV-3 must be examined. The maximum lethal effects for *Escherichia coli* are obtained on the average near 2650 Å, and it takes about 14×10^{-6} erg per bacterium to produce death.

Inactivation data by Hollaender and Emmons [1939] on the skin fungus *Trichophyton mentagrophytes* indicate that 2537 Å is the most effective region. It takes about 7×10^{-4} erg to obtain 50 per cent inactivation of these spores.

In the destruction of yeast, *Saccharomyces cerevisiae*, the inhibitory and lethal effects, according to Oster [1934], are approximately the same for all wavelengths, while the destruction efficiency on the basis of a 50 per cent killing is a maximum at wavelengths between 2600 and 2700 Å. The energy required to suppress budding of 50 per cent of the cells irradiated ranges from 457 ergs/mm^2 at 2652 Å to 23,500 ergs/mm^2 at 3022 Å. Landen and Uber [1939] obtained 500 ergs/mm^2 as the destructive efficiency of 2650 Å for the yeast *Sacc. ellipsoideus*. Similar results were obtained by Sharp [1938], for *Bacillus anthraci* using the strong ultraviolet mercury line 2537 Å. Summer sunlight cannot produce comparable effects since the normal atmosphere absorbs all lethal radiation shorter than 2950 Å.

Gates [1929] concludes from his study of the bactericidal action of ultraviolet light on *S. aureus* that: (1) in the initial period of exposure no bacteria succumb; (2) after this initial exposure a considerable number of bacteria, between 20 and 30 per cent, are destroyed, and in this group are found the young ones; (3) the remainder to about 70 or 80 per cent of the total number succumb along an energy gradient that appears to have an exponential relationship to the lethal effects; and finally (4) a number of organisms remain which require an excess of energy to kill them.

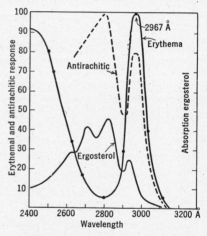

The evidence, therefore, shows that the most effective bactericidal region lies in the range 2500 to 2650 Å, with a possible maximum effectiveness at 2650 Å. The absorption maxima for proteins, yeast, and pepsin also extend from 2700 to 2800 Å, from which it may be inferred that bacteria are destroyed by the photochemical ionization induced in the protein body material of the bacterium (Fig. IV–19), if the surface of the bacterium and the medium in which it is investigated are excluded. Since at 2700 Å it takes about 25×10^{-6} erg per bacterium (Herčík [1936])

FIG. IV–19. The antirachitic response for an equal energy spectrum is shown as compared with the spectral absorption of ergosterol and the average erythemic reaction of the untanned skin to an equal energy spectrum.

Antirachitic data from Knudson and Benford [1938].

Ergosterol data from Bills, Honeywell, and MacNair [1928].

Erythema data from Luckiesh, Holladay, and Taylor [1930] or Coblentz, Starr, and Hogue [1932].

to produce death, it follows that about three million photons are necessary to cause death.

The lethal action of the ultraviolet energy is not brought about by a chemical change of the medium surrounding the organism. The fundamental reaction which causes death is produced inside the cell by the radiant energy that can penetrate to this depth. The reaction is probably unimolecular, on the basis of the assumption that the number of bacteria killed should be proportional to the radiant energy intercepted by a critical volume in the organism.

Rentschler [1940] found that the bactericidal action is determined by the amount of radiant energy to which the bacterium is exposed, regardless of whether a high intensity is applied for a short time or a low intensity is applied for a correspondingly long time, provided that the product, intensity $\times$ time, is the same.

The lethal action is independent of the temperature of the bacteria at the time of exposure.

The sensitivity of an organism to ultraviolet radiation varies appreciably at different stages of its life cycle. It has been found that younger cells are more sensitive than older cells to all forms of absorbed ionizing radiations.

ULTRAVIOLET ACTIVATION

In 1924 Hess and Steenbock independently and almost simultaneously announced the discovery that exposure of edible materials to ultraviolet light endows them with antirachitic activity. It has developed that this activation is relatively permanent and that it is not a process of oxidation.

The second stage in the development was reached when it was demonstrated that sterols became antirachitic upon irradiation. With the introduction of the quartz spectrograph for investigating the spectral absorption of the material under examination the problem entered its quantitative phase.

It was found that in foodstuffs the sterol fraction contained the " acceptor " of the activating rays. The trend of the investigation then turned to the solution of the chemical changes induced by the radiation in the sterols. It was found that ordinary cholesterol was somewhat opaque to ultraviolet light and that irradiation decreased its opacity.

Schultz and Morse, working with cod-liver oil in 1925, found that the absorption spectrum of ordinary cholesterol contained a definite band structure, with maxima of absorption at about 2940 and 2830 Å. The bands disappeared after irradiation and only general absorption remained. They assumed that the cholesterol was contaminated by a small amount of an impurity which produced the selective absorption. In December, 1926, reports from three separate laboratories confirmed the contamination hypothesis. The contamination was subsequently identified as ergosterol. The names of Rosenheim, Webster, Heilbron, Kamm, Morton, and Pohl are associated with the work of identifying the absorption spectrum of ergosterol. Heilbron, Kamm, and Morton [1927] reported that the fractional crystallization of cholesterol led to the accumulation in the least-soluble fraction of the substance responsible for the characteristic absorption spectrum, and identified three absorption bands at 2935, 2820, and 2690 Å. Irradiation destroyed the three bands, leaving only a general absorption.

Subsequently, Bills, Honeywell, and MacNair [1928] showed that ergosterol was the contaminant provitamin. With the aid of a continuous ultraviolet source of radiation supplied by a hydrogen discharge tube, they found that ordinary cholesterol possessed a fourth absorption band at 2600 Å (Fig. IV–19), and that ergosterol possessed similar absorption bands at 2935, 2820, and 2700 Å. This absorption disappears under irradiation, which produces *activation* that yields therapeutically valuable vitamin D.

In Fig. IV–19, the spectral antirachitic efficiency curve of ultraviolet radiation is plotted. Along with this curve, the absorption curve of ergosterol and the erythema curve are given. Note how the antirachitic curve follows the general contours of the absorption curve of ergosterol, and that the most effective antirachitic wavelength, 2804 Å, gives the least erythema. One may conclude that a measurement of the erythema effectiveness does not give an index to the effectiveness of ultraviolet irradiation in the cure or prevention of rickets.

Origin of Molecular Absorption Bands

If the irradiated atoms or molecules of the tissue become ionized, it is possible that this ionization will lead to chemical changes resulting in the destruction of the cell. On what part of the living cell the radiation acts and what primary changes result are still some of the questions to be answered. The primary process may consist in absorption by a complex molecule which is part of the nucleus. Since the molecules are relatively close together and interact strongly with each other, the absorption will not be limited to a sharply defined wavelength, but will spread over a more or less narrow band of wavelengths.

A single absorption band is characterized by a group of absorption lines so close together that in a spectrogram obtained with a spectrograph of small dispersion the lines fuse together. With higher dispersion the band will be found to have its lines crowded closer together at one end, called the band head.

The complex organic molecules that have been considered as participating in absorption are said to be in their lowest molecular energy state, E_0. A photon of energy content $h\nu$, absorbed by such a molecule, will alter its energy state from E_0 to E_1. This means that the molecule absorbs energy $E_1 - E_0$ from the radiant energy passing over it, in which these E's are definite energy states characteristic of the molecule and not of the radiant energy. Thus a molecule in a liquid might absorb light of frequency ν in such a way that $\nu = (E_1 - E_0)/h$, where h is the usual Planck's constant.

For simplicity's sake, let us consider a molecule of hydrochloric acid in which the hydrogen and chlorine atoms are a definite distance apart. This molecule, by acquiring additional energy through absorption, can respond in three ways: (1) There may result a vibration of the two atoms along their axis of connection. (2) There may result a rotation about an axis at right angles to the above axis. (3) There may be changes in radii of the orbital electrons of the atoms, i.e., quantized changes in the electron energies. The spectroscopic evidence shows that the vibrational energy $E_v = (n + \frac{1}{2})h\nu_v$, where n can take on only integer values 0, 1, 2, etc. This implies that the vibrational energy is quantized and that, the larger n, the farther the electron is removed from the nucleus.

The rotational energy is also quantized so that increase in its energy states proceeds as

$$E_r = \frac{(r + \frac{1}{2})^2 h^2}{8\pi^2 I}$$

where r changes by integers 0, 1, 2, etc. I, the moment of inertia, is included because the rotational characteristic of the molecule changes with increase in orbital radii of the electrons. The electronic energy E_e may also change, owing to electronic rearrangements when a quantum is absorbed by either atom. Thus the total energy of the molecule may initially be

$$E = E_e + E_v + E_r$$

Now, changes in any one, any two, or all three may take place when energy is absorbed. The absorption bands under consideration are found in the near ultraviolet; as a result the energy of the absorbed photon is chiefly used in electronic excitation.

We may picture the energy change involved thus: the initial energy of subscript zero, $E_{e0} + E_{v0} + E_{r0}$ becomes $E_{en} + E_{v0} + E_{r1}$. The energy changes involved in the vibrational changes may be comparatively small and do not enter into the picture; hence, E_{v0} is very small. Therefore, for some one electron change from its lowest energy state $n = 0$ to some higher energy state $n = 1$, the frequency of the absorbed energy is

$$\nu = \nu_e + B \pm 2Br + Cr^2$$

where ν_e is due to an electronic change, B and C are constants for the band, and r takes successive values of 0, 1, 2, 3, etc. Thus each line in such a band corresponds to the same electronic shift and to the same vibrational shift. If this relation is plotted for various values of r a parabola of two branches is obtained. The theoretical band for a diatomic molecule has the appearance of possessing a sharp edge at the long-wavelength end and gradually decreasing in intensity towards the short-wavelength end. Somewhat similar properties are exhibited by the experimental absorption bands previously discussed.

Instead of computing the theoretical energy values and from them the spectral frequencies, the problem usually is the converse, viz., obtaining the energy values from the experimentally determined spectrum and trying to arrive at their theoretical significance through an equation similar to that developed above.

The observed facts, however, have far outstripped our understanding of the mechanism of absorption. Although only a superficial elementary analysis of electronic band spectra has been given, it should be sufficient to enable the reader to appreciate the difficulties and the direction in which progress in this field is now being made.

STERILIZATION OF WATER WITH ULTRAVIOLET RADIATION

In order to appreciate the limitations set by water, either as a solvent or for immersion, on the lethal action of ultraviolet radiation, it is necessary to examine the transmission factors of water for ultraviolet spectral radiation. Information on the absorption characteristics of water in the ultraviolet is meager.

In general it is known that an absorption band exists at 6000 Å with probably two weaker bands at 6500 and 5200 Å. These give to water the predominant blue color when viewed through thick layers.

In the ultraviolet the absorption has been traced from 3000 Å to its opaque limit just below 1800 Å. These results are summarized in Fig. IV–20. This curve shows why water becomes opaque near 1800 Å. Since midsummer sunlight is limited at 2950 Å by the opacity of the atmosphere, it becomes apparent that sunlight cannot exert a lethal action on bacteria immersed in water at any great depth. To sterilize water it would be necessary to use a source of ultraviolet radiation from a quartz mercury-vapor lamp of high intensity. This type of lamp is especially rich in ultraviolet radiation at 2536, and 2654 Å, and even

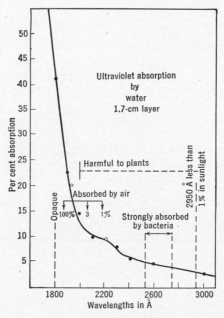

Fig. IV-20. This curve is constructed from data by Kreusler [1901]. It shows the opacity of a layer of water 1.7 cm thick to a source of artificial ultraviolet radiation. Air does not transmit sunlight below 2950 Å. Note that bacteria cannot be killed by wavelength region around 2600 Å, if immersed in water to any great depth. Coefficient of absorption is 0.0025 for water at 2600 Å.

this form of radiation cannot be efficient if water is treated in layers greater than 2 cm thick, and if the flow is so fast that a single bacterium cannot absorb its lethal dose of 25×10^{-6} erg.

ULTRAVIOLET ABSORPTION IN AIR

In the ultraviolet the absorption at atmospheric pressure of a layer of air 1 meter thick is negligible for wavelengths greater than 2300 Å. It is about 1 per cent at 2200 Å and 2 per cent at 2050 Å, and increases rapidly towards shorter wavelengths. This absorption is due to the presence of oxygen. It sets a lower limit of about 1850 Å to the wavelength of the ultraviolet radiation which can be recorded with an optical instrument in which the beam traverses 50 cm of air at atmospheric pressure.

If air 1 meter thick at 760 mm pressure shows a negligible absorption for wavelengths greater than 2050 Å, why is it that we find a rather sharp cut-off in transmission of sunlight at 2950 Å, so that no rays lethal to bacteria (2500 to 2800 Å) reach the earth? This opacity of the atmosphere is attributable to the presence of ozone at high altitudes. Ozone shows a pronounced absorption band extending from 2200 to 2900 Å. Below 2200 Å ozone is transparent again, but the dense oxygen in the lower atmosphere is relatively opaque to wavelengths 2200 to 2000 so that the opacity increases rapidly from 1850 to shorter wavelengths.

It, therefore, follows that midsummer sunlight reaches the earth without containing an appreciable amount of ultraviolet energy destructive to bacteria. Apparently, sunlight as a means of sterilizing the lower strata of air is of questionable value. For this task, therefore, one must resort to other ultraviolet sources which possess pronounced energy radiations near 2650 Å.

STERILIZATION OF AIR WITH ULTRAVIOLET RADIANT ENERGY

The sterilization of the air in an operating room has been successfully accomplished with the aid of a Westinghouse " Sterilamp " by Hart and Gardner [1937]. Their work proved that the presence of staphylococci in the air in the operating room was a source of wound contamination rather than contamination from the skin of the patient or personnel, or by other contacts.

They showed that the transportation of pathogenic bacteria through the air to the wound can be eliminated to a great extent by laying down a barrage of ultraviolet radiant energy around the operative incision and exposed sterile supplies.

Barriers of ultraviolet rays have been shown to be effective in preventing the spread of infection in an isolation ward. Wells' work [1940] shows that an organism in air is about 20 times more vulnerable to the ultraviolet range 2000 to 3000 Å than when suspended in water. Vulnerability values were found to be reduced tenfold paralleling an increase in relative humidity from 46 to 91 per cent. For this effect no acceptable explanation has been proposed.

The available information indicates that bacteria are killed by about the same amount of ionizing energy no matter what its wavelength. The cell damage caused by ionizing radiations must be attributed directly to the liberated ions and to the chemical changes that these ions induce. The nature of these changes has been the subject of much experimentation. Tentatively, we may state that the number of ions produced by lethal doses of radiation is small compared with the enormous number of atoms in the tissue that is radiated. Ionic recombinations take place so rapidly that the chemical changes leading to the death of the cell are minimal, but they are of such a nature that the metabolism of the cell does not readily repair them. In spite of the large amount of work that has already been done, it will probably take a long time to solve so complex a problem.

BIBLIOGRAPHY

1901 KREUSLER, H., *Ann. Physik*, 6, 412.
1915 BURGE, W. E., *Am. J. Physiol.*, 36, 21.
1917 LUCKIESH, M., *J. Franklin Inst.*, 184, 227.
1919 MOLL, W. J. H., *Colorimetry and Nephelometry*, Verlag Akad. Wet. Amsterdam, 28, 1001.
1919 NEWCOMER, H. S., *J. Biol. Chem.*, 37, 465.
1925 MÜLLER, R. H., and G. F. KINNEY, *J. Optical Soc. Am.*, 25, 342.
1925 Report of the Optical Society of America, Committee on Spectrophotometry, *J. Optical Soc. Am.*, 10, 169.
1927 HEILBRON, I. M., E. D. KAMM, and R. A. MORTON, *Biochem. J.*, 21, 78.
1928 BILLS, C. E., E. M. HONEYWELL, and W. A. MACNAIR, *J. Biol. Chem.*, 76, 251.
1928 CLARK, W. M., *Determination of Hydrogen Ions*, Williams and Wilkins Company, Baltimore, Md.
1928 RIVERS, T. M., and F. L. GATES, *J. Exptl. Med.*, 47, 45.
1928 YOE, H. H., *Photometric Chemical Analysis, Colorimetry*, Vol. I; *Nephelometry*, Vol. II; John Wiley & Sons, New York.
1929 GATES, F. L., *J. Gen. Physiol.*, 13, 231; 13, 249.
1929 SMITH, F. C., *Proc. Roy. Soc. London*, B104, 198.
1930 GATES, F. L., *J. Gen. Physiol.*, 14, 31.
1930 LUCKIESH, M., L. L. HOLLADAY, and A. H. TAYLOR, *J. Optical Soc. Am.*, 421, 20.
1930 WYCKOFF, R. W. G., *J. Exptl. Med.*, 52, 769.
1931 CLARK, J. H., *J. Optical Soc. Am.*, 21, 240.
1931 EHRISMANN, O., and W. NOETHLING, *Z. Hyg. Infektionskrakh.*, 113, 597.
1931 FORSYTHE, W. E., B. T. BARNES, and M. A. EASLEY, *J. Optical Soc. Am.*, 21, 30.
1931 LUCAS, N. S., *Biochem. J.*, 25, 57.
1931 TAYLOR, A. H., *J. Optical Soc. Am.*, 21, 20.
1931 WYCKOFF, R. W. G., *J. Gen. Physiol.*, 15, 351.
1932 COBLENTZ, W. W., R. STARR, and J. M. HOGUE, *J. Research Natl. Bur. Standards*, 8, 541.
1932 COUNCIL ON PHYSICAL THERAPY, "Acceptance of Sunlamps," *J. Am. Med. Assoc.*, 99, 31; 100, 1863.
1933 GATES, F. L., *J. Gen. Physiol.*, 17, 797.
1934 COBLENTZ, W. W., *J. Am. Med. Assoc.*, 103, 183 and 254.
1934 COUNCIL ON PHYSICAL THERAPY, *J. Am. Med. Assoc.*, 102, 42.
1934 GATES, F. L., *J. Gen. Physiol.*, 18, 265.
1934 GIESE, A. C., and P. A. LEIGHTON, *J. Gen. Physiol.*, 18, 557.
1934 OSTER, R. H., *J. Gen. Physiol.*, 18, 251.
1934 TWYMAN, F., and C. B. ALLSOPP, *Absorption Spectrophotometry with Hilger Instruments*, 2d Ed., Adam Hilger, London.

1934   WALD, G., *J. Gen. Physiol.*, **18**, 905.
1935   ARMSTRONG, E. L., and M. L. KUDER, *J. Lab. Clin. Med.*, **21**, 181:
1935   ARNOW, L. E., *J. Biol. Chem.*, **110**, 43.
1935   COULTER, C. B., F. M. STONE, and E. A. KABAT, *J. Gen. Physiol.*, **19**, 739.
1935   HOLLAENDER, A., and W. D. CLAUS, *J. Gen. Physiol.*, **19**, 753.
1935   MORTON, R. A., *The Application of Absorption Spectra to the Study of Vitamins and Hormones*, Adam Hilger, London.
1936   Circular Letter LC–473, KSG : AEH IV–3, U. S. Dept. Commerce, Natl. Bur. Standards, Washington, D. C.
1936   EVELYN, K. A., *J. Biol. Chem.*, **115**, 65; **117**, 365 (1937).
1936   HERČÍK, F., *J. Gen. Physiol.*, **20**, 589.
1936   SNELL, D. S., *Methods of Colorimetric Analysis*, D. Van Nostrand Company, New York.
1937   HART, D., and C. E. GARDNER, *Trans. South. Surg. Assoc.*, **49**, 377.
1938   COBLENTZ, W. W., *J. Am. Med. Assoc.*, **111**, 419.
1938   CREW, W. H., and C. H. WHITTLE, *J. Physiol.*, **93**, 335.
1938   HAUSSER, I., *Strahlentherapie*, **62**, 315.
1938   HECHT, S., *J. Applied Phys.*, **9**, 156.
1938   KNUDSON, A., and F. BENFORD, *J. Biol. Chem.*, **124**, 287.
1938   SHARP, D. G., *J. Bact.*, **37**, 447.
1939   BRODE, W. R., *Chemical Spectrophotometry and Its Application*, Adam Hilger, London.
1939   BUTTOLPH, L. J., *J. Optical Soc. Am.*, **29**, 124.
1939   EDWARDS, E. A., and S. Q. DUNTLEY, *Am. J. Anat.*, **65**, 1.
1939   HENSCHKE, U., and R. SCHULZE, *Strahlentherapie*, **64**, 14.
1939   HOLLAENDER, A., and C. W. EMMONS, *J. Cellular Comp. Physiol.*, **13**, 391.
1939   LANDEN, E. W., and F. M. UBER, *Proc. Soc. Exptl. Biol. Med.*, **42**, 559.
1940   LOOFBOUROW, J. R., " Borderland Problems in Biology and Physics," *Rev. Modern Phys.*, **12**, 270.
1940   RENTSCHLER, H. C., *Trans. Ill. Eng. Soc.*, **35**, 960.
1940   WELLS, W. F., *J. Franklin Inst.*, **229**, 347.
1941   BLUM, H. F., *Photodynamic Action and Diseases Caused by Light*, Am. Chem. Soc. Mono. 85.   Reinhold Publishing Corporation, New York.
1941   ELLIS, C., and A. A. WELLS, *The Chemical Action of Ultraviolet Rays*, 2d Ed. F. F. HEYROTH, Reinhold Publishing Corporation, New York.
1941   LAURENS, H., " The Physiological Effects of Radiant Energy," *Ann. Rev. Physiol.*, **3**, 21.

Chapter V

THE STRUCTURE AND PROPERTIES OF SURFACES AND MEMBRANES

In the previous chapters some of the fundamental phenomena causing the destruction of the metabolic equilibrium of the normal cell after x-radiation and gamma radiation absorption were examined. Many substances will also decompose as the result of absorption of ultraviolet rays. If these radiations can produce a modification in the surrounding medium in which a cell is embedded, the resulting toxic products may affect the life history of the cell. On the other hand, the energy may be absorbed in such a way as to change directly the colloidal states of the cytoplasm, causing a modification of the surface structure of the cell and the accompanying alteration of the normal cellular permeability. These modifications will permit the entrance of toxic chemical substances which are normally unable to enter the cell.

A great deal of information exists regarding the passage of dissolved substances into living cells and the accompanying changes in osmotic pressure, but the interpretation of the data, particularly in regard to the possible existence of plasmatic membranes, is rendered difficult by the complexity of the system involved. In general, two points of view have developed: (1) that the cytoplasmic surface is covered with a thin layer of specially differentiated substances of a lipoid nature or with a mosaic of alternate lipoid and protein material; (2) that no special membrane exists on the surface of a cell, but that permeability phenomena are governed by absorption of water by colloids and by the difference in electrical potential which is developed as a result of the concentration of ions unable to cross the border of the cell.

How far the membrane hypothesis is adaptable as an explanation of cellular permeability and osmosis is left to the judgment of the reader after he has acquainted himself with the phenomena contributing to the changes in surface energy of liquids, existing either as free surfaces or as surfaces of separation associated with partitions through which osmosis can take place.

LIQUID SURFACES

A liquid in a large-surfaced open container at rest and under the influence of gravity develops a free horizontal surface. Below this free

170

surface of the liquid the molecules exert an attractive force on one another. This attractive force is appreciable because the molecules are within very minute distances of one another. Since in the interior of the liquid each molecule is surrounded by others on every side, it is therefore subject to attraction in all directions. On the average, over long periods of time as compared with the molecular temperature vibrations, the attraction of any molecule is uniform in all directions; hence the molecule is in equilibrium.

At the surface, however, the molecules of the liquid are attracted only inward and to each side by their neighbors; there is no outward attraction to balance the inward force. The result is that every surface molecule is subjected to a resultant inward attraction directed perpendicular to the surface. It is this inward attraction that causes a free surface to maintain its unique shape for given external conditions. It is also this resultant inward attraction that produces the reduction of the area of a free surface.

The fundamental property of liquid surfaces is that they tend to contract to the smallest possible area permissible by their environment. This tendency is illustrated by the spherical form assumed by small drops of liquid and small gas bubbles, and the shapes assumed by soap films. The departure from spherical forms, noticed in larger liquid drops or gas bubbles, is due to the gravitational effect. The diskoidal form of the mammalian erythrocyte is not well understood, and no satisfactory mathematical expression for the contour has been found.

SURFACE ENERGY

The fact that an undisturbed liquid surface tends to contract shows that surface energy is associated with it, for energy must be expended to extend such a surface. If we view this extension of the surface from an internal point and in terms of the molecules which form the surface, we observe that, as the surface is extended, more and more molecules must be brought from the interior to be added to the expanding surface. In this molecular rearrangement, work is done to move the internal molecules into the surface; hence energy is being expended against the inward-directed molecular forces. An expanding surface is therefore accumulating a greater potential surface energy, and a contracting surface is accompanied by a loss in surface energy. When a surface contracts, either it must wrinkle, or molecules must be forced out of it. If an appreciable surface molecular attraction comparable to what might be called tangential tension exists, then a liquid surface must wrinkle on contraction. This result is contrary to experimental evidence; hence no tangential surface force can exist.

Adam [1930] has shown at great length that the surface energy due to the inward pull on the molecules forming the surface is the fundamental property of surfaces. This potential surface energy is of fundamental importance, for a large number of problems relating to the equilibrium of surfaces can be solved without a knowledge of more than the magnitude of this surface energy. In the solution of such problems a mathematical device is used to simplify the analysis. We substitute for the surface energy a hypothetical tension acting in all directions tangent to the surface, and equal to the magnitude of the surface energy per unit area. This *hypothetical tension* is what is generally understood by the term *surface tension*.

The *surface energy per unit area is denoted by the number of ergs per square centimeter.* This is analogous in dimensions to surface tension expressed in dynes per centimeter. To illustrate its usage by an elementary example, let us analyze the surface energy of a circular surface of radius r having an area πr^2. Next, let us assume a hypothetical force acting at right angles to the circumference of the surface. This force will act along the radii of the circle tending to shrink the surface. Let its magnitude be T dynes per centimeter of circumference. In order to increase the area, energy must be expended. Let the available energy be sufficient to expand it to an area having a radius $(r + dr)$ cm. The energy used to produce this expansion is $dE = 2\pi r T dr$, which upon integration becomes $E = \pi r^2 T$. Hence the energy per unit area measured in ergs per square centimeter has the same dimensions as T, the so-called surface tension measured in dynes per centimeter. This hypothetical surface tension which is supposed to act in the face of the plane surface is also treated as acting tangentially to any curved surface. To treat it as a vector will often lead to fallacious results. Its use may be illustrated in calculating the surface energy of a spherical bubble immersed in a liquid, a common biophysical phenomenon.

The pressure inside a bubble of gas immersed in a liquid must be greater than the external pressure existing at the surface by an amount equal to the internally directed molecular forces per unit area. If T is the hypothetical surface tension in dynes per centimeter at the liquid-gas interface of a bubble of area $4\pi r^2$, then the surface energy at this interface is $E = 4\pi r^2 T$. If the bubble is allowed to expand so that its radius increases to $r + dr$, then the work done in this expansion is $dE = 8\pi r T dr$. If the pressure directed along the radius of the bubble is p dynes per square centimeter, and an increase in volume dV results, then the work done is $dE = pdV$, or $p \cdot 4\pi r^2 dr = 8\pi r T dr$. Hence

$$p = \frac{2T}{r}$$

If, as in the structure of a soap bubble, two surfaces of external radius R_2 and internal radius R_1 are involved, then the internal pressure is

$$p = 2T \left(\frac{1}{R_2} + \frac{1}{R_1} \right)$$

or for very thin soap bubbles where R_1 may be considered equal to R_2

$$p = \frac{4T}{R}$$

TEMPERATURE EFFECTS ON SURFACE ENERGY

As the temperature of a liquid rises, the kinetic agitations of the molecules increase. It has been found experimentally that the surface energy decreases with rising temperature. Table V–1 shows that the reduction in surface-energy measurements with rise in temperature,

TABLE V–1

TEMPERATURE EFFECTS ON SURFACE ENERGY

A liquid-air interface. Changes in T indicated in ergs per square centimeter. Standard T for water-air interface at 20° C is 72.75 ± 0.05 erg/cm². Air pressure, standard conditions.

Water	$t°$ C	10	15	20	25	30	35	40	50	100
	T	74.22	73.49	72.75	71.97	71.18	70.38	69.56	67.91	58.85
Ethyl Ether	$t°$ C	20	50	100						
	T	17.01	13.47	7.97						

over long ranges of temperature, is practically linear. The temperature effect is caused by a decrease in the inward pull on the surface molecules which results in a decrease in surface energy.

LIQUID-GAS INTERFACE

Under ideal conditions surface-energy measurements are made on an uncontaminated liquid surface subjected to a gas pressure of 1 atmosphere at 20° C. The surface is then referred to as a liquid-gas interface. The accepted reference standard of interface-energy measurements is water in the presence of air at 20° C and 760 mm pressure. Its magnitude is 72.75 ± 0.05 erg/cm². Benzene, which is sometimes used as a reference standard, has under the same conditions an interface surface energy equal to 28.88 ± 0.03 erg/cm². Water has the highest interface surface energy of the liquids except mercury, which may pos-

sess as high a value as 465 ergs/cm^2. The surface energy possessed by
some of the more common physiological fluids is shown in Table V–2,
each of which has a surface energy lower than water.

TABLE V–2

LIQUID–LIQUID INTERFACE SURFACE ENERGY

Interfacial energy T in ergs per square centimeter, 20° C

Liquid	Liquid-Water T	Liquid-Air T
Water		72.75
Aniline	5.8	42.90
Benzene	35.0	28.88
Carbon disulphide	45.0	32.33
Carbon tetrachloride	45.0	26.77
Chloroform	32.8	27.14
Ethyl ether	10.7	17.01
Bile		48
Milk		50
Serum (mammalian)		60
Urine (normal)		66
Urine (icteric)		55

LIQUID-LIQUID INTERFACE

Interface energy also exists at the surface between two immiscible
liquids. It has been found that the interfacial energy between two
liquids is less than the energy of the liquid possessing the higher surface
energy when in contact with air. In this case the reduction in energy
is a measure of the reduction of the surface energy of the boundary due
to the presence of the superimposed liquid.

Here one liquid surface is in close contact with a second liquid surface.
The molecules of one liquid surface attract the molecules lying in the
opposite face of the adjoining liquid across the contact boundary. This
attraction diminishes the effective pull exerted by each of the liquids on
its own surface molecules. The condition for complete miscibility of
two liquids is that this interfacial energy shall be zero. Table V–2
shows how much the interfacial energy of water in contact with an
organic liquid has been reduced below that of water in contact with air.

EFFECTS OF SUBSTANCES IN SOLUTION ON SURFACE ENERGY

Substances dissolved in a liquid may either lower or raise the surface
energy at the interface between liquid and air. When many inorganic

salts, such as sodium and potassium chloride, are dissolved in water, the interface energy is raised to a marked degree. This rise is shown in Table V-3. On the other hand, bile salts, tannic acid, starch, and lecithin reduce the surface energy of water. Kopaczewski's [1933] experiments show that " human serum at $20°$ C has a tension of 67.7 dynes per cm," which increases to " 68.3 dynes per cm on dilution with water to form a 50 per cent concentration." If a dissolved substance lowers the surface energy of the solvent, it will tend to become concentrated in the surface layer. It has been observed that the surface energy of stored samples of serum falls slowly with time. This decrease in surface energy may be due to adsorption of air or other gases at the liquid-gas interface. Substances which cause a decrease in surface energy and are as a result concentrated at the surface of the solvent can produce very large changes in surface energy for very minute quantities dissolved.

TABLE V-3

SURFACE ENERGY OF AQUEOUS SOLUTIONS

Interface, liquid-air. For M moles per kilogram of solvent an increase in T is shown. Units of ΔT, ergs per square centimeter. Temperature $20°$ C.

	NaCl	KCl
M	ΔT	ΔT
0.025	0.055	...
0.05	0.09	...
0.10	0.17	0.16
0.25	0.42	0.35
0.5	0.82	0.70
1.0	1.64	1.4
2.0	3.28	2.8
3.0	4.90	4.2
4.0	6.50	5.5
5.0	8.17	7.0

A substance which increases the surface energy of the solvent, as for instance sodium chloride, will tend to flow out of the surface layer, leaving it less concentrated than the solution in the interior of the solvent.

The Hay test for the presence of bile in urine takes advantage of the fact that the surface energy is decreased because of the concentration of bile salts in the surface layer. If sublimed sulphur is sprinkled on the surface of normal urine or pure water, the sulphur is not wetted but floats on the surface. If the sublimed sulphur is sprinkled on icteric urine, from patients suffering from jaundice, the sulphur sinks to the bottom of the urine. The surface energy of the normal urine, because of the presence of the bile salts, is changed from about 66 to 55 ergs/cm^2.

Oil is sprayed on water as a larvicide to suppress mosquitoes. The larvae of mosquitoes normally suspend themselves from the water-air interface by means of three hairlike appendages attached to their breathing tubes. Substituting a water-oil interface for the water-air interface reduces the surface energy. To be effective the oil must reduce the surface energy sufficiently to prevent the larvae from suspending themselves by their breathing tubes, so that they sink and suffocate.

SURFACE ENERGY IN LIVING SYSTEMS

Since living cells are immersed in liquids, it follows that the interface surface energy must be much less than that found at air-water interfaces. Recent work shows that invariable, very low tensions exist between the cell and liquid interface. Protoplasm in sea water, for instance, may have a surface energy as low as 1 erg/cm^2. The work by Harvey [1938] on the physical properties of protoplasm shows that such "naked" cells as amebas, leucocytes, and plant cells removed from their cellulose walls possess surface energies even less than 1 erg/cm^2. With the microscope centrifuge, first constructed by Harvey in 1932, some very low values for this interface tension were found for numerous invertebrate eggs.

PLATEAU'S PRINCIPLE OF MINIMAL AREA

When the disturbing effects of gravity are absent to distort the shape of a fluid body at rest, liquid surfaces always assume a curvature such that the mean curvature along two planes at right angles is constant.

$$\frac{1}{R_1} + \frac{1}{R_2} = \text{Constant}$$

where R_1 and R_2 are these principal radii of curvature at any point. Hence, when one decreases the other must increase to keep the reciprocals of the sum constant. A spherical soap bubble, for example, has two equal curvatures along two planes at right angles. If this bubble is stretched, one radius of curvature increases as the one at right angles decreases. Geometrically it can be shown that surfaces to which this equation applies are surfaces of minimum area.

The forms of living cells and protoplasmic masses, such as vacuoles, plasmolyzed protoplasts, and amebas, are also illustrations of this principle. Barnes [1937] even found that fatty material in such cells as intestinal epithelium occurs as spherical droplets.

This law of constant mean curvature is also illustrated by the structure of emulsions. Emulsions are systems of two liquids insoluble in each other, consisting of small globules of one liquid suspended in a second liquid with which it does not mix. The conditions necessary to produce a stable emulsion are such that, when two incompletely miscible liquids are mechanically agitated so as to disperse one in the o ther in the form of globules, a minimum of work must be done upon the system, which is equal to the product of the interfacial surface energy per unit area by the increase in surface due to the globule formation. That this is an appreciable amount of energy, and that the resulting dispersion is unstable, can be shown by the fact that as the coalescence of the globules takes place a measurable amount of energy is liberated. To stabilize an emulsion, it is necessary to add a third substance (the emulsifier) which will form an adsorbed film on the globules. This will prevent their coalescence if the surface energy of each globule is reduced to a minimum. In general, the more the emulsifier decreases this surface energy, the more stable is the resulting emulsion. The most effective emulsifiers for fat-water systems are polysaccharide gums, proteins, soaps, lipoids, bile salts, and saponins.

THE COALESCENCE OF LIQUID SPHERES

The coalescence of spherical droplets in suspension is primarily attributable to the reduction in the potential surface energy. Taylor's [1921] study of this problem convinced him that coalescence of liquid spheres is not due to a molecular attraction, so long as the spheres do not touch. When contact occurs, a " force " comes into play which causes them to coalesce and become one sphere. This occurs with all liquids, independent of the relative size of the spheres, and at all temperatures.

A fundamental property of the surface energy is to maintain the area of a liquid surface at a minimum. The minimum area that can be attained by any unconstrained mass is spherical. Therefore, if several small spheres, each of surface energy e, were to coalesce, a new sphere, having surface energy E, must be formed. Upon the large sphere a redistribution of surface energy must take place in such a way that the surface energy E is less than the sum of the surface energies of the small spheres.

Taylor [1921] calculated this redistribution of energy for the coalescence of three spheres of water whose diameters were 0.3, 0.4, and 0.5 cm. The potential surface energy of these three spheres is

$$E = \pi\{(0.3)^2 + (0.4)^2 + (0.5)^2\}T$$

or $0.50\pi T$ ergs per square centimeter, where T is the interface tension in dynes per centimeter.   If these spheres are brought in contact they will coalesce to form one sphere whose diameter is 0.6 cm and whose potential surface energy is $E = 0.36\pi T$ ergs per square centimeter.   The difference, or $0.14\pi T$, is the loss in potential surface energy that has been transformed into kinetic energy, which manifests itself as a rise in temperature of the newly formed sphere.   For water, where $T = 72.75$ ergs/cm^2 at 20° C, this rise amounts to 7.5×10^{-7} calorie.   The converse case possesses physiological interest.   How much energy would be used to break the above drop into ten thousand equal spherical fragments?

Surface Energy of Spreading Cells

In the response of living cells to contact with solid bodies, the surface energy and contact angles developed at the interfaces play an important part, if not a major one, in determining the physical response of cells to changes in environment.

The behavior of a cell towards a horizontal flat surface with which it may come in contact and attain an equilibrated shape or, if surface conditions are favorable, spread to molecular film thickness has many biological implications.   The familiar adhesiveness exhibited by blood cells and the spreading of phagocytes in the process of ingesting small particles are typical examples.

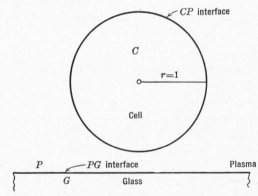

Fig. V–1.   Cell immersed in plasma before contact with glass surface.

The complex phenomena of the response of a living cell to a flat surface or spherical particle with which it makes contact is best understood if an idealized simple case is first analyzed and examined for the physical implications involved.   The existence of a perfect fluid is assumed which is immersed in plasma of the same density as the cell.

In this environment the cell is spherical and possesses potential surface energy equal to $4\pi r^2 T_{CP}$ ergs per square centimeter, where T_{CP} is the tension attributed to the cell-plasma interface. The spherical cell is then allowed to come in contact with a glass plate G shown in Fig. V–1, which is also immersed in plasma. As the cell makes contact with the glass surface it exchanges a cell-plasma (CP) interface, of area πa^2, for a cell-glass (CG) interface of equal area (Fig. V–2). If the cell spreads over the glass surface, this area increases until the cell has expanded and formed a layer one molecule thick.

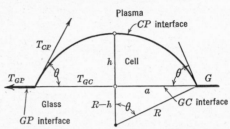

FIG. V–2. Cell immersed in plasma in equilibrium position with respect to glass surface. θ = contact angle.

The fundamental question is whether the cell will always spread to monomolecular thickness or whether an intermediate equilibrium position will be attained, owing to the character of the interfaces. Fenn's [1921] theoretical analysis of this situation showed that for a given environment the surface energy of the cell, while spreading, would decrease and reach a minimum value when the cell attained its equilibrium position on a given surface.

To verify this analysis the spherical cell C is represented as in Fig. V–1. This cell with cell-plasma interface and of unit radius is about to come in contact with the surface G in the presence of the plasma P. As the cell touches the glass surface it assumes the shape shown in Fig. V–2. The problem is to determine the height h of the distorted cell above the horizontal surface G at equilibrium in terms of its surface energy. In its new environment it now possesses cell-plasma (CP), cell-glass (CG), and glass-plasma (GP) interfaces differing in area from those in Fig. V–1.

In assuming the equilibrium position on the glass surface, part of the cell-plasma interface, of area πa^2, is replaced by an equal area of cell-glass interface. At the circular edge of contact between the three media are located the tensions T_{GP} due to the glass-plasma interface, T_{GC} due to the glass-cell interface, and T_{CP} due to the cell-plasma interface. At the junction of these three phases the cell-plasma interface makes an angle θ with the glass-cell interface, which defines the contact angle.

The cell, if free to spread, must decrease its potential surface energy in the act of spreading. This act of spreading enlarges the glass-cell contact area until equilibrium has been attained. In this state the surface energy is at a minimum. The surface energy of the contacted cell is made up of two parts: the area of the curved surface of the spherical segment with surface energy equal to $(\pi h^2 + \pi a^2)T_{CP}$, and the circular interface with surface energy equal to $\pi a^2(T_{GC} - T_{GP})$ ergs per square centimeter. Then the total energy is

$$E = \pi(h^2 + a^2)T_{CP} + \pi a^2(T_{GC} - T_{GP})$$

where T represents the tensions designated by the three different interfacial subscripts.

Let $T_{CP} \equiv n$ and $T_{GC} - T_{GP} \equiv m$. The above equation may then be rewritten as

$$E = n\pi(h^2 + a^2) + m\pi a^2$$

where, because the volume of the cell remains constant,

$$a^2 = \frac{8}{3h} - \frac{h^2}{3}$$

In the process of spreading, the volume of the cell is assumed to remain constant, so that the problem reduces itself to ascertaining the magnitude of the height h of the cell at equilibrium for given values of cell, surface, and plasma characteristics, i.e., for values of m and n or values of m/n.

Substituting for a its values in terms of h in the above equation for E, and differentiating the result with respect to h, gives

$$\frac{dE}{dh} = \frac{\pi h^3 \left[2n - \frac{2}{3}(m+n) - \frac{8\pi}{3}(m+n) \right]}{3h^2}$$

Since at equilibrium the surface energy must be a minimum, i.e., $dE/dh = 0$, it follows that $h^3 = \dfrac{4(m+n)}{2n - m}$. Geometrically it can be seen from Fig. V–2 that

$$\cos\theta = \frac{4 - 2h^3}{4 + h^3}$$

Substituting the above value of h^3 in this relation, we find that

$$\cos\theta = -\frac{m}{n} \equiv \frac{T_{GP} - T_{GC}}{T_{CP}}$$

It is possible to use this expression to predict what will happen when a cell of uniform density, immersed in plasma of the same density, makes contact with a horizontal surface. Suppose that it spreads until its contact angle is 90°. What is the height of the cell under these circumstances? This height may be obtained by setting $\theta = 90°$, $\cos \theta = 0$, $-m/n = 0$. Then $h^3 = 2$, and $h = 1.26$. The cell has therefore assumed the shape of a hemisphere having a volume equal to the original spherical cell.

If the nature of the surface G is then changed so that the contact angle $\theta = 0$, then $\cos \theta = +1$; hence $-m/n = +1$, i.e., the cell spreads " to infinity."

If the surface G is such that the cell does not spread at all, then $\theta = 180°$ and $\cos \theta = -1$; hence $-m/n = -1$. The cell is a free sphere.

The conclusions are that values of $-m/n$ between $+1$ and -1 will produce all possible degrees of spreading and that the surface characteristics of cell, plasma, and plane determine the magnitude of the contact angle in its equilibrium position. To produce further spreading of the cell, either work must be done on it or the surface characteristics of the interfaces must be changed.

PHAGOCYTOSIS

If a small spherical insoluble particle is substituted for the plane surface, comparable changes in the contact area of the cell and particle will take place because of the spreading of the cell over the particle. This factor led Fenn to propose the above analysis as a method of approach in the understanding of the very important biological phenomenon known as phagocytosis.

Phagocytosis may be defined as the ingestion of a particle by a living cell. The particle may be a non-living piece of matter, a bacterium, or other cell structure. The problem is not to investigate the fate of the ingested particle, but to attempt to analyze the mechanism of phagocytosis in terms of the surface energy existing at the interfaces created by the contact of the cell with the particle in the presence of plasma.

The above theory of cell spreading may be extended to cover cases where the surface G over which the cell spreads is curved to such an extent that G may be considered a small sphere. Under these circumstances the following questions may arise. What is the physical adjustment of the cell, and how does the total surface energy vary as the small spherical particle is progressively ingested?

It frequently happens in phagocytosis that the cell is about ten times greater in radius than the particle to be ingested, as for instance when a particle in the form of a *Staphylococcus aureus* of average diameter from 0.7 to 1.0 μ is about to make contact with a large mononuclear lymphocyte with average diameter 12 to 15 μ. In this example, according to Lyddane and Stuhlman [1940], the above theory shows that the surface energy of the expanding cell, as it progressively ingests the particle, drops to a minimum at some specific depth of penetration, where the cell and particle are then in equilibrium. Under these conditions, whether the particle is partly or completely ingested, the surface energy between coccus and cell is at a minimum. If as a result of ingestion the cell-particle interface changes, it is possible that further ingestion goes on at the expense of the internal energy of the cell, or that the particle is ejected.

PHAGOCYTOSIS A PHENOMENON OF SPREADING

The above analysis is supported by experimental evidence (Mudd [1933]), which proves that the ability of a phagocyte to spread over the surface of a particle undergoing ingestion is one of the principal factors in determining phagocytosis. It has been found that, in the presence of dilute sensitizing serum, adhesion of particles to the phagocytes may take place with little evidence of complete ingestion. If the sensitizing serum is more concentrated, however, the particles adhere to the phago-cytes and are subsequently covered by their cytoplasm. The conclusion that may be drawn is that the phagocytosis-promoting substances of immune sera, opsonin or bacteriotropin, resurface the particles with at least a monomolecular layer of an interfacial-surface-energy depressant, a surface deposit upon which phagocytes can spread very readily.

Phagocytosis in the body can be promoted by the deposition, on the particle or on a bacterium, of a film of serum globulin which gives the surface a low interfacial tension against the leucocyte and a high inter-facial tension against the medium in which the particle is suspended. Since it is practically impossible to measure the three interfacial tensions in a phagocyte-particle-liquid system, inferences must be drawn from such theoretical situations and indirect experimental evidence as out-lined above (Mudd, McCutcheon, and Lucke [1934]).

The influence of sulphanilamide upon phagocytic activity is still uncertain. Recent work, however, indicates that sulphanilamide and sulphapyridine are more effective therapeutically in conjunction with immune serum than if either drug or serum is given alone, a result sug-gesting that phagocytosis may play a part in the final disposal of the infective agents.

STALAGMOMETER

A rather usual method for measuring surface energy is by determining the weight of the drops which detach themselves slowly from the tip of a calibrated vertical glass tube of small bore. A rather crude formula is then applied in which the weight of the drop W is proportional to the surface energy and radius of the tube.

$$W = 2\pi r T$$

It is assumed that the tension of the liquid acts vertically around the rim of the tube from which the drop is suspended and subsequently necks off.

It can be shown theoretically and verified experimentally that drops necking off from a vertical tube are always smaller than $2\pi r T$, often by

Fig. V–3. Progressive stages in the formation of a drop of water separating itself from a clean polished surface at the end of a glass capillary tube. Freehand sketch.

more than 40 per cent. High-speed photographs by Guye and Perrot [1903] show that the suspended drop becomes unstable before it leaves the end of the tube. Then a constricted portion develops, as seen in Fig. V–3, which narrows and subsequently allows the drop to form after breaking off near the end. The stretched column between the lower drop and the tube then separates itself from the tube and forms an additional small drop; finally, the remainder of the column retracts, allowing some of the liquid to remain suspended from the end of the tube.

In any drop-weight method both the large and small drops must be counted together as " one drop."

Harkins and Brown [1919] showed by careful measurements that the weight of a drop is conditioned by the radius of the tube from which the drop falls and is also a function of the inverse cube root of V, the volume of the drop. The more exact relation between these quantities is

$$w = 2\pi r T f\left(\frac{r}{V^{1/3}}\right)$$

or more simply

$$T = \frac{mg}{r}F$$

where F is a correction factor and equal to $\dfrac{1}{2\pi f(r/V^{1/3})}$ and m is the mass of
the drop falling from a tube of radius r. A table of correction factors
compiled by Harkins and Brown can be found in the *International Critical Tables*, Vol. 4, p. 435. With the aid of these tables the error in determining the surface energy is reducible to 0.1 per cent.

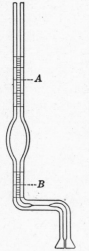

A convenient form of dropping tube, or stalagmometer, is shown in Fig. V–4. It is essentially a capillary tube the end of which is flattened by compression, carefully ground flat, and polished. The tube is filled, with the liquid under examination, to the major engraving A. The number of drops which break away from the lower plane surface C are counted while the liquid level falls from the upper mark A to the lower mark B.

Since the measured surface energy decreases in magnitude with rise in temperature, all observations must be made at constant temperature. The experimental results that can be obtained by this method are least subject to error when the lower polished flat release-surface possesses a sharp edge and the drops are allowed to form slowly. Adam [1930] recommends a total time of about ten minutes for the formation of

Fig. V–4. Stalagmometer after Traube.

each drop. The surface-energy values will be found too large if the drop forms too rapidly. The time of formation can be shortened if the initial stages of drop formation are rapid and if the final necking is allowed to develop very slowly, for example during one minute, so that the drop eases off very gently.

In the use of a stalagmometer great care must be exercised to avoid the contamination of the polished release-surface by grease. The slightest trace of grease greatly lowers the surface energy of the water which is used to calibrate the stalagmometer. In order that determinations may be carried out at constant temperature and in the presence of saturated vapor, drops must be allowed to form in a closed, temperature-controlled vessel.

The Suspended-Ring Method

If a biological fluid possesses a low content of surface-active solute, a tensiometer method, which measures the force required to detach a circular ring from the surface, is highly recommended. A metal ring dipped below the surface and then carefully pulled vertically upwards will drag with it a film of the liquid. If we assume that this film becomes vertical before rupture takes place, then the downward pull P on the ring must be equal to twice the product of mean circumference of ring by surface energy. To the first approximation

$$P = 4\pi RT$$

To increase the accuracy, the exact dimensions of the ring and the diameter $2r$ of the wire of which it is made must be taken into consideration. On account of the incompleteness of the theory, Harkins, Young, and Cheng [1926] have increased the reliability of the method to better than 1 per cent by introducing an experimental correction factor F, so that the working equation becomes

$$T = \frac{mg}{4\pi R} \cdot F$$

To obtain an unknown surface energy the maximum pull in dynes to raise the ring when the surface is on the point of rupture is obtained, experimentally, as $p = mg/4\pi R$, where R is the mean radius of the ring. The volume of the liquid V raised by means of the ring above the plane surface of the liquid, which corresponds with the above maximum pull, is $V = m/(d - \rho)$, where d is the density of the liquid, ρ is the density of air saturated with vapor of the liquid, and m is the mass of the raised liquid.

It was found that for the proper values of the ratio of R/r the correction factor F is determined by the value of R^3/V. Hence, the values of R, r, and the experimentally determined value of V being known, the surface energy may be determined to a high degree of precision with the aid of a table of these correction factors as

$$T = p \cdot F$$

In the hands of du Noüy [1919] this method was brought to a high degree of precision. He adopted a ring of platinum (10 per cent iridium) which hangs from an inverted V frame of the same kind of wire fused to the ring. This ring can be cleaned by simply heating it white hot. It is suspended from the arm of a specially designed torsion balance, as in the Cenco-du Noüy tensiometer (Fig. V-5). The wire ring is of circular section about 0.3 mm in diameter with a mean circumference of 4 cm. The torsion wire is made of steel piano wire of diameter 0.25 mm. The liquid is placed in a shallow crystallizing dish or watch glass into which the ring is allowed to dip. The pointer attached to the torsion wire rotates over a fixed circular scale as the ring is raised to the point where it breaks through the liquid surface. The liquid surface is adjusted so that, for its final reading at rupture, the beam lies in a horizontal position. If the ring has a mean circumference of 4.00 cm and is used on pure

water at room temperature, the value of the correction factor F will be approximately 0.990. Since F can be determined for any given case, the apparatus is sensitive to a force of about 0.1 dyne and has the advantage of being able to use small quantities of liquid at high operating speeds.

Certain experimental precautions are essential if a moderately high degree of precision is desired in the use of this instrument:

1. The liquid should be covered by an inverted glass funnel to prevent cooling by evaporation.

2. The liquid and the vapor above it must be kept at a constant temperature.

FIG. V–5. Cenco-du Noüy precision tensiometer. (Courtesy Central Scientific Company.)

3. The vessel used to contain the sample should be of such a shape and size that the surface need not be corrected for curvature of meniscus of the liquid.

4. The design of the vessel should be such that the surface of the liquid may be renewed or swept by a clean glass bar. Tables of correction factors are supplied by the manufacturers of this instrument for the particular ring adopted.

Since the surface energy of water and other liquids increases appreciably with a decrease in temperature, it is necessary to know the temperature and the temperature coefficient of the liquid under test. The temperature coefficient of water between 15 and 25° C is, according to Harkins, 0.154 erg/cm^2/°C; between 10 and 60° C its surface energy may be expressed by

$$T = 75.796 - 0.145t - 0.00024t^2$$

THE EFFECT OF SURFACE IMPURITIES ON SURFACE-ENERGY MEASUREMENTS

In determining the speed with which a substance spreads over the surface of a liquid, the ring method of measuring surface energy is used to compare the surface energy at points on the circumference of a circle at whose center the spreading substance touches the liquid. Substances like myristic acid are found to spread in two stages. In the first stage the surface is covered by a unimolecular " expanded " film under no compression. The second stage follows when the expanded film becomes more closely packed and still maintains its unimolecular thickness.

The ring method was used by Cary and Rideal [1925] to follow surface-energy changes as illustrated by the progressive film formation of a crystal of a fatty acid, as, for instance, myristic acid, when it was brought into contact with the surface of a 0.01 N solution of hydrochloric acid in water. The velocity of spreading on water was found to be of the order of 20 cm/sec.

Water, having a high cohesion, does not spread on organic liquids. Organic liquids of moderately high cohesion spread on water. Any diminution of the surface energy of the water, by an adsorbed film, diminishes the tendency of the upper liquid to spread.

The property of castor oil to spread rapidly as a thin film would seem to help explain the rapidity and thoroughness with which it coats the intestinal walls when it is used as a purgative. It has also been demonstrated that castor oil is a better lubricant for machinery than mineral oil of equal viscosity.

PERMEABILITY OF STATIC MEMBRANES

It has been found possible to construct partitions which, when used to separate pure water from a solution of crystalloids like sugar or salt, will allow the water to diffuse through them, but not the dissolved crystalloids. A film of colloid (glue-like) material such as starch coated on a supporting sheet of porous paper, if used as a partition between pure water and a solution of crystalloids and colloids, will allow the crystalloids to pass through and diffuse into the water, but it will entirely block the passage of the colloids. If the partition is a structure which allows only the solvents to pass through, it is designated as semi-permeable. Some animal bladders and parchment sheets will allow water and dissolved crystalloids to pass through but will prevent the passage of colloidal substances. Animal and vegetable membranes that have the property of allowing the solvent to pass through them and of preventing some or all of the solute from passing are also considered semi-permeable.

The botanist de Vries [1888] was one of the first to attribute the shrinkage of plant cells, placed in dilute sugar solutions, to the semi-permeability of the cell membrane. He observed, with the aid of a microscope, that plant cells had comparatively rigid cellulose walls enclosing a membrane filled with protoplasm. Reproductions of his original osmotic experiments on the middle nerve leaf of *Tradescantia discolor* are shown in Fig. V–6. In diagram *A* note how the sap fills the normal cell until its bulging sides touch the cellulose walls. When such a structure was immersed in a 10 per cent sugar solution, the protoplasm was found to shrink gradually and draw away from the walls, as shown in *B*. When the cell was immersed in a strong solution of potassium nitrate, the sap was observed to shrink into globular masses like those shown in *C*.

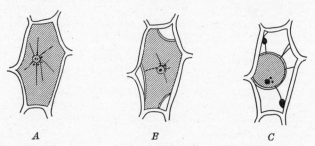

A   B   C

Fig. V–6.   Cells from the middle nerve leaf *Tradescantia discolor*.   *A*, normal cell.   *B*, plasmolysis started, cytoplasm shrinks from cell wall.   *C*, strong plasmolysis due to 1.0 *M* potassium nitrate.   (After H. de Vries [1888].)

De Vries found that such a shrinkage was produced by the passage of the water content of the cell through the cell membrane while the leaf was immersed in a sugar or salt solution.

He also discovered that many plant cells, after having undergone what he termed *plasmolysis*, could be restored to their natural fluid conditions by placing them in pure water. This experiment proved that the membrane was permeable to water in either direction.

He concluded that the dead cellulose walls were freely permeable to the sugar and salt solutions, but that the membrane boundary of the cell protoplasm was impermeable to the crystalloids but permeable to water.

A familiar example of membrane permeability is the swelling of seeds when steeped in pure water. They will increase as much as 70 per cent in weight from the transmission of water through the semi-permeable covering with which they are surrounded.

The apparent " selective " permeability of seed coverings to certain substances is illustrated by the use of copper sulphate as a fungicide for wheat. This salt, though highly poisonous for the fungus spores adhering to it, will not affect the vitality of the wheat seed because the seed covering is impermeable to it. Other examples of selective permeability are furnished by the many marine forms in which the sodium-potassium ratio of the cell content is very different from that found in sea water. The marine plant *Valonia*, for instance, was found by Osterhout [1936] to possess a cell content which has about one fifth the sodium concentration and fifty times the potassium concentration of sea water in which it normally exists.

In a certain sense, the human skin may be considered as functioning like a semi-permeable membrane. The work of Whitehouse, Hancock, and Haldane [1932] has shown that a large proportion of the moisture which is given off from the skin during rest under ordinary conditions of temperature passes through the skin by osmosis or diffusion. The osmotic loss was demonstrated through different effects of baths in pure water and strong salt solutions. They found that osmotic loss increased very rapidly as the temperature of the skin rose, but that, with a sufficient rise, a point was reached where the presence of liquid sweat over the whole skin interrupted the process completely.

Since the introduction of the cell theory in 1838 the general conclusion that living matter must be enclosed in a protective membrane in order to survive in its environment has become definitely established. A fundamental property of a living cell is the semi-permeability of its limiting membrane. Upon the death of the cell the semi-permeability of its membrane is usually entirely lost. The limiting membrane of protoplasm is not a dead partition, but an intricate dynamic structure maintaining the control between its internal and external environment. The external environment is usually a dilute solution containing a changing amount of nutrient material.

Osmosis

Osmosis may be defined as the passage of a fluid or fluids through a membrane which separates two liquid phases consisting of a common solvent and one or more solutes with different concentrations in the two phases.

The unfertilized eggs of the sea urchin are typical natural osmometers. They are normally spherical in shape, which readily permits their change in volume to be determined by measuring their diameters. The eggs can be swollen by introducing them into diluted sea water. Shrinkage will take place when they are transferred from diluted to concentrated sea water. McCutcheon and Lucke [1927] discovered that the rate at which water passed through the membrane in *exosmosis* as well as *endosmosis* in the unfertilized sea-urchin egg followed the same law as that expressing the velocity of a monomolecular chemical reaction, namely, that

$$\frac{dx}{dt} = k(c - x)$$

where x was the change of volume during time t, c the original volume, and k the velocity constant. It was also found that the speed of osmosis was greatly increased as the temperature increased. The speed of penetration was found to be much greater than if simple diffusion through a membrane took place.

OSMOTIC PRESSURE

The osmotic pressure of a solution can be defined as the maximum hydrostatic pressure ($P = hdg$) produced when a solution and solvent are separated by a perfect semi-permeable membrane. It may also be defined as the equivalent of the external pressure which must be applied to a solution in order to prevent the passage of the solvent into it through a perfect semi-permeable membrane.

MEASUREMENTS OF OSMOTIC PRESSURE

In the search for an ideal semi-permeable partition, Traube, as early as 1867, discovered that a flexible film of cupric ferrocyanide has semipermeable properties. He found that, when a dilute solution of copper sulphate is mixed with a dilute solution of potassium ferrocyanide, a brown precipitate of cupric ferrocyanide is formed. This precipitate, if used as a partition, will permit the passage of water, but will prevent the passage of both copper sulphate and potassium ferrocyanide, as well as of many other crystalloids.

A very realistic model of a growing cell may be constructed by introducing a moderately concentrated solution of potassium ferrocyanide, in the form of a drop, below the surface of a dilute copper sulphate solution. A brown precipitated film of cupric ferrocyanide is formed around the drop, which subsequently ruptures at some point as the result of the increasing osmotic pressure caused by osmotic flow of water through the membrane. The rupture, however, is rapidly mended by a new patch of precipitated cupric ferrocyanide. The osmotic pressure again enlarges the drop until by a succession of ruptures and subsequent repairs the drop has grown until its internal and external pressures have attained equilibrium.

Since this type of unsupported membrane is rather fragile, the botanist Pfeffer (1877) supported the gelatinous cupric ferrocyanide film by the framework of a porous earthenware pot. He used an unglazed porcelain cylindrical vessel from which he had removed the air occluded in the pores and then allowed them to fill with water. By placing this water-saturated pot in a 3 per cent solution of copper sulphate and pouring into the interior a 3 per cent solution of potassium ferrocyanide, he succeeded in precipitating the semi-permeable membrane in the framework of the vessel, where the two liquids met in the porous wall.

Figure V–7 shows the form of the apparatus used by Pfeffer to measure osmotic pressures. The earthenware pot was a white unglazed porcelain cell *z* with the glass pieces *v* and *t* inserted as air-tight stoppers. The

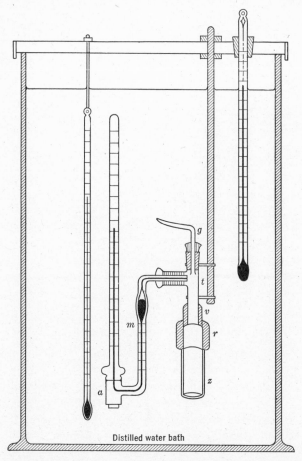

Fig. V–7. A precision method for measuring osmotic pressures according to Pfeffer.

porcelain cell was about 4.6 cm high and had an internal diameter of about 1.6 cm with walls from 1.25 to 2 mm thick. A manometer *m* was attached to measure the pressure. The tube *g* was sealed off after air bubbles had been removed at the joints *t*. The solution whose osmotic pressure was to be determined was introduced into the apparatus through *g*. The porous cell was then totally immersed in distilled water, and after osmotic equilibrium had been attained the pressure was read on the manometer.

Using dilute solutions of cane sugar, Pfeffer discovered that the osmotic pressures developed by them were proportional to their concentrations and that the osmotic pressure increased with rise in temperature. He found that the osmotic forces developed by his solutions were astonishingly large. A 10 per cent sugar solution, for instance, actually developed an osmotic pressure of nearly 7 atmospheres, or a force of more than 100 lb/in.[2]

Van't Hoff's Discovery

Ten years later van't Hoff pointed out the remarkable parallelism between the properties of gases and the osmotic behavior of dilute solutions. The experimental evidence showed that the osmotic pressure of a dilute solution was directly proportional (1) to the concentration of the solute and (2) to the absolute temperature.

If it could be proved that the ultimate material particles in the solvent behave as if they were entities having the properties of gas molecules, the application of the general gas law to osmotic-pressure phenomena would be justified. Or, conversely, if the general gas law could be used to predict the osmotic pressure of a solution, the conclusion is that, to the first approximation, the entities in the solvent of a dilute solution had properties analogous to those of gas molecules.

The first step is the justification of Boyle's law. In order to apply it the pressure must be shown to be inversely proportional to the volume, provided that the temperature is kept constant. Since the measured hydrostatic pressure $P = hdg$ and the density of this column of liquid $d = m/V$, it follows that $PV = hmg$. When the osmotic pressure developed by sucrose, as indicated in Table V–4, is examined, it can be seen that a 0.2 M concentration develops a pressure of 5.11 atmospheres at 20° C. It should follow that a 0.4 M concentration must develop a pressure of 10.22 atmospheres, and 0.6 M concentration, a pressure of 15.33 atmospheres. The corresponding experimental values are 10.22 and 15.52 atmospheres, respectively. The agreement is surprisingly good. The conclusion is that the osmotic pressure is proportional to the concentration expressed in gram-molecular weights per 1000 grams of water; i.e., P is proportional to mg/V.

The gram-molecular weight is the weight of a substance in grams numerically equal to its molecular weight. A gram-molecular weight of any substance contains the same number of molecules (6.064×10^{23}) as a gram-molecular weight of any other substance. The concentration of a substance is defined as the number of gram-molecular weights M contained in 1000 grams of water.

As a second step another aspect of the general gas law must be justified, namely: the pressure developed by a given mass of gas, at constant volume, is proportional to the absolute temperature. The restatement of the law as applied to dilute solutions would read: the osmotic pressure developed by a given concentration is proportional to the absolute temperature. Table V–4 shows that a sucrose concentration of 0.4 M

TABLE V–4

Osmotic Pressure of Sucrose

Concentrations in gram-molecular weights per 1000 grams water.
Sucrose $C_{12}H_{22}O_{11}$. Temperatures in degrees Centigrade.
Osmotic pressure in atmospheres, standard conditions.
$C = M/1000$, where $M = 342.2$.

C	Temperature, °C				
---	0	10	20	30	40
0.1	2.48	2.52	2.61	2.50	2.58
0.2	4.76	4.93	5.11	5.09	5.21
0.3	7.14	7.39	7.67	7.71	7.91
0.4	9.52	9.87	10.22	10.38	10.69
0.5	12.00	12.40	12.86	13.09	13.47
0.6	14.50	14.98	15.52	15.85	16.28

By Courtesy of Morse, Holland, Myers, Cash, and Zinn, Am. Chem., J., **48**, 29 *(1912).*

at 10° C can develop an osmotic pressure of 9.87 atmospheres while the same concentration at 20° C should, according to the general gas law, develop a pressure of 10.21 atmospheres. The data show that this sucrose solution can develop an osmotic pressure of 10.22 atmosphere. The conclusion is that, at any given temperature, all equal concentrations of dilute solutions of non-electrolytes have the same osmotic pressure. Hence, the molecular weight of a non-electrolyte being known, the general gas law can be used to calculate the amount of a substance that must be dissolved in 1000 grams of solvent to obtain any desired osmotic pressure.

Isotonic Solutions

Solutions developing the same osmotic pressure are isosmotic or isotonic. Hypotonic solutions are solutions that have a lower osmotic pressure, and hypertonic solutions possess a greater osmotic pressure, than plant or animal cell contents when the cells are placed in such solutions.

If a cell is placed in a solution having a higher osmotic pressure (hypertonic solution) than the cell contents, water tends to flow out of the cell, thus reducing its internal osmotic pressure. The cell therefore shrinks in size. If the solution in which a cell is introduced has a lower osmotic pressure (hypotonic solution), then water tends to flow into the cell, which expands, eventually bursting as the result of the increased internal osmotic pressure.

Hamburger, a Dutch physiologist, was probably the first to apply physical laws to animal physiology. He showed, as early as 1886, that erythrocytes from different species of animals have different limits of fragibility and that in no case was the solution producing hemolysis (stretching of red blood cells so that pigment escapes) isotonic with the cell content. He found that an isotonic solution of sodium chloride containing 0.951 gram of NaCl per 100 grams of water could be used to prevent the rupture of the membrane of human red corpuscles.

OSMOTIC PRESSURE OF ELECTROLYTES

We find experimentally that an aqueous solution of sucrose ($M = 342.2$) having a molar concentration of $0.2\,M$ at $0°$ C develops an osmotic pressure equal to 4.76 atmospheres. A similar concentration of sodium chloride ($M = 58.5$) develops an osmotic pressure of 8.75 atmospheres. The sodium chloride behaves osmotically as if its concentration were nearly twice as great as that of sucrose.

This abnormal osmotic activity of salt solutions was first observed by the botanist de Vries during his investigation of the previously mentioned experiments on the plasmolysis of plant cells.

If "normal" means the values calculated in accordance with the van't Hoff laws of osmotic pressure and molecular weights of nonelectrolytes, then electrolytes may be said to possess an abnormally high osmotic pressure. This abnormality is found to become more pronounced by diluting the solution.

The explanation is found in the fact that salts, acids, and alkalies dissociate when dissolved in water. The molecules in solution dissociate into positively and negatively charged entities called ions. These ions participate in creating the osmotic pressure just as if they were individual particles. Sodium chloride, in water, dissociates into one positively charged entity, the sodium ion, and one negatively charged entity, the chloride ion. If all the molecules which make up a solution of sodium chloride in water were completely dissociated, then such a salt solution should have an osmotic pressure twice that of a sugar solution of the same molecular concentration.

TABLE V–5

DEGREE OF IONIZATION OF SODIUM CHLORIDE IN WATER
WITH CHANGES IN CONCENTRATION

C = the concentration in gram-molecules per 1000 grams water.
α = the degree of ionization or the fraction dissociated.
i = the isotonic coefficient.

$t°$ C	C	1.000	0.5	0.2	0.1	0.05	0.02	0.01	0.001	0.0001
18° C	α	0.68	0.77	0.82	0.85	0.88	0.92	0.94	0.96	0.99
	i	1.68	1.77	1.82	1.85	1.88	1.92	1.94	1.96	1.99
25° C	α	0.847	0.828	0.849	0.874	0.899	0.929	0.944	0.96	0.99
	i	1.847	1.828	1.849	1.874	1.899	1.929	1.944	1.96	1.99

TABLE V–6

DEGREE OF IONIZATION OF ELECTROLYTES

α = the degree of ionization or fraction dissociated.
n = the number of ions into which the molecule dissociates.
Concentration of all solutions 0.01 M at 25° C.

	NaCl	KCl	MgSO$_4$	Na$_2$SO$_4$	HCl
M	58.46	74.56	60.19	71.03	36.47
α	0.944	0.940	0.596	0.87	0.952
n	2	2	2	3	2
i	1.944	1.940	1.596	1.87	1.952

It has been found that the situation is more complex inasmuch as the salt in solution is ionized to a greater degree in a dilute solution than in a concentrated solution, and both the ions and also the undissociated salt molecules participate additively to produce the osmotic pressure. The experimental evidence to support these statements is indicated in Tables V–5 and V–6, which show, respectively, the degree of ionization of sodium chloride with decreasing concentration and the degree of ionization as the molecular structure changes.

According to Table V–4, the osmotic pressure developed by a 0.5 M sugar solution at 18° C is 12.8 atmospheres, while a similar sodium chloride solution develops an osmotic pressure 1.77 times as great, or 22.7 atmospheres. If the dissolved sodium chloride dissociates completely, the solution will produce a pressure of 2 times 12.8 atmospheres. The sodium chloride is apparently not completely dissociated. Table V–5 shows that its degree of ionization α is 77 per cent, that this degree of ionization increases with dilution, and that only at infinite dilutions would one expect the degree of ionization to be 100 per cent. The osmotic pressure of a 0.5 M sodium chloride solution is due to 77 positive ions, 77 negative ions, and 23 undissociated molecules per 100 sodium chloride molecules found in the solvent at this concentration. These ions additively develop an osmotic pressure equal to 1.77 times 12.8 or 22.7 atmospheres.

ISOTONIC COEFFICIENT

The van't Hoff isotonic coefficient (i) is a number by which the osmotic pressure, calculated from the general gas law, must be multiplied in order to give the expected osmotic pressure of an acid, base, or salt.

If n is the number of ions into which the molecule dissociates when introduced into a solvent and α is the fraction of the molecules ionized at a given concentration, called the degree of ionization, then the isotonic coefficient is defined by

$$i = n\alpha + (1 - \alpha)$$

Table V–5 shows some typical results obtained from sodium chloride dissolved in water; of special importance is the fact that the isotonic coefficient increases with dilution because of the increase in degree of ionization. Only for very dilute solutions ($C < 0.0001$) is the dissociation so complete that each molecule appears as two ions in the solvent to produce the expected osmotic pressure.

THE FREEZING POINT

The construction of an adequate semi-permeable membrane with which to determine the osmotic pressure of most physiological liquids has often entailed insurmountable difficulties. An indirect method can be resorted to which will give adequate quantitative results. Advantage is taken of the relation that exists between the freezing point of a solution and its molal concentration on the one hand and its molal concentration and osmotic pressure on the other hand.

The temperature at which a liquid substance exists in equilibrium with its solid crystalline state is termed its *freezing point*. This must not be confused with the melting point; for instance, a fat like mutton tallow solidifies between 36° and 41° C, but melts around 44° C; butter solidifies near 21.5° C, but melts at about 30° C.

Both the melting point of ice and the freezing point of water are 0° C under standard conditions.

In a mixture of ice and water at 0° C, the less dense ice (0.91674 gram/cc) floats on the water (0.99987 gram/cc). Since water expands on solidification, increasing the pressure will lower the freezing point. If the material contracts on freezing, like paraffin, then an increase in pressure will raise the freezing point. For water, an increase in pressure of 1 atmosphere will lower the freezing point 0.0075° C. Therefore, in making freezing-point measurements which involve water as a solvent, the very minute correction due to changes in atmospheric pressure can be disregarded.

The freezing point of any solution is invariably lower than that of the pure solvent. The temperature at which a solution freezes is lower the greater the amount of substance dissolved. When such a solution begins to freeze, it is only the solvent which freezes out at first. As a result, the remainder of the solute is more concentrated. The freezing point of this concentrate is in turn still lower. The process continues until the solution becomes saturated. At this point the dissolved substance and the solvent freeze out so that the concentration of both remains unchanged during solidification.

FREEZING POINT OF A DILUTE SOLUTION OF A NON-ELECTROLYTE

When a solid like sugar is dissolved in water to form a dilute solution the freezing point of the solution is below the freezing point of pure water. We refer to this lowered freezing temperature as the depressed freezing point. It is designated by Δ and is expressed in terms of the number of Centigrade degrees below the freezing point of distilled water taken as zero. Experimentally it is found that a solution containing 3.42 grams of sucrose dissolved in 1000 grams of water, i.e., a concentration of 0.01 M, freezes at -0.0186° C. The depression of the freezing point $\Delta = 0.0186$. As the concentration is decreased, the freezing-point depression is proportionally decreased. At concentration 0.001 (Table V–7), $\Delta = 0.00186$, and proportionally lower values are obtained as the concentration decreases until at infinite dilution (zero concentration) the freezing-point depression is zero.

If other non-electrolytes are dissolved in water and examined in a similar manner, it is found that all those solutions containing 0.01 gram-molecular weight per 1000 grams of water have a common freezing point, namely, -0.0186° C. They all possess Δ values which are smaller for proportionally smaller concentrations.

As a result of such experiments Blagden formulated a law which states that the depression of the freezing point of a dilute non-electrolyte is proportional to the concentration of the solute. Raoult later found that, for the same solvent, equimolecular amounts of different solute depressed the freezing point to the same extent, so that the conclusion is that equimolecular dilute solutions have the same freezing point or the same Δ value.

TABLE V–7

FREEZING POINTS OF SOME COMMON SALTS OF PHYSIOLOGICAL IMPORTANCE, COMPARED WITH SUCROSE

Concentration in gram-molecular weights per 1000 grams water

Δ value of	Concentration			M
	0.001	0.01	0.1	
Sucrose	0.00186	0.0186	0.188	342.2
NaCl	0.00366	0.0360	0.348	58.46
KCl	0.00366	0.0361	0.345	74.56
BaCl$_2$	0.00530	0.0503	0.470	208.29
MgSO$_4$	0.00338	0.0285	0.225	60.19

0.1 M is not considered a dilute solution.
Glucose, $M = 180.09$, $C = 0.1 M$, $\Delta = 0.192$.   Morse, Frazer, and Lovelace [1907].

Osmotic-pressure experiments have furnished data showing that all equimolecular dilute solutions of non-electrolytes have the same osmotic pressure.   Another conclusion is that dilute non-electrolyte solutions of equimolecular concentrations have freezing points that are directly proportional to their osmotic pressure.

According to the van't Hoff's law, the osmotic pressure of a dilute solution containing 0.01 gram molecule of non-electrolyte in 1000 grams of water will develop an osmotic pressure of 0.224 atmosphere at 0° C. It will freeze at −0.0186° C.   Hence a depression of the freezing point of 0.1° corresponds with an increase in osmotic pressure of 1.204 atmospheres or 915 mm of mercury (1219.5 millibars) at 0° C.

FREEZING POINT OF A DILUTE SOLUTION OF ELECTROLYTE

Equimolecular dilute solutions of electrolytes do not freeze at the same temperature.   This departure from the simple relations obtained for non-electrolytes can be observed in Table V–7.   Here are tabulated some of the common salts of physiological importance which have freezing points differing from the freezing point of sucrose by as much as a factor of 2 or 3.

Since the freezing point depends on the number of entities in solution, it must follow that the molecule of a salt like sodium chloride, which dissociates into a sodium ion and a chloride ion, would, for example, at

0.001 M concentration produce a lowering of the freezing point equal to twice that of a non-electrolyte, i.e., $2 \times 0.00186°$ or $0.00372°$. A similar solution of barium chloride which dissociates into three ions should show a freezing-point lowering equal to $3 \times 0.00186°$, or $0.00558°$. The corresponding experimental values shown in Table V–7 are $0.00366°$ and $0.00530°$. Since the experimental values are smaller than the theoretical values, it follows that not all the molecules in the solvent are dissociated into ions, so that at all concentrations we must allow for the fraction of undissociated molecules found even in very dilute solutions. In the classical theory of solution the undissociated entities are molecules; in the Debye-Hückel theory they are supposed to be ions surrounded by an atmosphere of oppositely charged ions, and under the influence of an electric field it is this atmosphere that is constantly changing instead of the ionic entities. In either theory a knowledge of the degree of dissociation is essential to determine the requisite freezing point and from it to calculate the expected osmotic pressure.

The degree of ionization of NaCl at 0.001 M concentration is 96 per cent. This means that out of every 100 sodium chloride molecules in the solvent 96 dissociate into sodium and chloride ions and 4 remain undissociated. It should follow that the expected freezing-point depression is $1.96 \times 0.00186°$, or $0.00365°$, which is in close agreement with the experimental value of $0.00366°$ of Table V–7. Since a depression of the freezing point of $0.1°$ corresponds with an increase in osmotic pressure of 1.204 atmospheres, the above solution can develop an osmotic pressure of 33.5 mm of mercury. How many millibars is this mercury pressure equivalent to?

EXPERIMENTAL DETERMINATION OF THE FREEZING POINT

One of the most practical indirect methods for determining the osmotic pressure, and one almost exclusively used by physiologists and in medical practice, is the cryoscopic method. Since most physiological fluids are in reality dilute solutions, as seen in Table V–8, they readily lend themselves to freezing-point determinations. An additional advantage is founded upon the fact that it makes practically no difference whether gross material is in suspension or whether more or less protein material is present. The freezing point of blood, for instance, may be obtained by using whole blood, blood plasma, or serum, since the corpuscles act as particles in suspension.

⟩ Since a change in the freezing point of $0.01°$ corresponds with an osmotic-pressure change of 91.5 mm of mercury, it is necessary to use a thermometer calibrated to $0.01°$ so that an estimated change of plus or minus one tenth of a calibrated division will introduce an error of not more than 9.15 mm of mercury in the osmotic-pressure observations.

TABLE V-8

PHYSIOLOGICAL FLUIDS

Data show mean per cent water content.

Normal sea water	98.8	Bladder bile	84
Valonia sap	98.4	Liver bile	97
Ringer solution	99	Cow's milk	87.1
Cell sap	97–98	Human milk	88.5
Blood plasma	91	Horse's serum*	93.32
Gastric juice	99.5	Horse aqueous humor*	99.69
Pancreatic juice	99.5	Horse vitreous humor*	99.68
Saliva	99.5	Red blood corpuscles	64

*W. S. Duke-Elder, *Physiol. Rev.*, **14**, 483 (1934).

In physiological or medical investigations, if the quantities of fluids available are not too small, a thermocouple or Beckmann thermometer having a range of 3° C with intervals calibrated in hundredths of a degree can be used. If only small quantities of fluid are available, a micro-Beckmann thermometer can be used. The micro-Beckmann thermometer has an overall length of 28 cm with a linear spread of 3.5 cm per degree. Since each tenth degree is calibrated into 10 divisions, it is possible, with the aid of a reading glass, to obtain a reliable freezing-point reading to 0.002° C.

The freezing-point apparatus as assembled is shown in Fig. V-8. The Beckmann thermometer B and stirrer C are inserted into the freezing-

TABLE V-9

FREEZING MIXTURES

Proportion of substance I to be added to proportion of substance II to produce a freezing mixture having temperature $t°$ C

Substance	I	II	$t°$ C
Ammonium chloride	3	10 water	−5.1
Potassium iodide	14	10 water	−11.7
Calcium chloride	3	10 ice	−10.9
Ammon um chloride	1	4 ice	−15.4
Sodium nitrate	1	2 ice	−17.75
Sodium chloride	1	3 ice	−21.3
$CaCl_2 + 6H_2O$	100	7 ice	−54.9
Chloroform	Solid CO_2		−77.0
Ether	Solid CO_2		−77.0

Courtesy Chemical Rubber Publishing Company, Cleveland, Ohio.

point tube *F*. This tube is surrounded by an air chamber *A*, which assures a slower and more uniform rate of cooling of the liquid under examination. A stirrer *S* and thermometer *T* are introduced into the beaker *E* which contains the freezing mixture of the desired tempera-

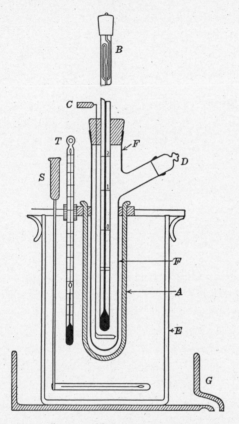

Fig. V–8. An assembled freezing-point apparatus.

ture as predetermined from Table V–9. A metal drain *G* is used to collect the moisture condensed on *E*.

The Beckmann is a mercury-in-glass differential thermometer, with scale readings in degrees Centigrade. It seldom happens that the distribution of mercury between its reservoir and bulb will be such that this thermometer will read exactly 0° C when water freezes. In order to locate this zero point on the Beckmann scale, distilled water is introduced into the freezing tube by way of the side arm *D* and the zero point is located experimentally. It will be observed that the temperature will fall until ice is formed and then remain constant. This constant-temperature reading is identified on the scale and constitutes 0° C. If there is a tendency to supercooling, a tiny crystal of ice may be added through the side tube D to start the crystallization of the water. If supercooling has taken place, the mercury in the thermometer will rise rapidly on crystallization to the true freezing point, where it will remain stationary for a time.

The water is then removed from the freezing tube, and the tube is dried and reassembled. About 25 cc of the solution whose freezing point is to be determined is then introduced through the arm D and the freezing point is determined in the same way as for water.

TABLE V–10

FREEZING POINT OF MAMMALIAN BLOOD

Δ indicates the average freezing-point depression in degrees Centigrade.
O.P. the osmotic pressure calculated for body temperature, 37° C.
The unit of O.P. is the atmosphere.

Mammal	Man	Ox	Horse	Rabbit	Sheep	Pig	Dog	Cat	Mean
Δ° C	0.560	0.585	0.564	0.592	0.619	0.615	0.571	0.638	0.59
O.P.	7.7	7.9	7.7	8.1	8.5	8.5	7.8	8.7	8.0

$\Delta = 0.1°$ C corresponds with an increase in 1.204 atmospheres at 0° C.
$\Delta = 0.59$ is equivalent to 8.0 atmospheres at 37° C.
A point to be emphasized is that at no time does mammalian blood exert such a pressure; all that is meant is that this is the osmotic pressure that would be produced by blood if it were separated from pure water by a semi-permeable membrane.

The difference between these two freezing points as read on the thermometer is the desired depression Δ of the freezing point, from which the osmotic pressure can be calculated.

Some freezing-point-depression data obtained by cryoscopic methods from mammalian blood are shown in Table V–10. The conclusion drawn from these data is that the blood of all these mammals develops about the same osmotic pressure, and that under normal circumstances the osmotic pressure of blood never departs from this mean value. It has been observed that shortly after meals the osmotic pressure of the blood is slightly higher; it is reduced slightly by large ingestion of water. The kidney as a mechanism exists for regulating the osmotic pressure of the blood so that the tissues may remain immersed in a fluid of constant osmotic pressure. This constancy of the osmotic pressure is attained through the excretion of the necessary amounts of water and solids.

OSMOTIC PRESSURE OF PROTEINS

Proteins are complex organic compounds of high molecular weight. The serum albumins, for example, have a molecular weight of 68,000, and the serum globulins have a higher value, averaging 175,000.   They are formed by living matter and occur in the tissues and liquids of plants and animals.   They are composed of carbon (50–55 per cent), hydrogen (6–7 per cent), nitrogen (15–18 per cent), oxygen (19–24 per cent), with some sulphur, phosphorus, or iron.

Since proteins are colloids they do not penetrate the semi-permeable boundaries of living cells and tissue structures, yet despite their giant molecular forms they can develop a small osmotic pressure.   As early as 1861 Graham suggested that plasma colloids might exert an osmotic pressure in the vascular system, but it remained for Starling [1896] to measure the osmotic pressure of colloidal solutions directly.   He took advantage of the fact that colloidal membranes, while permitting the passage of water and salts, are impermeable to colloids in solution. With this technique Starling [1936] found that blood serum containing about 7 per cent proteins developed, owing to the presence of the proteins, an excess osmotic pressure of about 35 mm mercury.   The osmotic pressure developed by blood plasma, which is about 6.4 atmospheres at 37° C, is due primarily to the presence of sodium chloride.   Its colloid osmotic pressure, which is of prime importance for the transfer of fluids from tissue to blood to urine, is mainly due to the presence of plasma proteins and is approximately 28 mm of mercury.   Equally low values were found by Pfeffer for egg albumen (1.25 weight per cent at 20° C), 22.4 mm of mercury.

Since a Δ change of 0.01° corresponds to a pressure change of 91.5 mm mercury, it can be concluded that the presence of proteins will change the freezing point only 0.0034°.   This quantity lies just within the limit of accuracy of the micro-Beckmann thermometer.   For all practical purposes, in the osmotic-pressure determinations of blood, the presence of proteins adds a negligible magnitude to the depression of the freezing-point determination.

Osmotic Pressures of Some Biological Fluids

One interesting hypothesis that has been used in discussing the theory that life originated in the sea is that in the blood of all vertebrates the content of sodium, potassium, calcium, and magnesium is proportional to that of Archean sea water.

In certain marine invertebrates the body fluids contain the ions of the above salts in almost the same concentrations in which they occur in sea water.   The tissue fluids of the jellyfish are very much like sea water when one compares their relative concentrations of sodium, potassium, calcium, and magnesium ions.   The serum of the lobster, which is of a higher order in the scale of evolution, contains a concentration of sodium and magnesium between that of the jellyfish and the mammal. Macallum [1917] suggested that these and a mass of other data point to the possibility that an animal not possessed of a kidney, or analogous organ, cannot accurately regulate the concentration of ions in its body fluids, and must through osmosis approximate the total ionic concentrations of its surrounding medium.

It is possible, for instance, to introduce a spider crab (*Maia verrucosa*) into diluted or concentrated sea water and find that the crab's body fluid can adjust itself through osmosis to its new environment. The fiddler crab (*Portunus depurator*), commonly found on our southern beaches, also has no regulative osmotic pressure capacity; hence, the osmotic pressure of its body fluid is that of normal sea water ($\Delta = 2.30$). As we ascend the animal scale and examine the migratory forms, such as the salmon, which leaves the deep sea to go up into fresh water, or the eel, which migrates thousands of miles into the Sargasso Sea in order to spawn, it is found that the osmotic pressure of their blood is only slightly modified. The blood of the sand shark has a freezing point whose Δ value is slightly below that of sea water. The blood of whales and other marine mammals, on the other hand, has the same freezing point as the blood of land mammals. Apparently, the more specialized the animal form, the more perfectly is it adapted to regulate the osmotic pressure of its fluids.

In the higher animal forms the kidney plays a very important role in regulating the osmotic pressure of the blood. The theories of kidney secretion, however, are outside the scope of this subject and can be reviewed in any textbook on general physiology, such as that by Mitchell [1938].

Model of a Cell Membrane

Despite the extensive research of the past years, the constitution and functions of the limiting surfaces of cells remain on the whole unsolved. As a rule, the limiting surfaces are ill defined, probably highly variable in structure and properties, and so closely bound up with the protoplasm of which they form a part that they cannot be clearly recognized as membranes. There is a body of evidence suggesting that the limiting layer of the protoplast is a thin membrane composed largely of fatty substances containing submicroscopic compartments composed of an aqueous phase which is chiefly responsible for determining the entrance or exclusion of substances into the cell. Another well-supported view is that the cell envelope is a fluid bimolecular layer of lipoid (fatlike) molecules. This membrane, however, cannot be homogeneous, since water penetrates with ease into cells.

Various optical attempts at measuring the thickness of the transition layer have given values that are less than 0.2×10^{-4} cm, i.e., unresolvable by a compound microscope (see Chapter VIII). That bacteria of the genus *Bacillus* possess cell walls was recently verified with the aid of the electron microscope. The photomicrograph (Fig. VIII–22) of human tubercle bacilli made with an RCA electron microscope shows the bacilli to be surrounded by what appears to be a membrane having a thickness less than 0.1×10^{-4} cm.

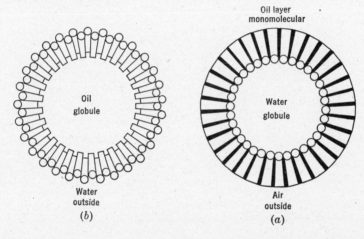

FIG. V–9. (a) A conventionalized picture of a drop of water covered with a monomolecular layer of oil, suspended in air. (b) A drop of oil suspended in water with oil molecules forming bounding phase. (By courtesy of W. D. Harkins and Chemical Catalog Company. [Reinhold Publishing Corporation], New York.)

These dimensions may be compared with those found by Langmuir [1925] for palmitic acid molecules when these molecules were steeply oriented to form a monomolecular surface film. Palmitic acid with its chain of sixteen carbons to the molecule has a cross section of 20.5 sq Å and a length measured perpendicular to a supporting surface of about 24.2 Å. The relative order of magnitudes indicates that the membrane of the cell is at most about 100 molecules thick.

If a closed membrane were one molecule thick, it could be pictured as in Fig. V–9. This highly conventionalized picture, used by Harkins [1925] in discussing the orientation of molecules in the surface of spherical liquid drops, shows a small spherical drop of water, Fig. V–9(a), covered with a monomolecular layer of oil suspended in air. Its surface can be represented as composed of closely packed molecules with their polar ends turned toward the water phase and the non-polar ends pointing outward.   If, however, a drop of oil is suspended in water as in (b), the oil molecules orient themselves in the opposite direction.

The fundamental principles involved in the structure of the interfaces are: The molecules in the surfaces of liquids seem to be arranged in such a way that the least polar groups are oriented towards the vapor phase. At the water-air interface the hydrogen atoms turn towards the vapor phase and the oxygen atoms toward the liquid phase.   At the liquid surfaces of organic paraffin derivatives the CH_3 groups turn outward, and the more active groups, such as NO_2, CN, $COOH$, CHO, OH, or groups which contain double bonds, turn toward the interior of the liquid.   If the organic compounds are soluble in water, their orientation is such as to place the active groups inward.

The stability of emulsoid particles seems to be brought about by the orientation of molecules at the interface.   In order to have the emulsoid particles stable, the molecules which make the transition from the interior of the drop to the dispersion medium must form what may be termed a bounding membrane.

If the thermal agitation is taken into consideration, it may be assumed that the molecules in a bounding surface, composed of flexible hydrocarbon chains, will orient themselves at any angle.   The only restriction on their motion is imposed by the condition that the lower end of each molecule must remain in contact with the underlying water.   Langmuir found that palmitic acid could be spread to form an expanded structure 13.6 Å thick, and that the film could also be compressed to form a structure 22.5 Å thick.   Thus an expanded film may be pictured in contradistinction to a compressed film, in which the oriented molecules, though still anchored to the underlying water, are set at any angle and hence loosely packed.

If for the sake of simplicity such a monomolecular structure is used to represent the superficial wall of a cell, then, to a good approximation, the cell wall may be represented as an expanded organic molecular film with a transition thickness of less than one hundred molecules.   Such a structure could possess semi-permeable properties and even change its surface energy by the reorientation of its structure.   Under the action of the temperature kinetic agitation it would be possible to find, on the average, areas not covered with molecules.   Such a membrane would allow for a shifting lattice structure and the adoption of a modified sieve theory for the basic pattern of a semi-permeable living membrane.

Some data may now be examined in support of the view that a cell has an outer boundary or cell wall (cell membrane) which fundamentally may have the structure of an expanded molecular film.   It has been shown that the walls of cells are made of substances which are colloidal in solution and more or less swollen by water. Overton suggested that lipoids have a tendency to concentrate at interfaces, where the substances could participate in producing the membrane structure. He then added that only those substances which are soluble in this lipoid structure were able to penetrate the interior. Overton's experiments support the view of the existence of such a structural framework. Later work by Loeb and others indicated that lipoid-soluble fatty acids readily penetrated the cell wall; on the other hand, acids which are practically lipoid-insoluble did not penetrate. Except for its static structural point of view a lipoid-solubility theory is as acceptable as any proposed to date.

In general, it has been found that living cells are readily permeable to lipoid-soluble non-electrolytes which possess an appreciable degree of water solubility. The work of Collander and Bärlund [1933] shows, however, that the penetration is limited to molecular sizes which are relatively small. It was found, for instance, that the relatively smaller molecules like formamide, acetimide, and ethylene glycol penetrated much more readily than much larger colloid molecules like albumin and hemoglobin. Apparently the average lattice spaces are therefore about 5×10^{-8} cm in diameter. The existence of lattice spaces explains why those gases that are readily soluble in physiological fluids can successfully pass through living membranes.

It has been found that both red cells and paramecia are affected by agents which penetrate or are adsorbed as lipoid and protein monomolecular layers; therefore, it can be concluded that their surface structures must contain lipoproteins or consist of a lipoid protein mosaic.

A cell wall cannot be smooth but must have distributed over its surface a multitude of irregular hills and valleys of atomic dimensions, an excellent surface for the adsorption of atoms, ions, and ion clusters. This structure can develop a difference in ionic concentration on the opposite sides of its wall. The result is a polarized ionic barrier acting as an effective control for ionic migrations.

It has been found, however, that cells are more permeable, on the average, to electrically neutral molecules than to ions. It is necessary therefore to have a structure that is electrically polarizable. It must, however, be able to change its degree and form of polarity in accordance with the kind of electrolyte in which the cell may be immersed.

The wall of the living cell has been found to be impermeable to polar compounds but permeable to a weak polar group such as the hydroxyl. The rate of entrance was found to be proportional to the ratio of the number of non-polar groups to the polar groups. A static structure, namely, a group of oriented molecules as found in the condensed stage of a film, cannot change its polarity very readily. The previously proposed expanded stage of a film membrane would conform to the demands of polarity made upon it as the result of the mosaic of pores and its relatively flexible molecular orientation.　It would depend for its degree of

TABLE V–11

CHEMICAL ANALYSES OF SAP COMPARED WITH NORMAL SEA WATER

Contents	Bermuda Sea Water	Valonia Sap[1]	Halicystis Sap[2]
Cl + Br	0.580	0.597	0.603
Na	0.498	0.09	0.557
K	0.012	0.5	0.0064
Ca	0.012	0.0017	0.008
Mg	0.057	Trace?	0.0167
SO₄	0.036	Trace?	Trace

[1] *Valonia macrophysa.*　[2] *Halicystis Osterhoutii.*

MEAN IONIC CONTENT OF BLOOD EXPRESSED IN PER CENT AND MILLIEQUIVALENT

Contents	Per Cent			Milliequivalent per 1000 cc*	
	Whole Blood	Plasma	Corpuscles	Serum	Cells
Na	0.20	0.335	0.065	135.1 ± 1.7	16.8 ± 3.5
K	0.20	0.019	0.42	4.6 ± 0.7	82.5 ± 4.9
Ca	0.006	0.011	0.001	5.3 ± 0.3	0.2 ± 0.3
Mg	0.003	0.0027	0.0066	1.6 ± 0.3	4.6 ± 0.5
Fe	0.5	0.00	0.10		
Cl	0.294	0.37	0.20		
HCO₃		0.164	0.002		
Total solids	22.0	9.3	34.6		
Hemoglobin	14.5	0.0	34.0		
Specific gravity	1.054–1.060	1.062	1.090		
Water	79–80	90–92	64–65		

By Courtesy of W. J. V. Osterhout [1936].
* By Courtesy of P. M. Hald and A. J. Eisenman [1937].
For effects and changes due to high altitude see D. B. Dill, J. H. Talbot, and W. V. Consolazio [1937].

polarity on the relative concentration of adsorbed ions and polar molecules at the two faces of the bounding film.　A shrinkage of such an expanded film would also more nearly orient the molecules to produce an increase in the degree of polarity and at the same time decrease the size and number of the pores of the mosaic.

In this connection Osterhout has shown that isotonic calcium chloride solution can render cells nearly impermeable to all ions, and that any excess of calcium over its normal sea-water concentration (Table V–11) tends to decrease the permeability of the cell.

If the calcium salts react chemically with the mobile external surface molecules in the presence of fatty acid molecules to form a calcium soap, the surface becomes more polarized for the soap molecules are more soluble in water than the original fatty acid molecules. The molecular structure may then be pictured as more closely packed and the openings of the mosaic pattern so reduced in area as to exclude the possibility of infiltration of most solute molecules.

A further important matter must be taken into consideration in setting up a hypothetical model of a semi-permeable dynamic cell wall, namely, the selective accumulative property of certain cells. This may be appreciated after examining the data of Table V–11. Of interest is the analysis of the cell sap of *Valonia macrophysa* by Osterhout [1936], which shows an unusually high potassium content as compared with sea water. Note also the amount of potassium in red corpuscles as compared with their plasma environment. It is difficult to explain these results since there can be no apparent differentiation by the membrane between sodium and potassium ions on the basis of their dimensions, mobility, or electric charge. Jacques' recent work on the nature of the protoplasmic surface of the cell in the marine plants *Valonia* and *Halicystis* and in the fresh-water *Nitella* indicates that the cell membranes are composed of non-aqueous layers at the inner and outer surfaces of the protoplasm which possess different solubilities for various salts, potassium being absorbed more rapidly than sodium in *Valonia*.

In any case the structure and the structural changes that account for the normal semi-permeability of the wall of the living cell (Rideal [1939]) await final analysis* and must remain matters of speculation until the biochemist and the biophysicist can furnish the necessary information about the chemical composition and electrical properties of plasma membranes.

BIBLIOGRAPHY

1888 DE VRIES, HUGO, *Z. physik. Chem.*, **2**, 415.
1896 STARLING, E. H., *J. Physiol.*, **19**, 312, and **24**, 317 (1899).
1903 GUYE, P. A., and F. L. PERROT, *Bull. univ. arch. sci. phys. nat.*, **15**, 132. Also H. E. EDGERTON and K. J. GERMESHAUSEN [1934].
1907 MORSE, H. N., J. C. W. FRAZER, and B. F. LOVELACE, *Am. Chem. J.*, **37**, 324.
1917 MACALLUM, A. B., *Trans. Coll. Physicians Phila.*, **39**, 289.
1919 DU NOÜY, P. L., *J. Gen. Physiol.*, **1**, 521.

* For a comprehensive discussion of the properties and functions of membranes and cell walls see " General Discussion " [1937].

1919   HARKINS, W. D., and F. E. BROWN, *J. Am. Chem. Soc.*, **41**, 499.

1921   FENN, W. O., *J. Gen. Physiol.*, **4**, 373.

1921   TAYLOR, W., *Phil. Mag.*, **41**, 877.

1922   OSTERHOUT, W. J. V., *Injury, Recovery and Death in Relation to Conductivity and Permeability*, J. B. Lippincott Company, Philadelphia, Pa.

1925   CARY, A., and E. K. RIDEAL, *Proc. Roy. Soc. London*, **A109**, 301.

1925   HARKINS, W. D., *Colloid Symposium Monograph*, II, 141, Chemical Catalog Company, (Reinhold Publishing Corporation), New York.

1925   LANGMUIR, I., *Colloid Symposium Monograph*, III, 48, Chemical Catalog Company, New York.

1926   HARKINS, W. D., T. F. YOUNG, and L. H. CHENG, *Science*, **64**, 333.

1926   McCLENDON, J. F., *Colloid Symposium Monograph*, IV, 224, Chemical Catalog Company, New York.

1927   McCUTCHEON, M., and B. LUCKE, *J. Gen. Physiol.*, **10**, 659.

1930   ADAM, N. K., *The Physics and Chemistry of Surfaces*, Clarendon Press, Oxford.

1930   HARKINS, W. D., and H. F. JORDAN, *J. Am. Chem. Soc.*, **52**, 1751.

1932   HARVEY, E. N., *J. Franklin Inst.*, **214**, 1.

1932   LILLIE, R. S., *Protoplasmic Action and Nervous Action*, University of Chicago Press.

1932   LUCKE, B., and M. McCUTCHEON, " The Living Cell as an Osmotic System and Its Permeability to Water," *Physiol. Rev.*, **12**, 68.

1932   WHITEHOUSE, A. G. R., W. HANCOCK, and J. S. HALDANE, *Proc. Roy. Soc. London*, **B111**, 412.

1933   COLLANDER, R., and H. BÄRLUND, *Acta Bot. Fennica*, **11**, 2.

1933   KOPACZEWSKI, W., *Protoplasma*, **19**, 255.

1933   MUDD, S., *Cold Spring Harbor Symposia Quant. Biol.*, **1**, 77.

1934   EDGERTON, H. E., and K. J. GERMESHAUSEN, *Am. Inst. Chem. Eng. Trans.*, **30**, 420.

1934   MUDD, S., M. McCUTCHEON, and B. LUCKE, *Physiol. Rev.*, **14**, 210.

1935   JACQUES, A. G., and W. J. V. OSTERHOUT, *J. Gen. Physiol.*, **18**, 967.

1936   OSTERHOUT, W. J. V., *Botan. Rev.*, **2**, 283.

1936   STARLING, *Principles of Human Physiology*, 7th Ed., Churchill, London. (Revised by C. L. EVANS.)

1937   BALDWIN, E., *An Introduction to Comparative Biochemistry*, Cambridge University Press.

1937   BARNES, T. C., *Textbook of General Physiology*, P. Blakiston's Son, Philadelphia, Pa.

1937   DILL, D. B., J. H. TALBOT, and W. V. CONSOLAZIO, *J. Biol. Chem.*, **118**, 649.

1937   General Discussion, " The Properties and Functions of Membranes, Natural and Artificial," *Trans. Faraday Soc.*, **33**, 911.

1937   HALD, P. M., and A. J. EISENMAN, *J. Biol. Chem.*, **118**, 275.

1938   HARVEY, E. N., *J. Applied Phys.*, **9**, 68.

1938   MITCHELL, P. H., *A Text Book of General Physiology*, 3rd Ed., McGraw-Hill Book Company, New York.

1939   RIDEAL, E. K., *Science*, **90**, 217.

1940   COLE, K. S., *Cold Spring Harbor Symposia Quant. Biol.*, **8**, 110. (Electrical properties of cell membranes.)

1940   LYDDANE, R. H., and O. STUHLMAN, JR., *J. Gen. Physiol.*, **23**, 521.

1941   MUDD, S., K. POLEVITZKY, J. F. ANDERSON, and L. A. CHAMBERS, *J. Bact.*, **42**, 251.

Chapter VI

THE BIOPHYSICAL PROBLEM OF NERVE CONDUCTION

A sensation invoked in the brain has no resemblance to the physical events which redirect the activity of the nervous system. The sensation of light may be aroused not only through absorption by the retinal receptors of radiant energy of a limited group of frequencies, but also by electrical or mechanical stimulation of the retina. The sensation called sound may be experienced by placing a low-frequency tuning fork with its base in contact with the head so that the vibrations are communicated to the bones of the skull. The same fork pressed to the surface of the skin produces a sensation of vibration, that is, a series of tactile impressions repeated at rapid intervals.

The experienced sensations are not the reproductions of the physical stimuli; they are, however, symbols of the stimuli that can be used to inform us of events occurring in our physical environment. Therefore it is important to inquire how nerves transport quantitative information about these stimuli to the central nervous system.

The experienced sensations are aroused by messages which are transmitted from the excited receptors by means of the nerves to the cerebrum. The problems of the kind of messages or nerve impulses and of the speed of their propagation have been under investigation since the time of Galvani and Volta, but not until 1908 did the researches initiated by Gotch and Keith Lucas make it possible to give a quantitative interpretation to the problem of nerve conduction.

The most general features of the so-called moving nerve impulses are best studied by first examining those irritable tissues or cells which can develop quantitatively interpretable responses to mechanical, thermal, chemical, or electrical stimulation, such as excised nerves and muscles of higher animals.

The impulse set up in response to an electric stimulus applied to tissue isolated from its normal environment is an artificial effect. The accumulated evidence, however, shows that its counterpart must be the fundamental activity of the nerve fiber in the body.

RELATION OF STIMULUS TO RESPONSE

The word " stimulus " will be used to mean any local artificial change in the environment of tissues which causes an *excitatory process* to be set up in the tissues localized at the point of stimulation.

211

The *threshold* value or *minimal* stimulus of a particular kind has a magnitude which is just sufficient to excite. A stimulus greater than threshold value will not produce a greater response. The magnitude of the response is independent of the magnitude of the stimulus, provided that it is not smaller than threshold. This general relation is known as the *all-or-none-law*. The implication is that the response is characteristic of the reacting structure and not of the energy employed to disturb the state of that structure.

Most living cells can be used as reacting structures in which the proper stimulus will set up a disturbance, or nervous impulse. With modern technique it is even possible to study the impulses set up in sensory nerve fibers by the appropriate stimulation of the sense organs so as to determine the frequency, the form, and the speed with which the messages are transmitted to the brain.

Various forms of energy can be employed as stimuli. In biophysical investigations of the excitability of nerve fibers it has become general practice to use a brief electric current as stimulus, for it is highly probable that the process of excitation itself is electrical.

ELECTRICAL STIMULI

Physiologists agree that an impulsive electrical discharge is by far the most effective and convenient means of artificially stimulating nerve fibers to set up a " nerve impulse," which travels over the whole length of the nerve fiber in both directions from the point of stimulation. Because the intensity and duration of an electric current can be very accurately controlled, it has become common practice to study the activity of an isolated nerve when stimulated by a brief electric shock. It has the advantage that such stimulation can be repeated without producing appreciable damage in the nerve fiber.

In most experimental work on the response of nerves to electric stimulation, current taken off the secondary of a mechanically interrupted induction coil has been used. A commercial 60-cycle alternating current has also been employed. For precision work, impulsive currents should be used with pulses timed by means of a mechanical regulator or more accurately by a variable-frequency stimulator.

INDUCTION COIL DISCHARGE

In every properly designed induction coil with mechanical interrupter a condenser is connected across the interrupter. Its capacitance must be so chosen as to quench the spark as quickly as possible when the mechanical interrupter opens the primary circuit. As a result, the break of the primary current is much quicker than the make. For a given primary current there is a corresponding capacitance which makes the potential across the terminals of the spark gap a maximum. The primary current I_p rises exponentially on the closing of the interrupter, as shown in Fig. VI-1. When the circuit is suddenly opened at C the current rapidly drops to D. Without the condenser this slope would be less steep.

Since the current builds up more slowly than it diminishes, the associated magnetic field builds up more slowly than it collapses. The induced electromotive force, and therefore the induced current in the secondary, are smaller when the primary circuit is closed than when it is open. This condition is illustrated by the broken-line curve I_s. The larger induced electromotive force at the break therefore lasts a shorter time than the smaller induced electromotive force at the make.

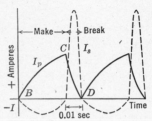

FIG. VI-1. An ideal rise and fall of the current in the primary and accompanying changes in current in the secondary of an induction coil with proper condenser connected across the mechanical interrupter.

The voltage across the terminals of the secondary, to which a stimulating electrode may be attached, is alternately positive and negative, but one cycle does not consist of two equal alternations of opposite sign. Therefore the discharge across the terminals of the stimulating electrode is, as seen in Fig. VI-1, predominantly in one direction.

STIMULATING ELECTRODE .

The electric stimulus can be applied to the irritable tissue with the aid of the two-pronged metal electrode shown in Fig. VI-2. The binding posts B are attached to the high-potential terminals of an induction coil or variable-frequency stimulator. The handle S is an insulating cover of hard rubber to facilitate handling. Platinum needles, Pt, spaced about 2.5 mm, are placed in direct contact with the tissue.

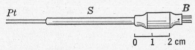

FIG. VI-2. A form of stimulating electrode in which the electrodes are pronged into a holder including a cord and plug. They can be sterilized. Overall length 4 in., tip length 1 in., tip spacing 0.1 in. Also available with longer electrodes. (By courtesy of Allen B. DuMont Laboratories, Passaic, New Jersey.)

If the response of an excised nerve is to be investigated, the platinum needle-electrodes are placed across and near one end of the preparation. When an adequate electrical discharge passes between the terminals of the electrodes, an excitatory impulse travels away from the point of stimulation.

THE DETECTION OF NERVE IMPULSES

As the impulse moves along the nerve, it is possible to detect its passage by placing in parallel with a section of the nerve a sensitive electrical-potential-recording instrument (see " Cathode-Ray Oscillograph "), terminating at two Ag|AgCl|Isotonic NaCl non-polarizable electrodes in contact with the surface of the nerve.   For most purposes silver wires, freshly coated by electrolysis, are placed in direct contact with the tissues.*

STRUCTURE OF NERVE FIBERS

A nerve is a bundle of separate nerve fibers.   Each is a thread of protoplasm (Fig. VI–3), either myelinated or unmyelinated, which functions as the conducting element of the nervous system.   The myelinated nerve consists of an axis cylinder surrounded by the myelin

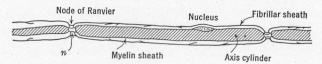

FIG. VI–3.   Very much enlarged myelinated nerve fiber of frog, semi-diagrammatic longitudinal section.   Axis cylinder appears structureless.   The neurilemma (n) is visible chiefly at a node as a thin delicate membrane.

sheath, which is a complex fatty substance of high specific resistance. External to it lies the neurilemma sheath.   At regular intervals along the fiber, constrictions occur in the sheath, which are known as nodes of Ranvier.   The unmyelinated fibers have no apparent myelin sheath. Those in the central nervous system are naked axis cylinders, but in the periphery they are covered by a very thin neurilemma sheath.

The axis cylinder is a soft, transparent, jellylike substance having much the same composition as that found inside other living cells.   Its specific resistance is low.   Its osmotic pressure is the same as that of blood.   The evidence seems to support the view that the axis cylinder is limited by a plasma membrane.   This limiting membrane is semi-permeable and electrically polarized, and it is probably the structure that participates in the propagation of the energy known as the nerve impulses.

The living fiber maintains a difference of potential across its surface which disappears when the nerve is deprived of oxygen.   It maintains

* Those designed by Adrian and Bronk [1929] are made of hypodermic needles with an insulated silver or copper core, the end of which is flush with the bevel of the needle.

its normal steady state only through a continuous expenditure of oxidative energy.

The electrolytic composition on the inside of the fiber differs from that on the outside primarily by its potassium-ion content. This difference as estimated by Fenn is about 65 times larger inside than outside. Such a difference in a concentration cell, according to Gasser's [1938] calculations, would produce about 100 millivolts. That such large differences of potential do exist was verified by Hodgkin [1939] from a single nerve fiber of a crab preparation. Such potentials may be accounted for by assuming the existence of a concentration gradient or of a diffusion gradient across the cell membrane in which the mobility of the potassium cation is the dominant factor.

A mode of exploring the cause of such a difference of potential is to investigate whether or not most of the potential may arise as the result of the existence of a possible polarized film of molecules at the surface of the fiber. A simple experiment involving the measurement of what is called the demarcation current proves the existence of a polarized surface possessing a difference of potential across its membrane-like covering.

DEMARCATION CURRENT OR CURRENT OF INJURY

If a nerve fiber is removed from the body, and two non-polarizable electrodes, in series with a sensitive electrometer, are applied to the

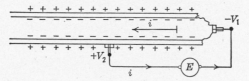

FIG. VI–4. The polarized state of a diagrammatic nerve fiber. Injury at the right end. $V_2 - V_1$ about 50 millivolts.

nerve in such a way that one is in contact with the surface of the nerve and the other is in contact with an injured end of the fiber (Fig. VI–4), a constant deflection of the electrometer will result as long as the tissue is alive. Such a deflection indicates that a difference of potential exists between the outside cell membrane and the exposed axis cylinder. The direction in which the electrometer deflects will indicate that the uninjured surface is at a higher potential than the injured end. This difference in potential is very small, usually about 50 millivolts. Until recently these small differences of potential have been measured by means of an Einthoven string galvanometer or a capillary electrometer. Millivolt potentials can now be measured with precision with modern galvanometers; if necessary, the potential may be amplified by means of a vacuum-tube voltage amplifier. The difference in potential maintains itself as long as the " injury " as such does not undergo a change in its physicochemical nature due to degeneration of the tissue. The injury does not produce the difference in potential; it merely allows the difference of potential to manifest itself as an active source of electromotive force.

THE ACTION POTENTIAL

Our definite knowledge of the response of living tissue to electrical excitation began with the celebrated investigations of du Bois-Reymond, extending from 1846 to 1860 and published under the title " Untersuchungen über thierische Elektrizität." By 1871 Bernstein had

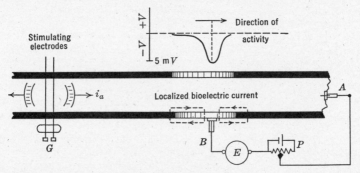

FIG. VI-5.   Monophasic action current pulse is shown traveling from the stimulating electrode G. Shading simulates degree of depolarization. Injury potential between A and B neutralized by counter emf from potentiometer P. If E is an oscillograph, the fluorescent screen will show the above monophasic action potential pulse as it passes the contact B.

demonstrated that when an excised muscle or nerve was stimulated at any point along the tissue a wave of activity ran along the nerve.   This wave was identified as a negative pulse of an electrical activity rising to a potential of about 5 millivolts.   The existence of a traveling pulse of activity may be demonstrated as illustrated in Fig. VI-5.   An excised nerve with its active end A placed in contact with a small metal electrode is connected through a potentiometer P and an electrometer E to a duplicate electrode B attached to the passive surface of the nerve sheath. The normal demarcation current is neutralized by a counter electromotive force from the potentiometer until the electrometer deflection is zero.

At G, several centimeters to the left of contact B, is placed a pair of stimulating electrodes.   The two platinum points are connected to the high-potential output of a small induction coil. When the key in the primary circuit of the induction coil is rapidly closed and opened, one or more 0.2-milliampere high-potential induction discharges stimulate the nerve fiber at this point and set up a nerve impulse i_a which travels away from G in both directions.

This impulse, in a thick mammalian nerve fiber, having a diameter of about 20 microns, may attain a speed of 100 meters per second; in unmyelinated nerve it may be as low as 1 meter per second.

The arrival of the pulse at B is shown by a deflection of the electric impulse recorder E. The successive changes in the deflections indicate that the external surface at the electrode B has been subjected to a rapid drop in potential, followed by a slower recovery to its former value. A record of the fall and rise of this action potential is inserted in the figure. The action is designated as monophasic. The inference is that the nerve impulse is an activity that travels with moderate speed, that it has an electrical origin, and that it is a pulse of activity with a rather steep wave front. It manifests itself as a local decrease and a slower recovery in the surface potential of the nerve.

DIPHASIC ACTION POTENTIAL

Another method of approach is to investigate the propagation of the nerve impulse uninfluenced by the complications introduced by the demarcation current. The experiment may be modified as shown in

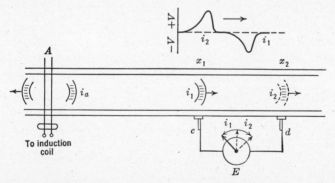

FIG. VI-6. Diphasic action potential i_1, i_2, due to a wave pulse i_a passing under contact c and then under contact d. The potential is amplified and presented as viewed on the fluorescent face of a cathode-ray oscillograph as two successive oppositely directed pulses.

Fig. VI-6. This diagram shows a normal nerve with the pick-up electrodes placed on its surface at the points $x_1 - x_2$. Under these circumstances no current flows through E either from c to d or from d to c, showing that *the external surface of the nerve is an electric equipotential surface.*

If, however, the stimulus, an electric discharge across A, is adjusted so as to excite a single nerve impulse (i_a), it signals its arrival at x_1 by a recordable impulsive deflection of the electric recorder E. The deflection takes place in such a direction as to indicate that a unidirectional impulsive current i_1 is traveling in the external circuit from d to c. After

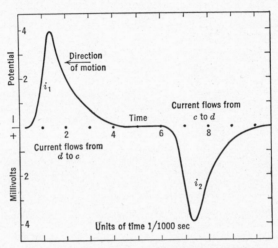

FIG. VI–7. Diphasic action potential reproduced to scale from an oscillograph record.

a very short interval of time a second impulsive electric deflection is observed, indicating that another momentary current pulse i_2 has passed in the opposite direction, i.e., from c to d. This reversed electric deflection takes place the instant the pulse of nerve excitation passes the point x_2. These externally recordable successive impulses of current, with the two phases of change in potential, are called the *diphasic action potential.* A scale drawing of this diphasic action is shown in Fig. VI–7. The time interval from crest to crest is proportional to the distance between the contacts c to d. The electrical implication is that the pulse of nerve excitation lowers the normal potential V_2 to V_1 on passing under the contact x_1; hence, a flow of current i_1 from d to c through the external circuit takes place. After the destructive activity has passed the point x_1, restoration sets in, accompanied by a slower return of the potential to its original value V_2.

After a short interval, depending on the distance $x_1 - x_2$, the nerve pulse reaches x_2, where in turn the normal surface potential V_2 at d is lowered to V_1, accompanied by the reversal of the previous electrical phenomena.

PHYSICAL CHARACTERISTICS OF THE ACTION POTENTIAL

The present evidence supports the hypothesis that the electric response is a true indication of the normal activity of the nerve and that it is not an artificial effect due to the type of stimulus employed. The energy manifesting itself as the nerve pulse is not obtained from the artificial stimulus. This stimulus only appears to upset an equilibrated electrochemical boundary condition, which may take the form of a destruction of a polarized electrical double layer and a subsequent slower repolarization at the expense of osmotic and chemical actions.

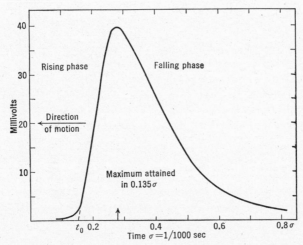

Fig. VI–8. Monophasic action potential plotted to scale. In large myelinated mammalian nerve fibers the phenomenon (spike) lasts about 0.4 millisecond. One third of the time is taken up by the phase of development, i.e., the rising phase of this curve.

If the electrical impulse is amplified and an inertialess recording instrument, in the form of a cathode-ray oscillograph, is used to record the nerve impulses, important details of nerve transmission can be observed.

In Fig. VI–8 is shown a monophasic action potential to scale. The original 40-millivolt pulse was amplified 8000 times with a 3-stage voltage amplifier, and the amplified potential changes were recorded with a cathode-ray oscillograph. The electric pulse is shown moving from right to left with the time recorded in milliseconds.

It will be noticed that the start of the activity, the foot of the rising phase, is not sudden or explosive. The gradual increase at the beginning of the rising phase of the curve may be attributed to the fact that the pick-up electrode is of finite width, so that the pulse may be considered as starting at t_0. The subsequent rapidly rising phase of the action potential is smooth, and its crest is reached in 0.135 millisecond. The falling phase is much slower, and its contour is usually not smooth.

The velocity of propagation of such a pulse, if taken from the saphenous nerve of the cat (Hursh [1939]), was found to be about 70 meters per second at 37° C, so that the crest is 0.95 cm behind the start.

It will be noticed that the rise and fall of the potential pulse is completed in about 0.5 millisecond. Erlanger and Gasser [1937] refer to it as a spike-like variation having the form of a skewed probability curve followed by after-potentials that may last for as much as 1 second (see Table VI-1).

COMPOSITE ACTION POTENTIAL OF A NERVE TRUNK

After the successful adoption of the variable-frequency stimulator and the cathode-ray oscillograph with the pre-amplification of the electrical potential impulses up to a millionfold, the study of nerve reactions to artificial electrical stimulation was given a new impetus.

The sciatic nerve of the bullfrog has served physiologists as a sort of standard in investigations of this type because it has the advantage of length and multiplicity of fibers. It consists of many hundreds of fibers of every size and variety. The diameters of the fibers range from 12 microns, which are myelinated, down to the smallest, which are unmyelinated.

Figure VI-9 shows some semi-diagrammatic typical results compiled from data obtained by Erlanger and Gasser [1937] from a peroneal nerve of a bullfrog, stimulated with an electric shock strong enough to excite all the fibers. Such an action potential record is divisible into three characteristic groups of elevations associated with (A) fibers of highest velocity, (B) those of intermediate velocity, and (C) the slowest pulse-propagating fibers. In group A are included the large myelinated fibers; in group C are included all unmyelinated fibers.

Experimentally, it was found that the threshold of stimulation for fast fibers is lower than that for slow ones. When the shock intensity was gradually raised, the α spike was developed first and with increasing intensity of shock the β and γ, and finally the B and C negative potential waves were developed.

This initial qualitative classification of nerve fibers in terms of their velocity of nerve pulse propagation has been justified by the recent experimental work of Gasser and Grundfest [1939] and by Grundfest [1939]. The view that nerve fibers of mammals may be divided into three groups, each of which possesses a characteristic action potential, seems to be well established.

The designation A refers to the somatic myelinated fibers; B to the autonomic myelinated fibers; and C to the unmyelinated fibers. Action in each starts with a spike. The only difference between the types is one of duration. The A spike has a duration of 0.4 millisecond, and the C a duration of more than 2 milliseconds. The spike is followed by an after-potential which is much smaller in size and much longer in duration.

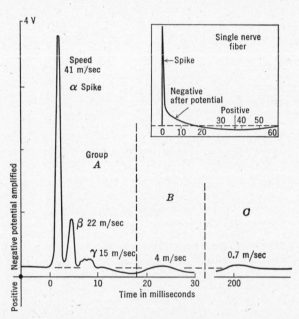

Fig. VI–9. The complete action potential of a bullfrog's peroneal nerve reconstructed semi-diagrammatically from oscillograph records. The electrical shock was strong enough to excite all the fibers. Composite curve drawn from data by Erlanger and Gasser [1937]. Insert, similar results from a single mammalian (group A) nerve fiber.

After-potentials vary as to form, size, and duration, depending on the kind of fiber. The complete sequence is a spike and a negative after-potential followed by a positive potential in the A and C fibers. In the B fibers the negative after-potential is extremely small in single responses but can be developed by special procedures.

Table VI–1 shows this classification applied by Grundfest [1940] to mammalian nerve fibers. Comparable correlations are not available for the action potentials of invertebrate nerves.

Grundfest points to two noteworthy correlations in the table: (1) the spike duration is constant for all A fibers within the experimental limits of 0.45 ± 0.5 millisecond and is independent of the size of these fibers; (2) the absolute refractory period is not independent of fiber size in group A, but increases as the fiber size decreases. Note that the positive after-potentials of the three groups persist more definitely as the fibers decrease in size. It is particularly noteworthy that no negative after-potential follows the action potential response of the group B fibers.

TABLE VI-1

PROPERTIES OF THREE GROUPS OF MAMMALIAN NERVE FIBERS

Group	A	B	C
Diameters of fibers, μ	20 to 1*†	< 3‡	unmyelinated
Velocity propagation, meters per second	100 to < 5*†	14 to < 3‡	< 2§
Spike duration, msec	0.4 to 0.5*	1.2‡	2.0§
Negative after-potential Amount, per cent of spike Duration, msec	3 to 5‖ 12 to 20‖ ¶	None‡ —	3 to 5§ 50 to 80§
Positive after-potential Amount, per cent of spike Duration, msec	0.2‖ 40 to 60‖ ¶	1.5 to 4.0‡ 100 to 300‡	1.5§ 300 to > 1000§
Absolute refractory period, msec	0.4 alpha*‖ 0.6 delta, cat* 1.0 delta, rabbit*	1.2‡	2.0‡
Order of susceptibility to asphyxia‡	2	1	3

By Courtesy of H. Grundfest [1940].

* Gasser and Grundfest [1939].   Delta (cat) are small A fibers.
† Hursh [1939].
‡ Grundfest [1939].
§ Grundfest and Gasser [1938].
‖ Gasser and Grundfest [1936].
¶ Lehmann [1937].

AFTER-POTENTIALS

In recording the monophasic action potential from a single nerve fiber (group A) as shown in the insert in Fig. VI–9, it has been found that the after-potentials run a course characteristic of the fiber. The spike potential in normal mammalian nerve fibers (group A) does not drop vertically back to the resting potential, but is followed by another negative potential (after the spike has passed) lasting about 15 milliseconds. This potential has a rising phase of its own and begins before the spike potential has returned to normality.

The negative after-potential is a separate phenomenon. The present evidence shows it to be depressed by lack of oxygen. It is abnormally prolonged by veratrine and depressed by carbon monoxide poisoning; its duration is decreased by monovalent ions (K^+) or increased by divalent cations such as Ca. Its basic significance, however, is still in doubt. The overall action potential drops below the resting potential, becomes positive, and returns to its normal value in about 50 milliseconds. The positive after-potential is probably intimately related to the spike potential, which is unquestionably the sign of the nerve impulse itself.

As an impulse travels along a nerve, the region of breakdown is in an *absolute refractory state* and the region immediately behind this is in a *relatively refractory state*. The importance of all these phenomena lies in the fact that they determine the excitability of the nerve.

Excitability is defined as the reciprocal of the threshold magnitude necessary to excite the tissue.

SUMMATION OF INADEQUATE STIMULI

If the stimulus is subliminal, no nerve impulse is developed. However, if a second subliminal stimulus follows the first within 1 millisecond or less and a nerve impulse is developed, the impulse is said to be due to the *summation of inadequate stimuli*. To account for this it has been suggested that any stimulus gives rise in a nerve fiber to a *local excitatory process* which does one of two things: if it is sufficiently great, it initiates a nerve impulse; if not, it reverses itself and subsides. If, during the reversal, a second subliminal stimulus is applied to bring the intensity of the process up to or above threshold, it will give rise to an impulse. Hence a stimulus, however weak or briefly applied, leaves the point of application in the nerve fiber in an altered state of excitability after the stimulus has ceased to act, and a time interval must elapse before complete recovery has set in.

If the stimulus is threshold so that a nerve impulse is initiated by the excitatory process, the excitability drops to zero immediately after the response has occurred: the cell or organ passes through an unexcitable state called the *completely refractory stage*. This *absolute refractory period* during which excitation is impossible is followed by a *relatively refractory period.* The excitability during this period of time is lower than normal; it is possible to set up an impulse, but the stimulus to accomplish it must be more intense than that which was needed to excite the normal pulse.

FREQUENCY OF IMPULSES

The relatively refractory period spaces the impulses so that the normal impulses are a minimum distance apart, making overlapping or continuous activity impossible. For instance, in the phrenic nerve of the cat, at 37° C under electric shock stimulation, it was found impossible to excite more than 1000 spike potentials per second.

The frequency of innervation of the motor units of muscle is ordinarily only 5 to 50 per second, depending on the intensity of muscular contraction (Adrian and Bronk [1929]). Even in extreme conditions it does not rise above 100 per second. In sensory fibers the frequencies of innervation are of about the same order of magnitude. Thus, for example, Adrian [1932] found that, when pressure was applied to the pad of a cat's foot, the nerve impulses propagated in single fibers varied from 9 to 100 per second, according to the magnitude of the pressure applied.

In general, it has been found that the rate of recovery of excitability in the most rapidly conducting and most excitable mammalian fibers is such that it would prevent conduction of as many as 1000 impulses per second.

SPEED OF PROPAGATION

It has been known since 1913, from the work of Lapique and Legendre, that the speed of propagation of nerve impulses increases with increase in fiber size.

Direct measurements on nerve fibers, ranging in diameter from 1 to 16 microns, have shown the speed of propagation of the nerve impulses to be proportional to the diameter of the fiber. Hursh [1939] found that in the nerves of four-day-old kittens the maximal velocity of propagation is 11 meters per second, as compared with 80 to 90 meters per second in the saphenous nerve of full-grown cats. As the kitten grows to maturity, the maximal velocity increases at a rate directly proportional to the diameter of the largest fibers. Gasser and Grundfest [1939], using myelinated fibers in the phrenic nerve of the cat, which vary in diameter from 1 to 14 microns, also found that the speed of propagation was proportional to the diameters of these fibers.

From the evidence on the relation between velocity of propagation and amplitudes of the recorded axon potentials, they concluded that the maximum axon potential was approximately directly proportional to the diameter of the active fiber. This conclusion is supported by theoretical considerations.

Whether the simple relation — the velocity of propagation of the nerve impulse is directly proportional to the diameter of the nerve fiber — can be extended to cover a much wider range of fiber diameters is still an open question in view of the measurements by Pumphrey and Young [1938]. These show that in cephalopod (squid) nerves, which contain fibers varying in diameter from 30 to 700 microns, measurements of the velocity of propagation were nearly proportional to the square root of the diameter, and that the smaller nerves of vertebrates (1 to 20 microns) gave values of velocity which were proportional to the diameter of the fiber.

The conduction properties of a nerve may be reduced by a drop in temperature to such an extent that a local application of ice acts as a nearly complete depressent to the nerve impulse as it passes through the low-temperature nerve section. The velocity of propagation, however, will be restored when the nerve regains its original temperature.

Anesthetics and narcotics, such as ether, chloroform, cocain, chloral, phenol, and alcohol, may be applied locally to a nerve trunk to decrease the conductivity and irritability, which are restored when the narcotic is removed.

ACCOMMODATION

When a stimulus in the form of an electric current is applied to a nerve for a short time, the critical value of current strength to excite — that is, the threshold value — is constant. Under these experimental conditions the applied current builds up a local excitatory process which sets the nerve impulse in motion when it reaches a critical value. If a stimulating electric current, insufficiently large to excite, is removed from a nerve, the excitatory process is assumed to revert to its resting value, according to the law of exponential decay.

If a subthreshold direct current is used as a stimulus and allowed to increase slowly with time, it is found that the current may attain a very high value without producing a response in the form of a moving nerve pulse. This result is possible if the rate at which the excitatory process decays is equal to, or greater than, its rate of increase.

If a constant subthreshold direct current passes through a length of nerve, the excitability of the nerve is increased at the cathode contact-point and decreased at the place where the anode makes contact. If the excitability at the cathode contact is examined as a function of time of application of a stimulus (Bishop [1928]), it is found that the excitability rapidly increases with time and passes through a maximum, from which it at first rapidly falls, and then decreases more slowly to attain a constant value. In frog nerve this maximum is attained in 3 milliseconds; in large mammalian nerve it is a fraction of a millisecond.

On breaking of the current, the excitability of the nerve abruptly decreases to a large value of inexcitability, from which it rapidly recovers to attain its resting value exponentially with time (Erlanger and Blair [1931]).

At the anode the inverse of this phenomenon takes place.

This change in excitability is called *accommodation*.

Complete accommodation means that the excitability of the nerve has returned completely to its resting value during the passage of a constant current. This is probably due to the neutralization of the depolarizing effect of the current by the repolarization activity of the nerve so that the two effects cancel, leaving the membrane at its resting value.

SEQUENCE OF EVENTS

From the above experimental evidence we may roughly piece together an explanation of the sequence of events which in the final analysis may lead to a correct interpretation of the origin and method of propagation of the impulsive wave of the nerve fiber.

In general, the biological potentials are of two types: the static potentials of the resting nerve indicating the relative difference of potential between the two points under examination, and the transient potentials accompanying the activity associated with pulse propagation.

Structurally the nerve fiber has the form of a cylindrical condenser or "submarine cable." The transmission of message pulses in an electrical cable, however, is entirely different from the propagation of pulse messages in nerve fiber.

The condenser-like properties of the nerve sheath and its potential difference between the axis cylinder and the outer surface are probably due to a difference in ionic concentration on the two sides of the boundary. This difference in potential gradually disappears when the nerve is deprived of oxygen. An explanation of this disappearance may be found in the associated osmotic-pressure phenomenon, for part of the potential is very probably due to the orientation of the organic molecules forming a polar boundary at the surface of the axis cylinder.

Suppose that these molecules are of the palmitic acid ($C_{15}H_{31}$—COOH) type, composed of a long (21×10^{-8} cm) cylindrical carbon chain terminating in an active polar group having a —COOH configuration. In a closely packed array* they stand upright so that a maximum number of

---

* Shaffer and Dingle [1938] find the monomolecular layer of crystalline egg albumin to be 40×10^{-8} cm thick.

active —COOH groups bury themselves in the water phase of the axis cylinder. If an increase in hydrogen-ion concentration of the water phase should now take place, it would diminish the attraction of the —COOH group for the water, and thus cause a change in the surface energy of the monomolecular array and consequently a change in potential.

When the nerve fiber becomes locally active a rearrangement in the monomolecular array may take place. The normal difference of potential suffers a transient decrease followed by a slower restoration so that a sensitive voltage-measuring device in contact with the point of excitation on the external surface of the nerve will show a pulse-like variation of potential with time. This transient lasts about 0.004 second. About one tenth of this time is used for the potential to rise to its maximum value.

The change in the state of the fiber that permits the development of this transient is not known. Any theory that may be proposed must be based on the following well-established facts. The duration of the spike-like pulse is constant for a restricted range of speeds of propagation and fiber diameters (Table VI–1). If the spike appears at all, it appears with the maximum size which the intrinsic properties of the nerve permit. The nerve pulse is independent of the nature of the stimulus which starts it. Its speed of propagation increases with the diameter of the fiber and increases with a rise in temperature. If its amplitude is locally depressed, it attains its full size when it emerges into a subsequent normal nerve section. The energy with which the action is maintained is supplied locally.

At various times, as the experimental data have accumulated, models of nerve excitation have been developed to coordinate the existing data. One of the early models designed to illustrate pulse propagation consisted of a wire-core axis cylinder while the interstitial fluid was replaced by an envelope of electrolytic solution. This was the so-called core conductor model which, however, lacks the equivalence of a bioelectrical membrane. Hermann used it to show that it duplicated the " passive " electrical properties of the nerve.

In spite of the perfected physical analogies attained by such models, one can duplicate biophysical conditions only very approximately, by substituting a polarizable organic interfacial membrane for the oxide film and a fluid conductor of physiological composition for the metallic core. Labes and Zain's [1927] model approached these conditions by using collodion sacs filled with a neutral solution of potassium phosphate for the cores, which were surrounded with sodium chloride solution isotonic with the phosphate mixture. The inner and outer solutions of a series of these collodion cells were placed in communication with each other through and with the external fluid by a series of fine glass capillaries with which the semi-permeable nature of the membrane was simulated.

The iron-wire model developed by Lillie [1923] carries the analogy into the dynamic stage, and it is generally accepted as the most complete model of the propagated nerve pulse.

LILLIE'S IRON-WIRE MODEL OF NERVE PROPAGATION

The model developed by Lillie to illustrate impulse transmission in a nerve fiber uses a pure iron wire that had been " conditioned " in strong nitric acid, which coated it with a layer of iron oxide. If such a wire is then placed in dilute nitric acid, no further chemical activity will take place; it is now said to be in its " passive " state. If the passive wire, in its dilute nitric acid bath, is scratched so that the oxide coating is penetrated, the dilute acid will attack the exposed underlying clean iron surface at this point. It is found that the exposed iron becomes electrically positive with respect to the adjacent edge of the oxide-coated surface. The electric eddy currents flowing across the edge of this surface fracture reduce the oxide coating to iron and oxidize the adjacent free iron surface, thus causing the exposed iron to become coated with an inactive surface.

This reduction-oxidation process travels along the wire, in both directions from the scratch, in the form of a local pulse-like electrical disturbance with the speed of about 15 cm/sec. This speed may be decreased by increasing the concentration of the acid.

After the initial formation of the passive surface on the iron wire a prolonged phase follows, during which a reexcitation of the wire by scratching produces only imperfect oxidation-reduction pulses. By degrees, however, the oxide-coated wire regains its original property of a recovered passive wire.

Similar properties are, as we have seen, exhibited by nerve fibers during their refractory period and again in the relative refractory period in which the speed of propagation gradually regains its normal value.

If the wire is enclosed in a tube filled with nitric acid, the velocity of transmission of the oxidation-reduction pulse is found to vary with the diameter of the tube. In a narrow tube the resistance through the electrolyte of neighboring points, between which the eddy currents flow, is increased. Hence, the currents are smaller and the time required to reduce the film is increased. This decrease in velocity with decrease in diameter is also one of the properties of nerve fibers.

The model is an excellent one provided that its limitations are realized. It is not, however, a theory of nerve activity, and it does not suggest one.

PHYSICOMATHEMATICAL ASPECTS OF EXCITATION AND PROPAGATION OF NERVE IMPULSES

Throughout the development of any physical experiment, one may observe the accumulated data presented in the form of tables. One column usually contains the independent variable and a parallel column the dependent variable. Another way of presenting the data is by drawing a graph or by expressing the results in a mathematical formula.

If, as in the problem of nerve conduction, one suspects that a basic physical law is involved, statements of relations are generally proposed between the rate of change of some quantity and other quantities developed by the experimental evidence. Such a relation presented in rigid mathematical terms is called a differential equation; it will contain derivatives of functions and also the functions themselves.

For instance, Newton's second law of motion states that the force equals the time rate of change of the momentum. Written in mathematical terms, this law is

$$F = \frac{d(mv)}{dt}$$

where mv is the momentum.

If the mass is constant we can rewrite the equation as

$$F = m \frac{dv}{dt}$$

which may be solved by direct integration.

On the other hand, if an effort is to be made to find relations between two phenomena, as, for instance, between the local excitatory process of a nerve and the stimulus, then the method of approach is as follows:

1. We start by assuming a working hypothesis. The data provide the clue.

2. We next set up a mathematical expression representing the rate of change of the two variables to be examined.

3. Then we integrate the equation in order to reproduce the working hypothesis in a mathematical form suitable for experimental verification.

Should subsequent experimental data force one to reject the solution, then the fundamental assumption upon which the solution rests must be modified so as to include the new data. As a result, we gradually build up a more comprehensive theory which may eventually give the clue to the fundamental law governing the phenomenon under investigation.

In this way the several mathematical versions of the phenomena involved in pulse propagation might have originated. The two simplest and most fruitful of these versions were proposed by Blair* [1932] in the form of a physicomathematical theory, and by Hill [1936] as a chemical wave theory of excitation and conduction in nerves.

Although the two theories start with somewhat different assumptions, the generalization of them by Offner [1937], by Young [1937], and by Katz [1939] shows that the fundamental time-intensity relations of nerve fibers are identical for all type of stimulating current; on the whole, therefore, the probable validity of the assumptions might be said to be verified.

Unfortunately, some recent experimental data by Katz [1939] on the stimulation of nerve with alternating currents do not satisfy the general equations.

A survey of the theories so oddly at variance, yet with so much in common, has failed to develop the fundamental laws governing the phenomena of nerve conduction. Despite these limitations the simple postulates set up as working hypotheses by Blair and extended by Rashevsky [1933] embody a very good representation of the methods of attack and are an excellent approximation representative of the experimental data.

Blair postulated the existence of a local excitatory process (p) and a stimulus (S). The growth of p in time, due to the stimulus, may be proportional to the applied stimulus (S), to the applied energy (S^2), or to both. In mathematical terms these assumptions are

$$\frac{dp}{dt} = KS \quad \text{or} \quad \frac{dp}{dt} = KS^2 \quad \text{or} \quad \frac{dp}{dt} = f(S, S^2)$$

Let us examine each one of these assumptions in terms of the known data. It was found that, when a nerve fiber was made part of a closed electric circuit and a stimulus in the form of a direct current was suddenly applied, the excitability of the nerve was increased at the cathode contact proportional to the intensity of the current strength. This fact makes the second and third postulates untenable. We therefore retain the assumption that the time rate at which the excitatory process (p) is built up is proportional to the applied stimulus.

$$\frac{dp}{dt} = KS$$

where K is the constant of proportionality, i.e., the growth per second per unit stimulus.

---

* Blair perfected his analysis and supported it by experimental evidence in 1933 and 1934.

The second hypothesis is a consequence of the observations that the local excitatory process p diminishes with time for all values of p. The simplest mathematical form of this statement is dp/dt decreases directly with p. Thus the process follows the natural law of depreciation of values with time, and

$$\frac{dp}{dt} = -kp$$

where k is the constant of proportionality or the coefficient of diminution of the excitatory process. The negative sign indicates that the activity diminishes as time goes on.

The third hypothesis is that the local excitatory process must attain a critical limiting value b in order that it may be adequate to initiate the nerve impulse. That is, p must reach a threshold value b such that

$$p = b \quad \text{or} \quad p > b$$

to start the nerve excitation.

Thus the whole phenomenon is described by the following differential equation

$$\frac{dp}{dt} = KS - kp$$

with excitation occurring when p is equal to or greater than b.

Since no stipulation was made as to what form S shall take, the stimulus may, therefore, be a type of electric current. The choice will be limited to the voltage derived from a direct or an alternating current, or from the discharge from a condenser. For simplicity's sake a direct current of potential V is chosen; then a statement for the time taken to build up an excitatory process to its threshold value is formulated by assuming that the excitatory process p attains its threshold value b in t_1 seconds. The mathematical equivalence of this statement is to integrate the excitatory process from its initial zero value to its final value b in time zero to t_1 seconds.

$$\int_0^b \frac{dp}{KV - kp} = \int_0^{t_1} dt$$

Integrating this expression with the aid of *A Short Table of Integrals*, by Peirce, and solving for the time, one obtains

$$t_1 = \frac{1}{k} \log \frac{KV}{KV - kp}$$

Thus a latent period of t_1 seconds must elapse between the moment of establishing the current and the moment of release or spread of the excitation. The minimum value of the potential V to accomplish this is V_0. Therefore we may write

$$kt_1 = \log \frac{V_0}{V_0 - B}$$

where $B = kb/K$.

The validity of this relation may be tested by plotting experimental values of $\log V_0/(V_0 - B)$ as a function of t_1. Blair used data obtained by Lapicque from such diverse types of tissue as *Spirogyra*, the sciatic gastrocnemius of the frog, and a nerve-muscle preparation of *Helix*; he found that these results were in good agreement with this solution except for occasional large values of time.

Rashevsky [1936] showed that Blair's original differential equation can express the velocity of propagation of the active current of the nerve. This velocity is strictly constant if the time in which the potential has risen to V_0 is not taken into consideration. He deduced the natural nerve-pulse velocity from electrochemical considerations to be equal to

$$v = \frac{I_0 - B}{B} \cdot \frac{k}{a}$$

Rashevsky took into consideration the gradual increase of the current as the depolarized section, associated with the pulse, advanced toward the region under examination. In the above relation I_0 is the maximum value of this current. Thus, when I_0 is less than B no propagation can occur. When $I_0 > B$ then $I_0 - B$ is the excess of the action current of the nerve over its minimal necessary value, and $a^2 = 2(\gamma - 1)\rho/\gamma\delta\rho'r$. Here γ denotes the ratio of the resistance of unit length of the core of the fiber to unit length of the outside medium while the nerve fiber is immersed in a conducting electrolyte. The axis cylinder has radius r and specific resistance ρ; its surrounding sheath of thickness δ has specific resistance ρ'. The value of a therefore depends on the dimensions and property of the fiber, and it has the dimensions of the reciprocal of length.

The theoretical value of the velocity as calculated from this equation can, of course, be only approximate since the values of the constants involved in a are not well known. Rashevsky [1933], however, showed that with reasonable assumptions for the less accurately known quantities the above relation leads to a value for the velocity of about 25 meters per second, which is, as was experimentally established, of the right order of magnitude.

Blair [1934] has also shown this equation to be in fair agreement with the data obtained by Blair and Erlanger [1933] for the velocity of propagation of pulses in single fibers.

Rheobase

The quantity $B = kb/K$ is technically known as the rheobase (*rheo* = to flow). If the equation for t_1 is rewritten

$$p = \frac{KV}{k} (1 - e^{-kt_1})$$

the excitatory process p increases exponentially with time to attain a maximum limiting value, when $t = \infty$, which is KV/k.

If B is the least voltage which will stimulate when the excitatory process has stopped growing, then

$$p_{\max} \equiv b = \frac{KB}{k}$$

Thus b is the magnitude of the local excitatory process necessary for the initiation of an impulse. Under these conditions, the so-called rheobase (Fig. VI–10) is

$$B = \frac{kb}{K}$$

that is, the rheobase is k times the amount of local excitatory process necessary for adequacy, divided by the growth per second of the excitatory process per unit stimulus (Blair [1935]). Since this method necessitates waiting a very long time, the chronaxie $(2B)$ is used instead of B to test for the threshold to initiate a nerve impulse.

Chronaxie

It has been found experimentally that, if the time of application of a stimulus is increased, the strength of the stimulus must be decreased in order to obtain the threshold quantity to initiate the nerve impulse.

Lapicque's [1926] data seemed to verify the assumption that the time of application must be inversely proportional to the strength of the stimulus in order to initiate the nerve impulse. Under these circumstances the strength-duration curves would be equilateral hyperbolas of the form $I \times t = $ constant when a current of intensity I is used. In terms of Blair's theory this statement describes the conditions only very approximately, since the expected relation is an exponential one.

In Fig. VI–10 are depicted more accurate data which show successive smaller stimuli of direct current that must be applied to initiate the nerve impulse during successively longer periods of time. This *strength-duration* relation is an exponential curve, as predicted by the theoretical analysis.

If the curve is graphically extrapolated until it becomes asymptotic to a line paralleling the time axis for a value of current equal to B, then B is called the *rheobase*.

The *chronaxie* is the time required for a strength $2B$ to excite activity in the nerve fiber. It is labeled T in Fig. VI–10. Thus, if it has taken an infinite time to initiate an impulse with 15 volts in frog nerve, it would take 1.75 milliseconds, i.e., chronaxie time, T, to initiate the impulse with 30 volts.

Analytically an expression for the chronaxie may be obtained from the equation

$$t = \frac{1}{k} \log \frac{V}{V - B}$$

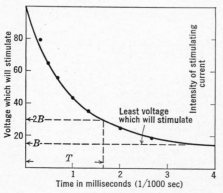

FIG. VI–10. A typical strength duration curve. T is the chronaxie, the shortest time that an intensity equal to $2B$ will initiate the nerve excitation.

When, as in Fig. VI–10, $V = 2B$, the chronaxie for direct current is

$$T = \frac{1}{k} \log_e 2 = \frac{0.693}{k}$$

Thus the chronaxie decreases with increase in k, the speed of subsidence of the excitatory process per unit state of excitation.

Experimentally an increase in temperature (Blair [1935]) is accompanied by an increase in the magnitude of the rheobase B together with an increase in k. If an increase in temperature implies an increase in excitability, an increase in k and its expected theoretical decrease in chronaxie must reflect an increase in the excitability of nerve fiber.

A tissue with a small coefficient of subsidence (k) must, therefore, in general have a slow rate of formation of the excitatory state or require a relatively large amount of excitatory process to initiate an impulse, or both. Tissue possessing small chronaxie can therefore be more easily excited.

In practice, in order to determine the chronaxie, all that is necessary is to find the threshold stimulus or rheobase (B), to double this value, and then, with a proper timing device, to find the shortest time of application of the stimulus $2B$ which will cause the least observable response of the tissue. The practical value of the chronaxie lies in the fact that it has been used as a definite measure of the excitability of a tissue.

Chronaxies may vary from 0.3 millisecond (frog sciatic) to 100 milliseconds (smooth muscle), or to such extreme values as 11,000 to 15,000 milliseconds (pigment cells, skin of frog). An interesting analysis has been made by Lewy [1935] in which he used the chronaxie in classifying 825 lead workers as to their over- and underexcitability resulting from certain pathological conditions.

We may conclude that the coefficient of diminution (k) of the excitatory process is characteristic of the tissue, that the rheobase (B) and the action potential taken together are not inconsistent with the above hypotheses, and that the action potential is prima-facie evidence of the transmission of nerve impulses. The simplicity of the hypotheses and the possibility of correlating future experimental data with the theoretical analysis will probably lead to an understanding of the actual mechanism of nerve conduction in biophysical terms.

ACTION POTENTIALS IN THE OPTIC NERVE

If two non-polarizable electrodes are placed on an excised eye, one electrode upon the cut face of the optic nerve and the other on the cornea, and then connected in series with an electrometer, the usual demarcation current is observed. If light is allowed to penetrate to the retina, the electrometer will indicate a change in the magnitude of the current, whose direction of flow is from the fundus to the cornea and therefore in the same direction as the demarcation current. These electric currents are a valuable index of the activity of the retina, but they do not indicate what retinal activity is propagated to the brain.

The effect of allowing visual radiant energy to illuminate the retina is to set up a series of nerve impulses in the retina which will be detected as action potentials in the optic nerve. Hartline [1938] has shown that the pattern of the discharge of impulses in a single optic-nerve fiber in the vertebrate eye, as a result of subjecting the retina to illumination, is similar to that for the whole optic nerve as originally obtained by Adrian and Matthews [1927] from the eye of the eel and later by Granit [1933] from the optic nerve of a mammal.

The optic nerve in a 3-lb *Conger vulgaris* specimen is about 15 mm long and thinner than sciatic nerve of the frog. The retina has the normal structure of the teleost eye, containing both rods and cones, and differs little from the mammalian retina except in the presence of the campanula and the absence of anything corresponding with the fovea. The number of fibers in this optic nerve is about 10,000.

The isolated eye and its optic nerve were mounted in a light-tight box at 16° C, and the nerve was supported by two electrodes. A source of illumination outside the box could be focused on the retina.

The action currents of the optic nerve in the dark showed the nerve to be " fairly quiet." A sudden exposure of the retina to illumination always produced a well-marked monophasic action current discharge. The average duration of one of these responses was 0.0015 second, which is about the same order of magnitude as that observed in a peripheral sensory nerve fiber. The frequency of the impulses was found to depend on the size of the retinal image and on the intensity of illumination.

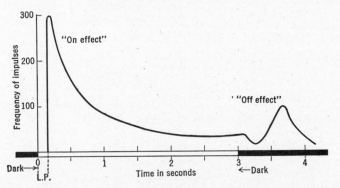

FIG. VI–11. The action currents of the optic nerve begin after a latent period (L.P.) less than 0.2 second after the light is turned on. After 3 seconds when the light is suddenly extinguished a second latent period appears, followed by a rise in frequency of the discharge, the "off effect." From data by Adrian and Matthews [1927].

The results show that the discharge frequency begins after a considerable latent period (L.P. in Fig. VI–11), rises to a maximum, then declines slowly. When the illumination is suddenly extinguished, it is followed by a sudden less prominent frequency increase which subsides gradually to zero frequency.

The general conclusion is that, the greater the intensity of the illumination, the shorter the latent period of the response, the greater the frequency of the discharge, and the greater the number of impulses in the initial burst of frequencies (Hartline [1938]).

The decline in frequency after the first burst may be correlated with our experience that a dimly outlined object appears in a dark room to decrease in brightness when the eye is prevented from moving while looking at it. After 20 seconds or less the object disappears and the field seems uniformly blurred.

These results mean that a changing visual field should produce a greater sensory experience than a stationary field; hence a movement will be more readily perceived than a steady pattern of light and shade.

When the entire retina was exposed to uniform illumination (Adrian and Matthews [1927]), the action current discharge in the optic nerve might consist of a series of regular pulses which usually varied between 15 and 5 per second. The frequency of the pulses varied with the light intensity and was found to decline as exposure continued.

They concluded that the intermittent discharges observed in the optic nerve may be attributed to nervous interconnection between the ganglion cells, but not to intermittent responses of the rods and cones to the continuous illumination. They also found that an increase in the size of the illuminated area paralled the effects of an increase in the intensity of the illumination. This, they decided, must be due to a nervous summation of the excitation from different points.

On extinction of the illumination (" off effect," Fig. VI–11) a latent period again develops comparable to that preceding the initial discharge lasting from 0.2 to 0.5 second. This latent period of the off effect is followed by a renewed outburst of impulses which lasts for about 1 second. It is difficult to say what causes this second, less violent, burst of impulses.

Whether the decline in frequency after the " on effect " is due to fatigue or to adaptation is still a matter of opinion. The impulses may vary in frequency but not in size, and the intervals between consecutive impulses cannot be shorter than the absolute refractory period of the fiber and must be long enough to allow for its complete recovery.

The electrical impulses detectable in the whole optic nerve when the retina is stimulated by light must represent the composite results of the activity of several thousand fibers. For instance, Hartline [1938] found that in 20 per cent of the isolated single fibers the initial burst of impulses of high frequency was followed by a much lower discharge frequency, which lasted throughout the duration of the illumination. When the illumination was extinguished, this discharge stopped. About 50 per cent of the fibers of the whole optic nerve responded with a short burst of impulses of high frequency when the light was turned on, but transmitted no impulses as long as the intensity of illumination was not changed. In about 30 per cent of the fibers no impulses appeared at all during illumination, but they showed a vigorous discharge of impulses when the light was extinguished.

Apparently it is the composite effect of these three groups of frequencies that is detected when the optic nerve as a whole is under examination. The burst of frequencies drops to half value in about a tenth of a second, so that a flicker whose frequency is greater than 10 per second should give the impression of continuous illumination. The motion-picture exposure frequency of about 12 frames per second will, as we know, cause no visual flicker.

The discharges in the optic nerve are of the same type as those observed in other sensory nerves. This is a very fundamental generalized conclusion.

ELECTROENCEPHALOGRAM

In 1929 Berger discovered that rapid changes in electrical potential could be detected between various points on the crown of the head. For instance, normal human subjects possessed a more or less regular rhythm of 10 pulses per second. The impulses had an average difference of potential of about 50 microvolts.

These electrical potential fluctuations, popularly called " brain waves," may be detected with the aid of two small pad-electrodes, moistened with electrocardiogram paste, which were placed on the scalp in circuit with an amplifier and a mechanical recording oscillograph. A sensitive instrument will resolve the electrical rhythm patterns so that at least four distinct, and more or less intense, frequencies can be identified. These wave patterns are classified as α (Berger), β, γ, and δ rhythmic electrical potentials.

The α rhythms appear as trains of waves lasting from 1 to 30 seconds. Their frequency for each individual is quite constant. They usually have a frequency of about 10, with extremes of 8.5 and 12.0 per second according to Pauline A. Davis [1941], and attain a maximum peak voltage of 200 microvolts, though typical voltages run from 25 to 75 microvolts.

The β rhythms have a frequency of over 20 per second and a peak voltage of 50 microvolts. They appear in short sequences or irregular groups. They are often difficult to distinguish from muscle potentials.

Fast γ rhythms have been described, but they are supposed to be difficult to distinguish from muscle potentials. Their frequency is over 35 per second. Their peak voltage is about 10 microvolts.

The δ rhythms have a frequency of 4 per second or less with a maximum peak voltage of 500 microvolts though typical voltages vary from 100 to 300 microvolts.

A freehand copy of a typical normal human electroencephalogram is shown in Fig. VI-12. Tuned electrical filters permit the passage of fairly narrow frequency bands, so that the recorded electroencephalograms take the forms shown in B, C, and D. Note especially how the amplitude of the α waves is modulated at a period of about 1 second. Such modulations are often quite irregular in some subjects. The α waves are nearly sinusoidal in form, though often very sharp and unsymmetrical.

The β activity is a universal feature of all records (Pauline A. Davis [1941]) and is present all over the brain.

Suppose that α and β activities were recorded as a pure sinusoidal wave of frequency 10 and 20 cycles per second, and possessed amplitudes

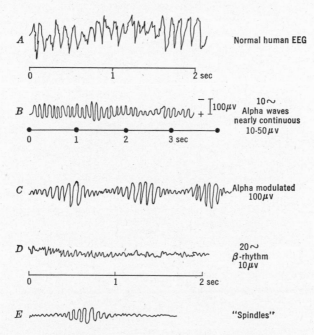

FIG. VI-12. Copies of typical fundamental rhythm patterns found in normal human electroencephalograms.

equal to 200 and 100 microvolts, respectively. They could be graphically represented as the broken lines in Fig. VI-13. The solid line represents their algebraic sum. This composite curve could then represent an idealized encephalogram. If this composite curve were being recorded as if it were an electroencephalogram, then, by the introduction of an electric filter in the recording circuit which would absorb the β wave form, the structure of the α rhythm could be obtained. The resulting wave train would then be similar to that represented by Fig. VI-12, B, except for the slight modulations shown.

Ever since the original observations by Berger, investigators have attempted to describe and interpret these records. A successful standardized recording has recently been reported by Pauline A. Davis [1941], which also contains a description of a standardized technique on a selected normal individual, a classification of fundamental types of electroencephalogram patterns, and a system of evaluation as to the degree of normality and abnormality.

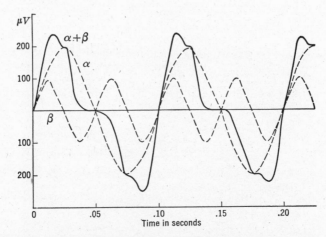

FIG. VI–13.   A synthetic encephalogram. Hypothetical α waves, 200-microvolt amplitude, 10-cycle frequency, superimposed on β waves, 100-microvolt amplitude and 20-cycle frequency.   Note similarity of composite graph (α + β) with electroencephalogram A in Fig. VI–12.

A selected normal individual is defined as one whose medical history reveals only the ordinary childhood diseases, who has had no psychiatric problem necessitating care, and whose behavior has been normal at home, at school, at work, and at play.   He must be known to be free of drugs, even as common a one as aspirin, for several days before the recording.

Upon examination, the person must be free from apprehension in relation to the procedure, comfortably relaxed but thoroughly awake with eyes closed, and on a bed in a diffusely lighted room.

The recording apparatus may be an ink-writing oscillograph with amplifiers and broad-band filters.   An available two-channel commercial form is shown in Fig. VI–14.   The speed of the recording tape is about 3 cm/sec.   Sensitivity is 1-cm deflection of the oscillograph pens per 100 millivolts.   Tuned electric filters may be used in the circuit. The 10-cycle filter has a broad peak at 10 cycles, and will pass 9, 8, and 7 cycles on one side and 11, 12, and 13 cycles on the other side; the higher- and lower-frequency filters have comparable breadth.

A three-pen recording can be obtained simultaneously.   The three matched amplifying systems are balanced with push-pull input stages, non-interfering and independent of one another.

As an example of cranial recording the "multiple monopolar method" recommended by Pauline A. Davis will be described. Figure VI–15 shows the arrangement of the electrode contacts. The lobe of the ear is used as a reference point since it is electrically much less active than points on the cranium.

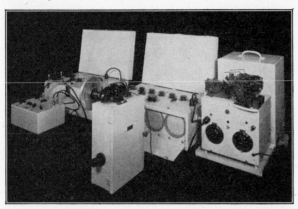

FIG. VI–14. A commercially available two-channel portable research electroencephalograph. Motion-picture camera in foreground, facing the two-channel oscillograph fluorescent screens. Mechanical two-pen recorder right end of display. Input amplifier. Sensitivity, 1 mm per microvolt. Voltage gain 20 million. Frequency range 1–10,000 cycles. Output amplifier. Power gain 4×10^{14} times. Cathode-ray screen, 5 in. Camera, 35-mm film. Power supply, 115 volts, 60 cycles, 400 watts. (By courtesy of the Electro-Medical Laboratory, Inc., Holliston, Mass.)

The electrodes are solder pellets covered with electrocardiogram paste. They are fastened to the head by covering them with collodion. The contact resistance should be less than 10,000 ohms.

In the encephalogram records examined by Pauline A. Davis [1941] it was found that the pattern of the occipital area in normal people was the most stable, and that if an α frequency were present it was more pronounced than from any other area. The temporal area usually showed less α activity than the motor area. The frontal electroencephalogram was found to be distorted by the

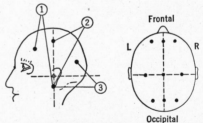

FIG. VI–15. Placements on head represent multiple monopolar recording technique. The numbers represent the amplifier channels. (By courtesy of Pauline A. Davis [1941].)

potentials generated by eye movements and muscle potentials.

A standard procedure is to determine the α index, which is the percentage of time the α frequency appears in a monopolar occipital record at a level 2 cm above the inion (Davis and Davis [1936]). This record is to be taken at least 10 seconds after the eyes have been closed.

The β activity is present all over the living brain. It represents physiological activity of the brain which is modified by physiological changes

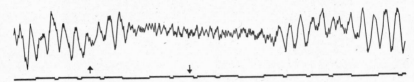

Fig. VI–16. A human electroencephalogram. The α rhythm is suppressed by visual stimulation. Subject in darkness with eyes open. Light turned on at first arrow and off at second. Note survival of β waves. Electrodes 5 mm apart and 5 cm lateral to midline over periparastriate area. Original record. (By courtesy of D. B. Lindsley [1938].)

such as sleep. One may identify the β activity of the brain as the residual occipital activity when the eyes are opened in a bright light. This type of encephalogram is illustrated in Fig. VI–16, which shows that the α activity ceases during illumination but resumes after light is cut off,

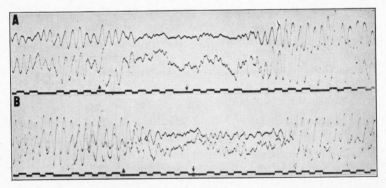

Fig. VI–17. A. This shows how the α rhythm of the right (top record) and left occipital areas differ in amplitude and blocking when a luminous stimulus is " turned on " at first arrow and " turned off " at second.

B. Blocking of α rhythm by an auditory stimulus (buzzer). On and off at arrows. (Original electroencephalograms by D. B. Lindsley [1938].)

but that the β waves are present at all times. Note that the composite wave at the right-hand edge resembles the composite $(\alpha + \beta)$ graph of Fig. VI–13.

It has been found that the β waves usually are diminished by apprehension or emotional attention, and reduced by drowsiness (Adrian and

Matthews [1934]). Many investigators have found that both auditory and tactile stimuli usually block the α rhythm. An electroencephalogram showing the effective blocking of the α rhythm by a luminus and auditory stimulus is presented in Fig. VI–17.

The pattern of the encephalogram changes systematically with the onset of sleep (Davis, Davis, Loomis, Harvey, and Hobart [1938]). In general, with the approach of drowsiness (" floating "), the α rhythm (10 cycles), if present in the waking record, diminishes in voltage and the time intervals between trains of α waves become longer. In the intervals between these trains the α waves are reduced. Moderately deep

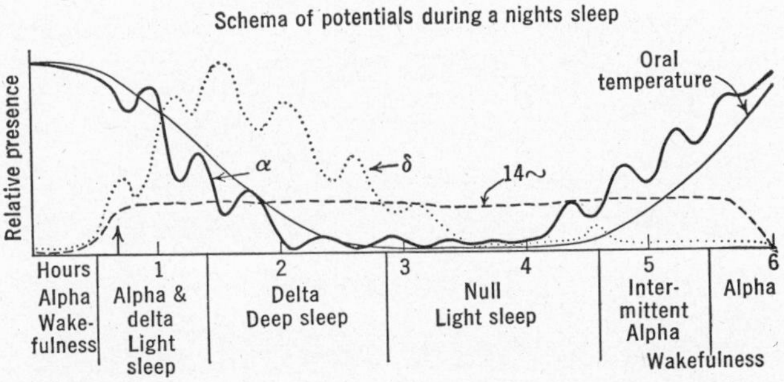

Schema of potentials during a nights sleep

Hours	1	2	3	4	5	6
Alpha Wakefulness	Alpha & delta Light sleep	Delta Deep sleep		Null Light sleep	Intermittent Alpha	Alpha
					Wakefulness	

Fig. VI–18. Predominance of brain potentials through the night. The α waves (black heavy line) in per cent presence; 14 per second waves (dashes) in per cent presence and δ waves (dots) in extent of predominance. Oral temperature (black thin line). Below the graph the stages of sleep are indicated. Record begun at time of retiring, arrow indicates beginning of sleep. Fluctuations represent changes due to shift of state of sleep. (By courtesy of H. Blake, R. W. Gerard, and N. Kleitman [1939].)

sleep shows well-developed 14-cycle " spindles " (Fig. VI–12, E) lasting for about 1 second, superimposed on a background of random oscillatory motion. As sleep becomes deeper, the random waves increase in voltage and wavelength; in very deep sleep, they may attain an amplitude of several hundred microvolts and last for 2 seconds or more.

An interesting graph summarizing the predominance of brain potentials through a night's sleep is shown in Fig. VI–18 (Blake, Gerard, and Kleitman [1939]). The heavy black line shows the percentage of α waves present. The dashed line indicates the percentage of 14-cycle waves. Delta waves are shown in extent of predominance by the dotted line. Note how the oral temperature parallels the percentage presence of α waves. This correlation is reasonable since α rhythm is closely associated with tonus (Jasper and Andrews [1938]).

The effect of drugs on the human encephalogram was summarized by Gibbs, Gibbs, and Lennox [1939] as follows: Drugs that cause a sleep-like state altered the encephalogram in the same general way as natural sleep.   The more nearly alike the clinical actions of two drugs are, the more nearly alike are the changes which they produce in the record.

An encephalogram obtained during epileptic seizures shows distinct and characteristic potential waves.   It was found that the rhythm which

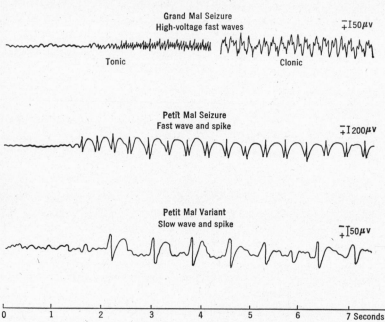

FIG. VI–19.   Types of abnormal activity encountered in epilepsy and the variety of seizure with which each is associated.   Grand mal seizure: typical pattern, electrodes on left frontal region and ear.   Petit mal seizure: left frontal region and ear. Petit mal variant: left occipital region and ear.   (By courtesy of F. A. Gibbs, E. L. Gibbs, and W. G. Lennox [1939].)

is developed during seizures is distinctive for the three main types of epilepsy.   Figure VI–19 shows the fast rhythm of " grand mal " and the alternating fast and slow rhythm of " petit mal."   The exact pattern tends to be characteristic for each patient.

The well-established facts are that the presence or the absence of the α rhythm is not correlated with intelligence and that different individuals differ widely from one another in general wave pattern, yet a given individual tends to reproduce his own record on successive tests.   The α rhythm content varies under different circumstances.   The onset of drowsiness, any startling stimulus, or conditions of embarrassment and apprehension may inhibit it.   Overactivity of a pathological sort illustrated by the grand mal epileptic seizures seen in humans is shown by the electrical activity building up to a climax in parallel with the muscular spasms or clonic jerks. In general, overexcitation of the cortex seems to be revealed by quick sequences of sharp spikes at relatively high voltage.

It is still uncertain how the differences of potential are generated by the brain and what the variations indicate. The groundwork of empirical observation and physiological analysis for the interpretation of the electrical activity of the brain is still being laid.

CATHODE-RAY OSCILLOGRAPH

Adequate study of the action currents in the central nervous system, or allied phenomena, can be carried out only with instruments of great sensitivity and resolving power. An amplifier must be available which can step up transient signals of the order of 1 or 2 microvolts and deliver them with enough power to operate a cathode-ray oscillograph.

This type of oscillograph uses a fine jet of electrons, emitted by an electron gun (see " Electron Microscope "), as a pencil to plot graphs on a fluorescent screen of one electrical quantity as a function of a second electrical quantity. In order to accomplish this, advantage is taken of the fact that a jet of high-speed electrons can be deflected by an electric field through which it passes. If the beam is allowed to impinge on a willemite ($ZnSiO_4$) fluorescent screen (see " Intensifying Screens "), a small spot of vivid green fluorescent light can be observed where the collisions of the electrons with the screen take place.

The deflection of the beam by an electric field, as observed by the motion of the fluorescent spot, serves as a measure of the strength of that field. Since such an electron beam is practically without inertia, a sudden change in the electric field strength or a reversal of polarity of the field is instantly recorded as a change in the position of the fluorescent spot.

Figure VI–20 shows the modern pear-shaped type of oscillograph vacuum tube with an electron gun at G emitting a fine pencil of high-speed electrons focused on the fluorescent screen by the electric lenses A_1 and A_2. The fluorescent material is placed on the inner surface of the glass face A. In the neck of the tube are two pairs of parallel " deflection plates," x and y. The electron beam passes between these plates along the central axis of the tube, after which it impinges on the fluorescent screen at A, where a small luminous spot may be observed. If coordinate axes are inscribed on the outer face of the tube any displacements of the spot can be described as movements referred to these coordinate axes.

If a difference of potential is now applied to the deflection plates marked y, a movement of the spot will take place from A to B_Y, or from A to C_Y, depending on whether the upper plate is positively or negatively charged.   A similar explanation applies to the movement of the spot on the X axis which is due to the position of the vertical deflection plates marked x.

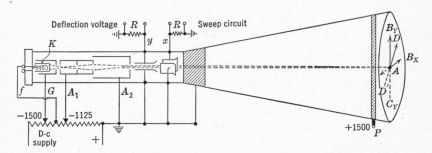

Fig. VI–20.   The essential elements of a high-vacuum cathode-ray oscillograph tube.   Electrons are emitted from the indirectly heated oxide-coated cathode K. Internal tungsten heater element f wound non-inductively. GA_1A_2 are the elements of an electron lens (see electron microscope). G, the grid, a nickel cylinder with small hole, controls intensity of beam. A_1, used to collimate the beam, is the first anode or focusing electrode. A_2, the second anode, accelerates the electrons toward the screen.   By varying its voltage, spot size and intensity may be regulated. P, the postaccelerating electrode (A. B. DuMont Laboratories, Inc.) or intensifier of the luminous spot.   It is a conducting ring placed on the innerside of the glass.   The potential between this electrode and A_2 is approximately equal to that between A_2 and K.   In order to avoid a loss in sensitivity due to P the anode A_2 is connected to the static internal shield. R is 1 megohm.   Overall length with a 20-cm screen is about 55 cm.

Suppose both the x and y plates to be charged electrically positive, and to the same potential, at the same time.   Then the spot will move along the diagonal from A to D.   Upon reversal of the polarity of the plates, the spot will move from A to D'.

If, for example, a sinusoidally varying voltage, such as the 60-cycle lighting source, is impressed on the x plates, the spot will move rapidly back and forth with simple harmonic motion to produce a horizontal fluorescent trace, the half length or amplitude of which is proportional to the voltage.   A similar trace along the Y axis will be obtained if the same voltage is attached to the y plates.   If the same alternating potential is connected to both the x plates and the y plates, the resultant pattern will be a straight line inclined at 45° as DAD'.   The fluorescent spot moves along this line as in simple harmonic motion, indicating that these two potentials are in phase.   If the magnitude of the two deflections remains the same but their phase-angle difference is increased until a circular trace of the spot is observed, then this circular pattern shows that the phase difference has become 90°.

If the x plates are connected to a source whose potential varies so that the fluorescent spot moves along the X axis with constant speed and very rapidly returns, then the circuit that produces such an effect is called a *sweep circuit.* If at the same time a 60-cycle alternating potential is applied to the y plates, the vertical harmonic trace would be swept from left to right at constant speed, and with proper timing of the sweep circuit one will observe, because of the persistence of vision, a stationary sine-wave pattern.

For the study of a transient bioelectrical phenomenon connected to the y deflection plates, a high-speed accurate linearly increasing potential is used as a sweep circuit to trace the varying pattern as a function of time. If the electrical activity is a monophasic action potential of a nerve, a curve similar to that of Fig. VI–8 will be developed.

The cathode-ray oscillograph is not a machine for performing any desired operation upon an electrical signal impressed upon the deflection plates of the instrument; it only traces on the fluorescent screen a pattern which must be interpreted. In interpreting this pattern it should be remembered that the unknown signal is always plotted as a function of some signal whose characteristics are known.

Voltage Sensitivity of the Cathode-Ray Oscillograph

A difference of potential connected across either pair of deflection plates of the oscillograph produces an electric field of strength E equal to the difference of potential divided by the distance between them. An electron of velocity v coming from a field-free space, on entering such a field at right angles to the lines of force, is deflected along a parabolic path (Fig. VI–21) as long as it remains in the electric field. After it clears the lower edge of the plate, it reenters a field-free space and moves in a straight line until it strikes the fluorescent screen. As a result, the beam is depressed through an angle θ. The resulting vertical deflection y, when the small distorting end effects of the field are neglected, is

$$y = \tfrac{1}{2}at^2$$

In its horizontal flight the electron travels the length of the plates x at right angles to the field such that

$$x = v_x t$$

The electric force acting on the electron to depress it is

$$Ee = ma = m\frac{2v_x^{\,2}y}{x^2}$$

then

$$y = \tfrac{1}{2}E\,\frac{e}{m}\frac{x^2}{v_x^{\,2}}$$

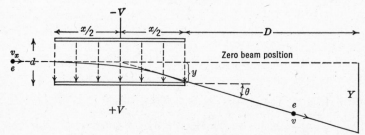

FIG. VI–21. The path of the electron e entering the idealized uniform electric field between a pair of deflection plates is parabolic. Upon leaving the field the electron moves in a straight line towards the screen Y.

After leaving the field, the electron travels with speed equal to v at an angle θ with the axis of the tube until it arrives at the screen, such that

$$\tan \theta = \frac{dy}{dx} = \frac{Eex}{mv_x^{\,2}}$$

From the dimensions of the tube

$$\tan \theta = \frac{Y - y}{D}$$

Equating we have

$$\frac{Eex}{mv_x^{\,2}} = \frac{Y - y}{D}$$

If D is made large in comparison with half the length of the deflection plate, then

$$Y = \frac{V}{d} \cdot \frac{e}{m} \cdot \frac{xD}{v_x^{\,2}}$$

where $E = V/d$. The sensitivity is the deflection of the fluorescent spot in centimeters per volt difference of potential applied to the deflection plates; thus

$$\text{Sensitivity} = \frac{1}{d} \cdot \frac{e}{m} \cdot \frac{x}{v_x^{\,2}} \cdot D$$

Since d, x, and D are all fixed by design in the tube and collected with e into the constant K', we have

$$\text{Sensitivity} = \frac{K'}{\frac{1}{2}mv_x^2} \equiv \frac{K}{V_a}$$

The sensitivity or ease with which the electron beam is deflected by the electric field of the deflection plates, varies inversely with the axial component of the kinetic energy of the electron leaving the electron gun. To increase the deflection, the time of flight of the electron must be increased as it passes through the field; i.e., the accelerating potential V_a on the electron gun must be decreased so that the axial velocity v_x of the electrons is small.

The reciprocal of the sensitivity is the deflection factor; it is usually expressed in d-c volts per inch. Thus as the potential of the (accelerating) electrode changes from 2000 to 1500 to 1000 volts, the deflection sensitivity increases from 0.23 to 0.30 to 0.45 mm/d-c volt (Du Mont, Type 208).

The intensity of the fluorescent spot increases, however, with the kinetic energy of the electrons. In order that a bright fluorescent spot may be obtained, and a high deflection sensitivity be retained, the electrons can be accelerated after they have passed through the deflection plates. This may be accomplished by introducing an electrostatic electron lens between the deflection plates and the screen (see " Electron Microscope "). This post accelerating electrode is called an intensifier.

Sweep Circuits

In modern cathode-ray oscillographs of the self-contained commercial form, a linear time-base generator has been built into the cabinet. The output voltage of this generator may be connected to the x deflection plates. In order to obtain a linear displacement of the fluorescent spot from left to right, the potential of the deflection plates must rise linearly with time and then at a given value drop to zero voltage so rapidly that the trace of the beam on the return movement is so faint that it cannot be confused with the fluorescent spot moving forward.

The device most commonly adopted for this purpose is the relaxation oscillator. It generates distorted currents in which the variations are due to the charge and discharge of a condenser through a resistor.

A relaxation oscillator circuit in its simplest form is shown in the insert of Fig. VI–22. It may be formed with a neon-gas-filled glow discharge tube G, in conjunction with a variable high resistor R, a variable condenser C, and a d-c voltage source. The discharge tube is connected across the frequency-controlling condenser C.

Current from the 620-volt d-c source flows through R, charging the condenser C. The charge on this condenser rises exponentially with time, as illustrated by the broken saturation curve in Fig. VI–22. The gas discharge tube does not allow this voltage to attain its maximum value V_m, because the gas in the tube ionizes at 120 volts. At the instant the voltage has reached this value (P on the curve) the tube flashes, discharging the condenser in the very short time Δt. During this discharge time the potential of the tube falls from P until it reaches a lower critical value V_C at O', where ionization ceases. At this potential the tube again becomes a nonconductor, and the condenser-charging cycle repeats itself, the potential rising from O' to P', etc. Thus the "sawtoothed" sweep-plate-voltage graph is generated.

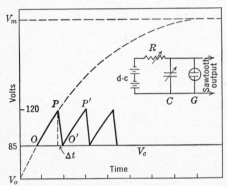

Fig. VI–22. Broken line shows the exponential voltage rise as the condenser C charges through the resistance R. Units of time depend on the product RC. With increase in RC the repetition rate diminishes. P, P' are the flash voltages of the tube G, while Δt is its deionization time. Insert is a simplified schematic diagram showing use of a gas-filled glow tube as a relaxation oscillator. If an 885 thyratron is used, the point P is attained at about 160 volts, and the maintaining voltage is about 16 volts.

If this generator is connected to the deflection plates of the oscillograph, the charging voltage sweeps the electron beam across the screen while the discharge cycle returns it to its starting point. The frequency with which this action occurs for a given flash-voltage of a gas discharge tube is determined by the time constant RC. Thus, either R or C, or both, may be increased to decrease the frequency of repetition rate of the fluorescent spot. In commercial forms of oscillographs this repetition rate can be varied from 2 to 50,000 sweeps per second.

If we examine the exponential rise in voltage in the interval from O to P or O' to P', it will be noticed that it is not quite linear so that the speed of the moving fluorescent spot is not quite constant. In order to obtain a more uniform speed of deflection a more linear charging interval of the curve must be used. This may be found nearer the origin. A gas discharge tube ionizing at a lower voltage moves the point P down the curve. The logarithmic curve being steeper and more linear near the origin, the rise in voltage is faster, so that the repetition rate is increased.

At no time is it possible to produce a truly linear horizontal motion of the fluorescent spot unless the control of the charging current is such that the flow is kept at a constant rate during the entire charging cycle. Various modifications of the above simple circuit are introduced into commercial equipment to attain such a linear time sweep.

When the repetition rate is equal to, is slightly less than, or is an integral divisor of, the frequency of the Y-axis signal, the pattern seen on the fluorescent screen appears stationary. The frequency, however, must be high enough to produce visual fusion of the images.

Detailed construction and applications of the low-voltage cathode-ray tube may be found in recent books by W. G. Dow [1937], G. Parr [1937], and J. Millman and S. Seeley [1941].

BIBLIOGRAPHY

1923 LILLIE, R. S., *Protoplasmic Action and Nervous Action*, University of Chicago Press.

1926 LAPICQUE, L., *l'Excitabilité en fonction du temps*, Paris, Les Presses Univ. de France.

1927 ADRIAN, E. D., and R. MATTHEWS, *J. Physiol.*, **63**, 378.

1927 GASSER, H. S., and J. ERLANGER, *Am. J. Physiol.*, **80**, 522.

1927 LABES, R., and H. ZAIN, *Arch. exptl. Path. Pharmakol.*, **126, 352**.

1928 ADRIAN, E. D., *The Basis of Sensation*, Christophers, London.

1928 ADRIAN, E. D., and D. W. BRONK, *J. Physiol.*, **66**, 81.

1928 BISHOP, G. H., *Am. J. Physiol.*, **84**, 417.

1929 ADRIAN, E. D., and D. W. BRONK, *J. Physiol.*, **67**, 119.

1931 ADRIAN, E. D., " The Messages in Sensory Fibers," *The Harvey Lectures*, **27**, 57.

1931 ERLANGER, J., and E. A. BLAIR, *Am. J. Physiol.*, **99**, 108; **99**, 129.

1932 ADRIAN, E. D., *The Mechanism of Nervous Action*, University of Pennsylvania Press, Philadelphia, Pa.

1932 BLAIR, H. A., *J. Gen. Physiol.*, **15**, 709.

1932 BLAIR, H. A., *J. Gen. Physiol.*, **16**, 165, 177.

1932 HILL, A. V., *Chemical Wave Transmission in Nerve*, Cambridge University Press.

1933 BLAIR, E. A., and J. ERLANGER, *Am. J. Physiol.*, **106**, 524.

1933 COLE, K. S., *Cold Spring Harbor Symposia Quant. Biol.*, **1, 131**.

1933 GRANIT, R., *J. Physiol.*, **77**, 207.

1933 RASHEVSKY, N., *Physics*, **4**, 341.

1934 ADRIAN, E. D., and B. H. C. MATTHEWS, *Brain*, **57**, 355.

1934 BLAIR, H. A., *J. Gen. Physiol.*, **18**, 125.

1935 BLAIR, H. A., *J. Gen. Physiol.*, **18**, 755.

1935 LEWY, F. H., *Am. J. Physiol.*, **113**, 87.

1935 RASHEVSKY, N., *Physics*, **6**, 308.

1936 BLAIR, H. A., *Cold Spring Harbor Symposia Quant. Biol.*, **4, 63**.

1936   DAVIS, H., and PAULINE A. DAVIS, *Arch. Neurol. Psychiat.*, **36**, 1214.
1936   GASSER, H. S., and H. GRUNDFEST, *Am. J. Physiol.*, **117**, 113.
1936   HILL, A. V., *Proc. Roy. Soc. London*, **B119**, 305.
1936   RASHEVSKY, N., *Cold Spring Harbor Symposia Quant. Biol.*, **4**, 90.
1937   DOW, W. G., *Fundamentals of Engineering Electronics*, John Wiley & Sons, New York.
1937   ERLANGER, J., and H. S. GASSER, *Electrical Signs of Nervous Activity*, University of Pennsylvania Press, Philadelphia, Pa.
1937   LEHMANN, J. E., *Am. J. Physiol.*, **118**, 600.
1937   OFFNER, E. A., unpublished; see YOUNG [1937].
1937   PARR, G., *The Low Voltage Cathode Ray Tube and Its Applications*, Chapman & Hall, London.
1937   YOUNG, G., *Psychometrika*, **2**, 103.
1938   DAVIS, H., *Tabulae Biologicae*, **16**, 116 (Berlin).
1938   DAVIS, H., *Am. J. Psychiat.*, **94**, 825.
1938   DAVIS, H., PAULINE A. DAVIS, A. L. LOOMIS, E. N. HARVEY, and G. HOBART, *J. Neurophysiol.*, **1**, 24.
1938   GASSER, H. S., *J. Applied Phys.*, **9**, 88.
1938   GRUNDFEST, H., and H. S. GASSER, *Am. J. Physiol.*, **123**, 307.
1938   HARTLINE, H. K., *Am. J. Physiol.*, **121**, 400.
1938   JASPER, H. H., and H. L. ANDREWS, *J. Neurophysiol.*, **1**, 87.
1938   LINDSLEY, D. B., *J. Gen. Psychol.*, **19**, 285.
1938   PUMPHREY, R. J., and J. Z. YOUNG, *J. Exptl. Biol.*, **15**, 453.
1938   SHAFFER, M. F., and J. H. DINGLE, *Proc. Soc. Exp. Biol. Med.*, **38**, 528.
1939   BLAKE, H., R. W. GERARD, and N. KLEITMAN, *J. Neurophysiol.*, **2**, 48.
1939   GASSER, H. S., and H. GRUNDFEST, *Am. J. Physiol.*, **127**, 393.
1939   GIBBS, F. A., E. L. GIBBS, and W. G. LENNOX, *Arch. Neurol. Psychiat.*, **41**, 1111.
1939   GRUNDFEST, H., *Am. J. Physiol.*, **127**, 253.
1939   HODGKIN, A. L., *J. Physiol.*, **94**, 560.
1939   HURSH, J. B., *Am. J. Physiol.*, **127**, 131, 140.
1939   KATZ, B., *Electric Excitation of Nerve*, Oxford University Press, London.
1940   GRUNDFEST, H., *Ann. Rev. Physiol.*, **2**, 213.
1940   RASHEVSKY, N., *Advances and Applications of Mathematical Biology*, University of Chicago Press.
1941   COLE, K. S., *J. Gen. Physiol.*, **25**, 29.
1941   DAVIS, PAULINE A., *J. Neurophysiol.*, **4**, 92.
1941   MILLMAN, J., and S. SEELEY, *Electronics*, McGraw-Hill Book Company, New York.

Chapter VII

AUDITORY BIOPHYSICS

In a physical sense, sound is a disturbance of a vibratory nature in an elastic medium. The disturbance may or may not be audible to a human ear. An auditory sensation may be produced by such a physical disturbance provided that its frequency lies within the response range of the auditory mechanism and its energy is sufficiently great to affect this mechanism sensibly.

The quantitative study of the vibrating disturbance lies academically in the province of the physicist. The analysis of the structure of the human response mechanism lies in the province of the anatomist. Its functional aspects are taken over by the physiologist; the psychologist more often than not will consider whatever is left untouched by the above specialists as his field of interest, especially the characteristics of sound as consciously heard or experienced.

The biophysical aspect merges all these provinces, deals with the effects of the external vibratory disturbances and the structure of the auditory mechanism, and analyzes the response characteristics of the structure in terms of fundamental physical laws.

The interest in biophysics is therefore in both aspects of sound: (1) the purely mechanical actions of the body producing the vibratory disturbances, the property of the elastic medium which transmits the vibrations to the eardrum and by way of the ossicles to the fluids of the inner ear; and (2) the bioelectrical response to the mechanical processes which are essential to the complex experience called hearing.

The Overall Aspect of the Auditory Process

The essential requirement for the auditory process is a vibrating object immersed in a medium, normal air under standard conditions, which may be called the object space. The vibrating object must be able to communicate its vibrations to the medium of the object space. The aural mechanism immersed in the object space must be able to transmit the objective phenomena to the cochlea, after which it is subjectively experienced as sound having attributes of loudness, pitch, and quality.

The mechanism making this transfer is composed of the external canal leading to the eardrum, an interlocking set of three bones, two muscles, a

253

large number of suspensory ligaments, a spirally converging fluid canal encased in a bony cochlea, and a complex set of end organs of the acoustic nerve located in the aural membrane immersed in this fluid. These end organs are stimulated by the hydrodynamic disturbances of the cochlea fluids to initiate the nerve impulses which are propagated to the brain via the acoustic nerve.

THE ACOUSTIC OBJECT SPACE

The eardrum is in contact with the air in which the human ear is normally immersed. The eardrum can move in and out as the result of pressure changes of the air in contact with its free faces.

An observer possessing normal ears placed in this object space experiences a sensation called a tone if the pressure disturbances at the eardrum are adequate and are repeated with a frequency of not less than 20 or more than 20,000 cycles per second.

This frequency range is presented to the ear in the form of longitudinal waves in the medium in contact with the eardrum. These *longitudinal waves* are basically the results of particles executing *simple harmonic motions* as an elastic medium. The acoustic intensity, or the energy per second that flows across each square centimeter of this medium, must be determined in order to evaluate the sensitivity range of the aural mechanism.

SIMPLE HARMONIC MOTION

If a small body were rotating with uniform speed in a horizontal circle, and you were to elevate the plane of the circle to the level of your eyes, you would see the body as if it were executing a sweep motion. The length of the sweep is equal to the diameter of the circle.

This will be called the " reference circle," and the sweep motion is its projected uniform circular motion on the diameter of the reference circle, designated as simple harmonic motion.

The velocity with which a point moves, in simple harmonic motion, is constantly changing in magnitude and direction. Its velocity at the two ends of its sweep is zero. As the particle attains its mid or equilibrium point from either direction, it has its greatest velocity. A corresponding acceleration is apparent. At its midpoint its acceleration is zero, and at the points of maximum displacement its acceleration is maximal.

Simple harmonic motion is described very accurately by stating that the restoring force is proportional to the displacement and that they are always opposite in direction.

Displacement of a Particle Executing Simple Harmonic Motion

Let P_1 in Fig. VII–1 be a particle on a reference circle of radius A moving with uniform speed. The projected position on the vertical axis is m_1. ᐧIf P_1 now moves with uniform speed around the circle to succes-

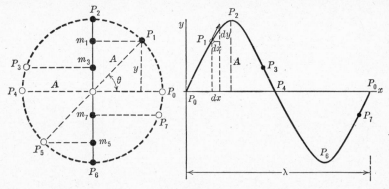

Fig. VII–1.

sive positions P_2, P_3, P_4, etc., m_1 will assume comparable positions m_2, m_3, m_4, etc., which are the projected positions of P on a diameter of the reference circle. The point m is executing simple harmonic motion. During one complete revolution of P, m will sweep across and back over a diameter taken as the y axis. The frequency with which this sweep occurs is equal to the number of revolutions of P per second. The time in seconds taken to make a complete revolution, or the completed sweep excursion along the diameter, is called the period. The angular displacement of P in one revolution is 2π radians. If the angular velocity is ω and the period of revolution is T seconds, then

$$2\pi = \omega T$$

The sweep motion of m is the simple harmonic counterpart of the circular motion of P, and its displacement at any instant is

$$y = A \sin \theta$$

In the reference circle any angular displacement $\theta = \omega t$. Thus

$$y = A \sin \frac{2\pi t}{T}$$

If this simple harmonic motion executed by m on the y axis were simulated by the point of a pencil held at right angles to the paper, and while doing this the hand is moved to the right with constant speed, you could generate the sine curve of Fig. VII–1 graphically. To produce this curve accurately you move to the right a distance λ centimeters in T seconds, or you move a proportional less distance x in t seconds, such that

$$\frac{x}{\lambda} = \frac{t}{T}$$

Then

$$y = A \sin 2\pi \frac{x}{\lambda}$$

would describe a wave motion in which λ represents the displacement equal to one wavelength.

The radius of the reference circle has the same magnitude as the amplitude A; it is the maximum value that y attains in the wave motion. It is also half the distance from crest to trough of the wave, or half the perpendicular distance over which the particle m vibrates.

FREQUENCY

The number of cycles or complete vibrations made by the vibrating particle in 1 second is its frequency.

$$n = \frac{1}{T}$$

where T is the period or time necessary for the particle P to move around the reference circle.

The phase angle is the angular position of the particle on the reference circle with respect to its initial position measured from the x axis in a counterclockwise direction. In Fig. VII–1, for example, the particle P_2 is out of phase with P_6; its phase angle is 180°, i.e., P_6 is π radians out of phase with P_2. In a similar manner P_3 is out of phase with P_7. Note their relative positions on the sine-wave curve.

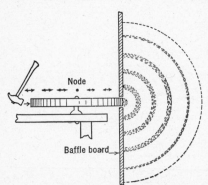

Node

Baffle board

FIG. VII–2. Acoustic waves are leaving the hole in the baffle board. Compressions and rarefactions of the air are shown as shaded and unshaded areas.

LONGITUDINAL WAVES

When the line of vibration of the particle is in the same direction the wave is traveling, the result is what is called a longitudinal wave. The oscillatory disturbances communicated by the rod to the air in Fig. VII–2 are longitudinal waves. The end of the rod is vibrating in its pistonlike motion in the same direction and in phase with the air particles. The resulting longitudinal air vibrations may be experienced as acoustical sensations.

VELOCITY OF A PARTICLE EXECUTING SIMPLE HARMONIC MOTION

An air particle swinging in a simple harmonic motion develops its maximum velocity as it passes through its midpoint; it decelerates as it moves away from this point until at maximum displacement it comes to rest. At this point it reverses its direction of motion and accelerates to attain its maximum velocity again at its midpoint. It continues until it comes to rest once more through deceleration at its opposite extreme displacement, where it again changes its direction, and accelerates to regain its maximum velocity at the middle of its swing.

The instantaneous velocity at any point on this path may be obtained with the aid of the velocity of the particle moving around the reference circle.

In Fig. VII–3 let v be the linear velocity of the reference particle P_1. The projection of v on the y axis is the simple-harmonic-motion velocity desired, which is the y component v_y of the linear velocity. From similar triangles $\cos \theta = \cos \omega t = v_y/v$ or

$$v_y = v \cos \omega t = \omega A \cos \omega t = \frac{2\pi}{T} A \cos \frac{2\pi t}{T}$$

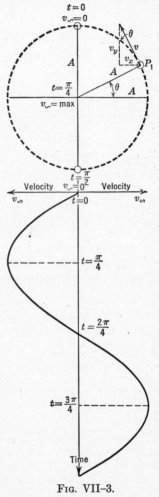

FIG. VII–3.

Note that, while the displacement is represented by a sine-wave curve, the accompanying velocity is a cosine-wave curve, identical except for a phase shift of $\pi/2$ radians. The maximum velocity of the particle is attained when it passes through the midpoint, i.e., when $t = T/4$, such that

$$v_{\max} = \frac{2\pi}{T} A \cos \frac{\pi}{2} = \frac{2\pi A}{T} = 2\pi n A$$

Energy of a Particle Executing Simple Harmonic Motion

The total energy content of the moving air particle is the sum of its kinetic and potential energies at any instance. Its kinetic energy, however, is a maximum at its midpoint, where its potential energy is zero. Its kinetic energy is $\frac{1}{2}mv^2_{max} = \frac{1}{2}m(2\pi nA)^2$, so that its energy at any point in its path is

$$E = 2\pi^2 mn^2 A^2$$

The energy of an air particle in a longitudinal wave, therefore, is proportional to its mass, to the square of the frequency, and to the square of the amplitude.

Intensity

The energy is passed along from particle to particle at the velocity of the propagating longitudinal wave. The rate at which this energy is transferred across unit area is called the intensity of the wave. The intensity is the product of the energy density, or energy per unit volume, and the velocity of energy propagation and hence is expressed in ergs per square centimeter times seconds or watts per square centimeter.

The energy per unit volume is

$$\frac{E}{\text{Unit volume}} = \frac{2\pi^2 mn^2 A^2}{m/\rho}$$

where ρ is the density of the medium. Let the velocity of energy propagation be V; then the intensity in ergs per square centimeter times seconds is

$$I = 2\pi^2 n^2 A^2 \rho V$$

If the longitudinal waves have a velocity V in air under standard conditions, and the frequency is in the acoustic range, the intensity of the acoustic energy in the object space is proportional to the square of the frequency and to the square of the amplitude.

It has been found experimentally that the minimum audible intensity is about 10^{-16} watt/cm^2 at a frequency of 1000 cycles. What is the amplitude of an air particle which produces this just-audible intensity? Here $n = 1000$, V (air) $= 343$ meters/sec for $\rho = 0.00121$ gram/cm^3 at 20° C, 760 mm pressure. $I = 10^{-16}$ watt/cm$^2 = 10^{-9}$ erg/cm$^2 \times$ sec. Solve for A in the intensity equation. Since

$$I = 2\pi^2 n^2 A^2 \rho V$$

$$10^{-9} = 2\pi^2 \times 10^6 \times A^2 \times 121 \times 10^{-5} \times 343 \times 10^2$$

$$A = 8 \times 10^{-10} \text{ cm}$$

The air particle which possesses this small amplitude is about 4×10^{-8} cm in diameter, so that the eardrum at threshold pressure executes displacements which are about one hundred times smaller than the diameter of a gas molecule.

ACOUSTIC PRESSURE

In the previous section it was shown that the displacement in simple harmonic motion is given by the expression $y = A \sin 2\pi t/T = A \sin (2\pi n t)$. The equation which describes the motion of all the particles in the wave is

$$y = A \sin 2\pi \left(\frac{t}{T} - \frac{x}{\lambda} \right) = A \sin 2\pi n \left(t - \frac{x}{V} \right)$$

where $V = n\lambda$. The definition of elasticity is

$$\text{Elasticity} = \frac{\text{Stress}}{\text{Strain}}$$

In a gas the stress or the force per unit area is the pressure, and the strain is the rate at which an element of unit cross section but of length dx changes with changes in values of the displacement dy. Hence

$$p = \text{Elasticity} \frac{dy}{dx}$$

Since

$$y = A \sin 2\pi n \left(t - \frac{x}{V} \right)$$

$$\frac{dy}{dx} = - \frac{A 2\pi n}{V} \cos 2\pi n \left(t - \frac{x}{V} \right)$$

Thus

$$p = \pm \text{Elasticity} \times \frac{2\pi n A}{V} \cos 2\pi n \left(t - \frac{x}{V} \right)$$

$$p = \pm \text{Elasticity} \frac{v}{V}$$

for a wave traveling with velocity V. Since

$$V = \sqrt{\frac{\text{Elasticity}}{\rho}}$$

$$p = \frac{V^2 \rho v}{V} = \rho v V$$

where p is the instantaneous-pressure change and v the instantaneous-velocity change of an air particle. At the midpoint of the simple harmonic displacement of the particle, where the maximum velocity (v_0) and the pressure (p_0) changes take place,

$$p_0 = \rho v_0 V$$

Acoustic Intensity in Terms of Acoustic Pressure

Since

$$I = 2\pi^2 n^2 A^2 \rho V$$

and

$$v_0 = 2\pi n A$$

$$I = \frac{v_0^2}{2} \rho V$$

$$I = \frac{p_0^2}{2\rho V} \text{ watts/cm}^2$$

The intensity may be expressed in effective or root mean square value of the pressure variation where $p_0 = \sqrt{2} p_e$.

In air under conditions where neither the density nor the velocity of propagation of the wave changes, the intensity is directly proportional to the square of the particle pressure.

If the minimum audible intensity is 10^{-16} watt /cm^2 at 1000 cycles, $\rho = 0.00121$ gram/cm^3, and $V = 343$ meters/sec at 20° C and 760 mm air pressure, the pressure associated with the threshold of minimum audibility is

$$10^{-9} = \frac{p_0^2}{2 \times 121 \times 10^{-5} \times 34{,}300}$$

$$p_0 = 2.9 \times 10^{-4} \text{ dyne/cm}^2$$

In the range of acoustic frequencies from 1000 to 6000 cycles Geffcken [1934] has observed that human ears can detect pressure changes even as low as 5×10^{-5} dyne/cm^2, thus justifying the above calculations.

Auditory Mechanism

The next problem to consider is the way the auditory mechanism responds to the changes in pressure set up in the object space. For the purpose of this discussion the structure of the ear may be divided into three parts.

I. The external ear is that portion of the acoustic mechanism upon which the sound waves impinge. It consists of the auricle (pinna), whose foundation is a framework of elastic cartilage, and the external acoustic meatus, a horizontal canal containing two slight bends, the first of which is directed upward and forward and the more internal portion is directed backward and downward. Its lower wall forms with the tympanic membrane an acute-angled depression. (See Fig. VII–8.) The canal is lined by a prolongation of the external skin, which also forms with a greatly diminished thickness the outer surface of the tympanic membrane. The tympanic membrane closes the canal and acts as a partition separating the outer from the middle ear.

II. The middle ear is essentially an air cavity lying in the temporal bone, lined with very thin mucous membrane. It contains the auditory ossicles and can be connected with the external air by way of the Eustachian tube, which communicates with the cavity of the nasopharynx.

III. The internal ear is contained in a bony cavity lying in the petrous portion of the temporal bone (Fig. VII–9). This cavity contains two chambers: one, called the vestibule, contains a series of organs which concern equilibrium (semicircular canals), but which have no connection with the hearing process; and the adjoining cavity called the cochlea.

PINNA

The surface of the pinna is not a reflector of sound, for reflection can take place only from a surface which is large in comparison with the incident wavelength. The pinna can scatter acoustic waves so that some of the scattered energy enters the ear canal. When a cupped hand is held near the pinna, passing acoustic waves are scattered by the hand and enter the ear canal, making the sound louder. Bringing the cupped hand in contact with the ear creates a resonance cavity composed of the palm of the hand, pinna, and ear canal. The response of this composite resonator may be heard.

EXTERNAL AUDITORY CANAL

The external opening of the auditory canal has an area of 0.3 to 0.5 sq cm, and according to Békésy [1932] it has an average volume of 1.04 cc, an average depth of 2.7 cm, and an average diameter of 0.7 cm.

If the resonance frequency of this cavity is calculated on the assumption that it is a Helmholtz resonator without neck, it is found to possess a fundamental frequency of 430 cycles. Whether the resonance frequency of the meatus contributes anything to the hearing process is not known.

MIDDLE-EAR CAVITY

The middle-ear cavity, also called the tympanic cavity, is separated from the external ear by the eardrum, or tympanic membrane. The mean volume of this cavity as measured by Békésy [1936] was found to be 2.0 cc. The ossicles and their suspensory ligaments occupy from 0.5 to 0.8 cc. In a study by the author of the middle-ear mechanism it was found that the bones themselves occupy only about 7 per cent of the volume of the cavity. The air cavity is therefore small so that its resonance frequency is high. Experimentally the natural frequency of the middle-ear cavity has been found to lie between 800 and 1500 cycles.

In order to change the air pressure in this cavity the nasal end of the Eustachian tube may be opened. The effect of changes in external air pressure experienced in moving elevators and airplanes, or on entering a compressed-air lock, may be relieved by swallowing. This action opens the Eustachian tube and allows the pressure on both sides of the eardrum to equalize.

TABLE VII-1

WRIGHTSON AND KEITH'S DIMENSIONS OF THE TYMPANIC MEMBRANE

Quadrant	Area, mm^2	Mean Radius
Anterior superior	13.5	3.8
Anterior inferior	14.5	8.7
Posterior inferior	22	8.0
Posterior superior	16	5.2
Vertical diameter	11.8	Mean area*
Horizontal diameter	8.9	52–90 mm^2

* Wrightson and Keith [1918]; Frank [1923]; Tröger [1930]; and Geffcken [1934].

TYMPANIC MEMBRANE

The so-called eardrum, or tympanic membrane, is a very thin, dense partition forming the boundary between the external-ear and middle-ear cavities. The area assigned to the tympanic membrane by various investigators varies from 0.52 to 0.90 sq cm, Wrightson's value of 0.66 herewith being accepted as a mean. Values adopted by Wrightson and Keith [1918] for the various detailed dimensions of the tympanic membrane are shown in Table VII-1. It is about 0.1 mm thick and composed of three layers of tissue. Its outer surface is a thin continuation of the external layer of skin; its inner surface, a continuation of the mucous membrane of the middle-ear cavity. Between these membranes is a thin fibrous layer.

The fibrous layer is built up of circular and radial fibers. The density of distribution of the circular fibers is more pronounced at the center and near the periphery. The radial fibers terminate in the fibrocartilaginous ring at the margin of the membrane. The manubrium or handle of the malleus (Fig. VII–4) is inserted between the mucous membrane and the inner fibrous layer.

The radial fibers terminate at the external lower end of the manubrium. When the tensor tympani muscle contracts, the handle of the

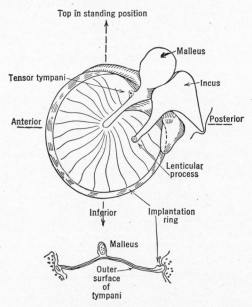

Fɪɢ. VII–4. A semi-diagrammatic view of the malleus-incus articulation looking at the inner convex surface of the eardrum. The lower figure is a diagonal section through the tympani showing the attached malleus.

malleus and the tympanic membrane are pulled inward, forming a shallow, unsymmetrically indented dish with a rolled edge and an eccentric hollow in its outer surface termed the umbo. Owing to the unsymmetrical suspension of the eardrum and its attachment to the manubrium, a fold of the membrane just below the head of the malleus is left in a flaccid state.

Helmholtz [1862] described the membrane as pulled tight but slightly curved outward at its edge and so constructed that a decrease in external pressure should increase this curvature. A large inward change in curvature at the center should produce a pronounced change just inside the fibrocartilaginous edge, where a circular layer of fibrous tissue strengthens the membrane. The circular fibrous layer is thickest close to the manubrium attachment. Between these two regions this layer is partially missing. Just within the fibrocartilage ring this layer ends abruptly.

On the hypothesis that adjoining modifications in tissue structure reflect the usage to which they are put, the circles of maximum strength in the eardrum indicate the regions of maximum deflection, and intermediate regions nearly devoid of reinforcing material indicate regions of minimum deflection.   The question then arises: does the tympanic membrane resemble a diaphragm subjected to partitioning into characteristic nodes and antinodes following the distribution of the reinforcements in the circular and radial fibrous layer?   An answer may be obtained by considering the eardrum as if it were a shallow conical shell.

Modes of Vibration of a Conical Shell

Owing to the difficulties involved in a mathematical analysis of a vibrating shallow conical shell, the analysis of its vibrations will be presented with the aid of a model.

An ideally rigid disk inserted in an infinite flat wall may be driven by an alternating force of constant magnitude at all audible frequencies. Under these circumstances it is found that the driving force is opposed by (a) the inertia of the disk and a certain quantity of air set in motion by the disk, and (b) the radiation of acoustic energy.   The first acts like a mass reactance, and the second like a mechanical resistance.   The mass of the disk is constant, but the mass of the air set in motion decreases with rise in frequency and at high frequencies becomes negligibly small.

If a disk is used as a model the resistance due to sound radiation is negligibly small. The acoustic output of a 20-cm disk, for example, is found to be constant up to 1000 cycles, after which it diminishes to 1/100 of this value at 8000 cycles.   It is, therefore, unsuited for reproduction of speech or music because, in the upper register, the acoustic output falls away too rapidly on account of the relatively large mass of the disk with its corresponding reduction of velocity.   For constant acoustic output its velocity should be the same for all frequencies, but unfortunately its velocity decreases inversely as its frequency.   Since acoustic power varies as the square of the velocity, its acoustic output thus decreases as the square of the frequency.   At high frequency its acoustic output is therefore very small.

Modifying the flat disks to a shallow cone structure improves the output at high frequencies.   A 20-cm (diameter), free-edged paper cone driven as an electrodynamic loud speaker exhibits radial modes of vibration which start below 100 cycles (McLachlan [1936]).   These may be suppressed by crimping and reinforcing the edge.

In commercial loud-speaker cones the radial modes of vibration are suppressed as much as possible, leaving the concentric nodal circles shown in Fig. VII–5 to function. These begin to be present at about 2000 cycles and then again at 5000 cycles.

The nodal circles occurring in such a narrow frequency range give the conical loud speaker a more pleasant tone than a disk loud speaker. If the paper cone is too stiff, however, its stiffness accentuates the higher frequencies, giving speech reproductions a harsh swishing quality.

Figure VII–5 shows the successive shapes of a homogeneous loss-free conical shell vibrating in the first and second center-moving symmetrical modes, in vacuo. Note particularly that on the forward thrust of the center a buckling action travels down the cone.

The response characteristics of the cone may be further modified by altering the apical angle and by adding circular corrugations and changing its construction so that its resonance quality is highly damped and its upper frequencies are more or less accentuated. These changes

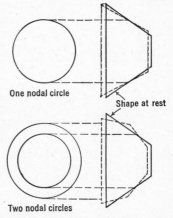

One nodal circle

Shape at rest

Two nodal circles

Fig. VII–5. The successive shapes of a vibrating conical shell.

produce a very complex response structure whose method of vibration is not completely understood. This model somewhat resembles the eardrum except that it is too symmetrical.

If the tissue structure of the eardrum is an indication of its response characteristics, the tympanum can be considered to be a shallow conical membrane which through adaptation has developed a structure possessing two nodal circles, of reinforced fibrous tissue. These allow the surface to attain its characteristic bowed structure under tension.

To complicate matters, the membrane is unsymmetrical in shape and unsymmetrically loaded by the attached malleus. The loud speaker is therefore only a very rough approximation of a very complex unsymmetrically loaded membrane whose response characteristics still await solution.

TYMPANIC DISPLACEMENTS

The tympanic membrane according to Geffcken [1934] possesses a greater relative stiffness for low frequencies than for high frequencies. Békésy's [1936] measurements show that, at a pressure of 9800 dynes/cm^2 and a frequency of 10 cycles, a tympanic displacement of 0.2 to 0.4 mm is

produced.   This very large deflection is detected as a tickle in the middle
ear due to one of the ossicles making contact with the tissue in the
cavity.   This sensation is the *threshold of feeling* and is experienced just
before the painful feelings, due to dangerously loud noises which may
cause injury to the aural membrane in the cochlea (Fig. VII–6).

To visualize what this means we may consider a gunner standing in the
midst of heavy ordnance gunfire.   He will be subjected to an amplitude
of air pressure equal to about 0.25 mm.   The air amplitude of nearby

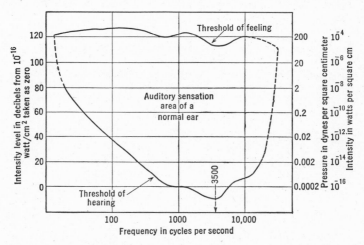

FIG. VII–6.   Intensity thresholds of the average human ear at various frequencies.

thunder is estimated at 0.1 mm.   For comparison, some measurements
by Shaw [1905] show that a telephone vibrating at 256 cycles will produce an audible tone when its double amplitude is 7×10^{-6} mm.   At
comfortable loudness it attains a total displacement of 0.0005 mm, and
at excessive uncomfortable loudness a value of 0.01 mm.

The displacement of the tympanic membrane at the threshold of
audibility of a 1000-cycle tone is, as previously shown, 8×10^{-10} cm.
At 2000 cycles Wilska [1935] found the tympanic membrane to move only
10^{-9} cm, and at 10,000 cycles 5×10^{-9} cm.   Of special interest is the
fact that at the threshold of hearing (Fig. VII–6) the movements of the
eardrum are of atomic dimensions.

If the response to amplitude changes is so microscopic, is it possible
for a human ear to be aware of the Brownian movement of the individual
air molecules that produce fluctuations in pressure on the eardrum?   An
approximate answer is found in some work by Sivian and White [1933],
who calculated that the mean pressure change caused by thermal noises
at ordinary temperatures are just below the threshold of audibility.   It

was estimated that the order of magnitude of these pressure changes was 10^{-5} dyne/cm^2. It has been found experimentally that the ear mechanism responds to as little as 10^{-2} dyne/cm^2 at 3000 cycles (Geffcken [1934]), which limit places the thermal noises just out of the response range.

Overall Response of the Acoustic Mechanism

The natural overall frequency of the human ear lies between 800 and 1500 cycles. By mounting miniature mirrors on the tympanic membrane, Békésy [1936] was able to show by means of a reflected light beam that explosive noises containing many intense harmonics were communicated to the malleus in a very suppressed form. When the overtones of the membrane were not excited, the natural response frequency of the membrane was highly damped. The logical conclusion is that this is due to the retarding force of the air, the internal friction of the diaphragm, and the frictional resistance introduced by the attached malleus and its suspensory ligaments.

In a specific example the natural frequency was found to be about 1400 cycles. There was a complete cessation of vibration after about 0.004 second. We may conclude that the overall vibration of the aural mechanism is highly but not quite critically damped.

Middle-Ear Mechanism

The mechanical function of the middle ear is to transfer the energy incident on the eardrum to the cochlear fluid of the inner ear. It is accomplished by means of a small pressure spread over the comparatively large area of the tympanic membrane, which converts it into a large pressure spread over a corresponding small area in the form of the footplate of the stapes where it makes contact with the cochlear fluid. If only a transfer of vibrations were desired, a much simpler mechanism would have sufficed, such as is found in reptiles and birds, in which the fundamental plan is a bone (columella) connecting a membranous window in the skull to the oval window set in the bony casing of the labyrinth (Beatty [1932]).

In discussing the biophysical transformer properties of the mechanism of the middle ear the tympanic membrane with its malleus and attached tympanic tensor will be treated as the first unit; the incus with its attached stapes and tensor stapedius as the second unit; and the footplate of the stapes inserted in the flexible ring of the oval window as the third unit.

THE MALLEUS

As the name implies, the malleus is a mallet-shaped bone. It has a handle and an irregular pestle-shaped head. The head (capitulum) is separated from the handle (manubrium) by a constriction, the neck (collum), to which the tendon of the tympanic tensor is attached.

Figure VII–7 shows the detailed construction of an average malleus, as adopted by Stuhlman [1937] for a comprehensive study of the transmission characteristics of the ossicle chain.

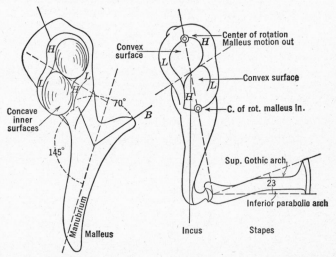

FIG. VII–7. Details of structure and articulation of malleus, incus, and attached stapes. To visualize their articulating positions, rotate malleus 180° to the right, placing concave surfaces over convex surfaces of incus. (Stuhlman [1937].)

The average mass of a malleus was found to be 23 mg. The average overall distance from the end of its processus brevis to the end of the manubrium or handle was about 5.8 mm. Its axis of rotation for small angular displacements was taken as passing through its center of gravity in the neck and continuing anteriorly through the anterior suspensory ligament. The length of the manubrium lever arm was taken as 3 mm.

The posterior surface of the head of the malleus possesses an 8-shaped double-socket concave facet where it articulates with the incus in corresponding convex surfaces to form an interlocking " saddle-shaped articulation."

TENSOR TYMPANI

The tympanic tensor may be considered as pulling inward and functioning as an equilibrator to govern the tension on the tympanic membrane and on the suspensory and capsular ligaments. This tensor and the one attached to the stapes pull in opposition to keep the articulating surfaces between malleus and incus in variable coupled contact. The effective magnitude of their tensions determines the characteristics of the transmitted energy from the tympanum-malleus to the incus-stapes transmission units.

The tensor tympani (Fig. VII–8) is a long, narrow muscle lying in a bony canal acoustically insulated until it almost reaches the tympanic cavity. Here it becomes converted into a round tendon (T) which passes through an eyelet to bend at right angles and terminates in the neck of the malleus opposite the lateral process.

If the tympanic tensor is stimulated to contract, it pulls inward, forward, and upward, thus applying tension to the lower segments of the tympanic membrane and to the ligaments attached to the malleus. The ligaments supporting the malleus are the anterior, the external, the superior, and the capsular ligaments bridging the malleus-incus articulation. If the tympanic tensor is under tension, the capsular ligament is under tension, a condition which pulls the malleus-incus articulating surfaces apart. This produces a loose coupling at this joint. As the tension on the tympanic tensor is reduced, the coupling becomes greater. If the tensor is cut, the coupling is maximal. Ossification of this joint produces rigid coupling.

It has been shown by Köhler [1910] and others that in man the aural muscles exhibit a reflex response to acoustic excitation of the eardrum. The pressure variation on the eardrum stimulates these muscles to contract. The effect of this contraction on the transmitted wave form will be discussed after the discussion of the part played by the stapedius tensor on the overall response of the mechanism. As a preliminary statement it may be said that the contraction of the interaural muscles reduces the overall sensitivity of the receptor mechanism for low frequencies and increases the ability to pass high frequencies.

Protection against rupture due to a sudden large increase in pressure, such as would be caused by a sharp blow over the ear by means of an open hand, is obtained from the articulation between the malleus and the incus, which can dislocate so that the excessive pressure is not communicated to the stapes. Under these circumstances the articulation acts as a protective device and the tensor as a snubber to prevent the drum from being pulled out too far as the result of the sudden external decompression.

THE INCUS

The incus is the auditory ossicle inserted between the malleus and the stapes. It has almost the shape of a molar tooth (Fig. VII–9). The

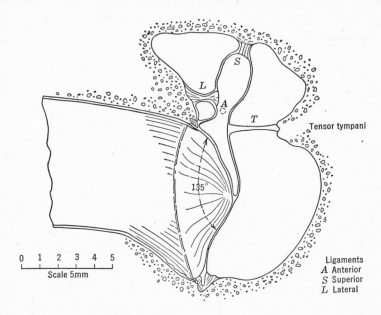

FIG. VII–8. Detailed scale structure of the attachments of the malleus and tympani. View of left ear. (Stuhlman.)

long crus lies about parallel to the manubrium of the malleus but behind it. The end of its long crus is turned up at an angle of about 23°. It terminates at the point where it articulates with the head of the stapes in the lenticular process, which is a planoconvex lenslike button with its rounded face set in a shallow socket at the top of the stapes. Its short crus is a compression member set practically at right angles to the face of the malleus-incus articulation. Its blunt end rests in a shallow hole, the fossa incudis of the tympanic cavity.

The incus is supported by two ligaments. The superior ligament extends from the top of the incus to the roof of the tympanic cavity, and the posterior, which is a short dense ligament attaching the end of the short crus, to the fossa incudis.

The average mass of this bone was found to be 27.5 ± 2.5 mg (Stuhlman [1937]). The angle between the short crus and long crus was found to be 85° to 90°. The incus has an average overall height, measured along the axis of the long crus, of 7.0 mm, and a horizontal length through the axis of the short crus of 5.0 mm. Its center of gravity lies 5.0 mm above the lenticular process on the axis of the long crus.

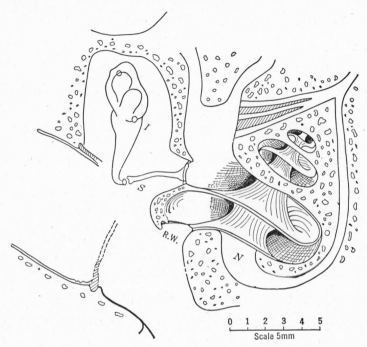

Fig. VII–9. Scale detailed structure of the incus (*I*) and attached stapes (*S*) with footplate inserted into its oval window. Note round window (*R. W.*) in the acoustic shadow of waves that may originate from vibrating ossicles and tympani. The section through the cochlea is taken just posterior to the axis of the modiolus. The acoustic nerve enters the modiolus at *N*. View of left ear with the section containing the malleus and tympani, whose edges are shown, removed. Figure VII–8 may be superimposed on this figure to give correct position of the ossicles. (Stuhlman.)

Mechanical Advantage of the Malleus-Incus Articulation

The malleus has a figure-8 convex articular surface, covered with cartilage, and the incus a corresponding concave surface; a capsule encloses these surfaces. Figure VII–7 shows these two surfaces with their liplike ridges, which are mirror images of each other. The ridges are higher at *H* and lower at *L*. The two rounded surfaces fit into each other like a shallow ball-and-socket joint and make close contact when the muscles are relaxed. This close-fitting position will be referred to as the locked or close-coupled position of the malleus-incus articulation.

In this locked position of the malleus-incus joint the manubrium lever arm is to the incus lever arm as 1.27 to 1. If the malleus-incus joint is coupled so that separation can take place, two centers of rotation develop in the faces of the articulation.   If the malleus moves outward, the center of rotation is located below the superior edge of the incus (Fig. VII–7), and on inward motion of the malleus a similar center of rotation is developed at a diagonally opposite point lying at the lower edge of the articulating surface.   The lengths of the lever arms malleus to incus on outward motion are 1 to 1; on an inward motion, nearly 2 to 1. These changes in length of the lever arms produce distortions in any symmetrical alternating force applied to the end of the manubrium. The degree of asymmetry depends on the rigidity of coupling of this articulation.

COUPLING

When two mechanisms are so placed or interconnected that energy may be transferred from one to the other they are said to be coupled. The extent to which mechanisms are coupled is expressed by the coupling coefficient.

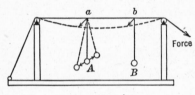

FIG. VII–10.

A simple piece of apparatus illustrating the factors governing the degree of coupling is shown in Fig. VII–10.   It consists of two uprights across the tops of which is fastened a string.   From the string at a and b are suspended two pendulums A and B; their lengths are adjustable, and they can be slid along the supporting string so that the points of support a and b can be varied.

Each of the pendulums has a natural period of its own, and as the pendulum swings it tends to make the other pendulum oscillate also.   If A is pulled to one side, bob B being stationary, it will pull the point of support, a, sidewise, and this pulls point b sidewise with it.   This induced motion of b will gradually set bob B into motion.

The coupling of the two pendulums depends, for a given length of pendulum, on the distance apart of the points of support a and b, and on the tension of the supporting string.   The greater the separation of a and b, the smaller is the coupling.   The greater the tension in the string between a and b, the smaller is the coupling.   In the transfer of the energy from A to B it can be observed that periodic variations in amplitude (beats) occur unless the coupling is small and highly damped.   Favorable conditions for beats to develop occur with large coupling and loose connections between a and b.   The transfer of energy from the first mechanism to the second and then back again is not marked as long as the coupling is kept small.   The transfer is then too slow for any appreciable surging to take place.

TRANSMISSION CHARACTERISTIC OF THE MALLEUS-INCUS ARTICULA-
TION

It was shown by Stuhlman [1937] that the malleus-incus articulation
functioned as an asymmetrical non-linear transmission mechanism except for very small displacements. He constructed an accurate 20-to-1
scale model of the ossicles so that their rather complicated relative motions

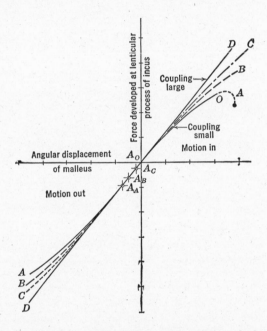

FIG. VII–11. Experimental transmission characteristics of the malleus-incus
coupling obtained from a 20 × model. Shift of the operating point of the characteristics from A to C shows increased coupling. The linear characteristic D indicates
rigid coupling. The typical basic operating curve for the malleus-incus articulation
is sigmoid shaped, as A, where the dotted line shows unstable condition attained as a
result of a slight dislocation when force directed inward becomes too large. (Stuhlman [1937].)

could be analyzed. Within the limitations set by the model in simulating the correct suspensions and articulations, it was found that, when a
simple vibratory motion was impressed at the end of the lever arm of
the malleus, it was transmitted to the end of the long crus (lenticula
process) of the incus after having undergone both asymmetrical and
non-linear distortion on passing through the malleus-incus articulation.

A characteristic family of transmission curves for various degrees of
coupling of the malleus-incus articulation is shown in Fig. VII–11. The
basic curve A is sigmoidal in shape. The upper branch, because of

inward motion of the eardrum, showed a discontinuity at the point O due to the dislocation of the joint at large deflections. The lower branch, because of outward motion, approached the displacement axis asymptotically for very large displacements of the lever arm of the malleus. The displacement of the malleus in this direction is limited by the tympanic tensor. The curve A has a point of inflection, A_0, at the origin. This point will be referred to as the symmetrical operating point. For small deflections the malleus displacement is a linear function of the force transmitted to the lenticular process of the incus. Under these operating conditions the malleus-incus articulation contributes no distorting component.

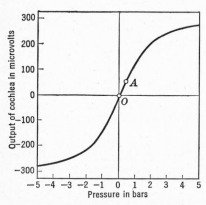

Fig. VII–12. Form of transmission characteristic proposed by Stevens and Newman [1936] to account for the bio-electric asymmetrical behavior of the ear.

A similar sigmoid operating curve (Fig. VII–12) was proposed by Stevens and Newman [1936] to explain the electrical response of the cochlea with changes in sound pressure on the tympanic membrane.

If the curve of Fig. VII–11A can be considered as the normal response characteristic of the malleus-incus articulation, then variations introduced into the slope of the curve and position of the operating point by changes in coupling of this articulation become functionally important. The linear relation, curve D, between malleus displacement and the force developed at the lenticular process of the incus was obtained when the malleus-incus joint was pressed together with sufficient force so that no slip was possible; this is the locked or close coupling position. Under these circumstances both stapedius and tympanic tensors are slack. As the malleus-incus articulating faces were allowed to slip progressively more freely, with respect to each other, curves C, B, and finally A were developed. In A the malleus-incus joint was loosely coupled. Such a condition can arise only when both tensors are applying sufficient antagonistic tension to separate the malleus-incus joint to the extreme position allowed by the capsular ligaments of the joint.

EFFECTS OF COUPLING ON THE CHARACTERISTIC TRANSMISSION CURVE

The family of transmission curves shown in Fig. VII–11 shows the results obtained with successively smaller coupling in the order D to A.

When the coupling became smaller, the characteristic not only developed a more asymmetrical shape but also shifted its operating point A more and more from its normal position A_0. This departure from linearity on shift is due to the interplay of the lipped edges upon which the malleus-incus joint moves with change in stiffness of the capsular ligament of the malleus-incus junction. Since the effective forces which produce the separation between malleus and incus are the interaural tensors and the elastic reactions of the capsular ligaments surrounding the joint, the asymmetrical non-linear transmission of the wave forms through the malleus-incus articulation must be progressively emphasized as the effective tension on the malleus-incus joint is increased (smaller coupling).

Evidence to support such a view can be found in the experimental work of Crowe [1932], who found that, when the tensor tympani of a cat was put under mechanical tension, as the load increased from 5 to 20 grams, the low-frequency sounds were more and more suppressed. Finally, for a load of 50 grams only frequencies above 2048 cycles were transmitted. This information confirmed many of the earlier experiments which indicated that, the greater the contraction of this tensor, the higher the pitch of the sounds heard.

If increased tension of the tensor tympani suppresses low-frequency reception, it should follow that decreased tension as obtained by cutting the tympanic tensor should favor low-frequency transmission. Bunch and Raiford [1931] showed experimentally that loss of transmission of high tones resulted from the cutting of the tensor tympani.

A change in coupling is also produced by a change in pressure of the external air. A temporary low-tone deafness is experienced when one rapidly descends in an elevator or enters a long vehicular tunnel which is subjected to pressure ventilation. Under these circumstances the tympanic membrane is first driven inward by the higher pressure, as if an increase in tension of the tympanic tensor had taken place, which produces low-tone deafness. Relief is afforded by swallowing, which opens the Eustachian tube and allows the pressure in the middle ear to increase to that prevailing in the outer ear canal.

The two interaural muscles normally function in opposition so that at various acoustic intensities the effective coupling of the malleus-incus joint is changed. The cutting of the tympanic tensor must produce an operating malleus-incus characteristic that is very asymmetrical and even very non-linear for low intensities. Figure VII–13A and B shows the progressive changes that may be expected in the output of a linear response mechanism as the slope of the characteristic changes with progressively smaller coupling. When the slope is 45° the impressed

wave is altered in neither amplitude nor shape.   If, however, the slope
is greater or less than 45°, the transmitted amplitude is magnified or
suppressed but the wave shape is not distorted.

If the characteristic becomes non-linear but remains symmetrical
with respect to the point of inflection A_0, which functions as the operating point, then the impressed wave form will be delivered as a symmetrically distorted wave whose
amplitude is enlarged or reduced
according to the slope of the characteristic. For very small amplitudes
this characteristic reproduces the
wave form as if it had the properties
of a linear characteristic because of
the small changes in slope just above
and below the operating point A_0.
On the other hand, if the operating
point lies on the lower or more pronounced non-linear part of the curve
so that the point of inflection A_0 has
been moved up, as shown in Fig.
VII–13D, then the transmitted wave
form is unsymmetrical both in shape
and amplitude.

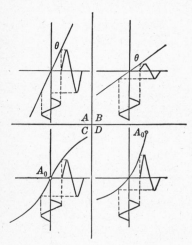

Fig. VII–13. A and B show a
linear characteristic of a coupled
mechanism. Input wave form plotted on y axis. Output wave form
on x axis. A shows amplification,
no distortion, angle θ less than 45°.
B shows an input-output 1 to 1 relation, θ equal to 45°. C and D characteristics are non-linear. C is non-
linear but symmetrical. The output
wave form is symmetrically distorted.
D is non-linear and asymmetrical.
The output wave form is unsymmetrically distorted.

That contraction of the interaural
muscles changes the efficiency of
transmission, i.e., changes the amplitude of the output which is comparable to producing a change in slope
of the malleus-incus characteristic,
is supported by the experiments of
Wiggers [1937]. Wiggers investigated
the effect of contraction of the intraaural muscles on sound transmission
in anesthetized guinea pigs and found
that in the frequency region 250 to 1000 cycles the efficiency was reduced when the muscles were under tension.   In the range 1000 to
1200 cycles no measurable change in intensity took place, and the frequency range 1300 to 1800 contained a peak of maximum efficiency at
1500 cycles where contraction augmented the efficiency in the transmission mechanism.

For a working hypothesis, the change in slope of an intraaural characteristic may be attributed to a change in intensity, and the shift of the

characteristic through the origin of coordinates to a change in the transmission frequency of the acoustic wave.

The degree of coupling of the malleus-incus joint must of necessity be governed by the ability of the muscles to react to the acoustic stimulations. Thus, the data gathered by Bunch [1929] and later confirmed by Montgomery [1932] indicate that with increased age the ears lose some of their high-tone responsiveness. At advanced age the transmission deafness of high tones is very pronounced, but the loss may be comparatively little for low frequencies. If with increased age the intraaural muscles cannot produce the necessary tension, the malleus-incus articulation functions as a close-coupled joint favoring the transmission of low frequencies.

Since the stapedius muscle and the tensor tympani muscle function antagonistically to produce an effective overall tension of the ligaments of the malleus-incus capsule, it follows that if the tendon of the tympanic tensor is cut, so that the effective tension can be produced only by the stapedius muscle, the result would be the production of an operating characteristic with an asymmetric large coupling factor which is favorable to the passage of low frequencies of high intensities. The experiments by Stevens, Davis, and Lurie [1935] on the localization of pitch perception on the basilar membrane, when the tensor tympani muscle had been inactivated, showed that the intense low tones which were transmitted very efficiently were responsible for disrupting the organ of Corti from the aural membrane.

On the whole the experiments seem to indicate that large coupling of the malleus-incus articulation due to the relaxation of the intraaural muscles and consequent close fit of the articulating surfaces is favorable to the passage of low-frequency, low-intensity sounds, whereas contraction of the intraaural muscles, producing a looser-coupled malleus-incus joint, is favorable to high-frequency, high-intensity transmission.

THE STAPES

The stapes is a stirrup-shaped bone (Fig. VII–14) having a head (*capitulum*), and an arch formed by the posterior and anterior *crura*, mounted on a kidney-shaped footplate. The head is connected with the lenticular process at the end of the long crus of the incus, with which it forms a ligament-covered, shallow-socket-and-hemispherical-ball articulation.

Inserted into the capitulum (C), close to the articulation of the lenticular process of the incus (I), is a tendon (T). The stapedius muscle makes its exit at the apex of a bone pyramid and pulls the tendon and attached head backward (posterior) and down (inferior).

The configuration, mass, structure, and size of the stapes are surprisingly uniform in adult man. Its average mass was found to be 2.5 mg (Stuhlman [1937]). Its average overall height is about 4.0 mm. The kidney-shaped footplate is 3.2 mm long and has a maximum width of 1.4 mm through its minor diameter, which lies off center towards its anterior edge (Fig. VII–14). It has an average area of 3.2 sq mm, confirming Wrightson and Keith's [1918] measurements on European source material.

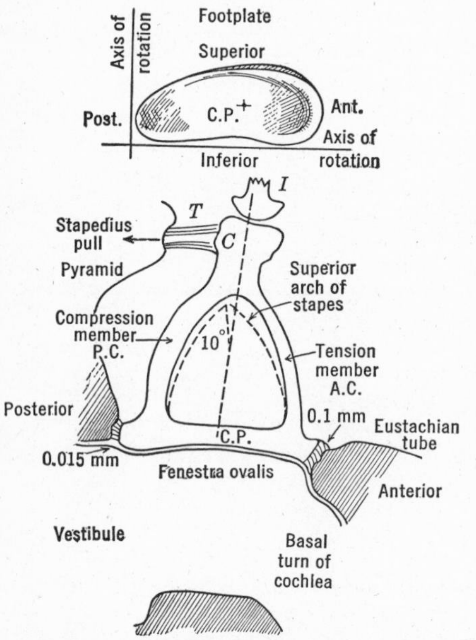

Fig. VII–14. Semi-diagrammatic view of stapes and footplate where it makes contact with the vestibular fluid. Note shading on footplate to indicate that anterior-superior edge is thickest. Diagrammatic position of stapes set in its oval window. Note position of posterior end of arch in its depressed position while its anterior end is under tension. The inferior arch is under pressure while its superior or Gothic arch is under tension. The axis of pressure is the broken line; it passes through the center of pressure C. P. in the footplate. Relative tilt of superior arch about 10° posterior.

Two hollow U-shaped crura form the arch, the capitulum forming the keystone. The arch is composed of a thick posterior crus (P.C.) the compression member, and an anterior (A.C.) less rugged crus which acts as a tension member to accommodate displacements, of a rolling variety, hinged at the posterior and inferior ends of the footplate.

The superior arched surface of the stapes forms a slightly elongated parabolic arch; the inferior arch takes the form of a slightly compressed parabolic curve.

The capitulum is bent down 23° and about 10° backward, but the footplate is set at right angles to the feet of the composite arch.

A thrust directed at the capitulum by the lenticular process tilts the footplate diagonally inward, the inferior and posterior edges acting as hinges. This thrust is the compression factor to which the much stronger parabolic arch reacts. On out motion of the lenticular process, a tension is applied to the capitulum and thence to the more fragile superior arch; this force tilts the stapes around the same hinges but outward.

The stapedius muscle pulls the capitulum in the inferior-posterior direction, thus sinking the inferior and posterior edges of the footplate into the oval window to a depth determined by the length of its annular ligaments. This pull of the stapedius tensor places the posterior crus of the stapes under compression and the anterior crus under tension. An unsymmetrical, pestle-like rolling motion (Stuhlman [1937]) applied to the capitulum by the lenticular process of the incus can therefore be duplicated by the footplate as it rests under the tension of the stapedius tensor in its oval window.

The structure of the stapes is such that it can readily conform to the two modes of vibration attributed to it by Békésy [1936]. One of these he observed to be a rocking motion about a major axis of the footplate at high acoustic pressures, which was observed suddenly to change to a rocking motion around the posterior end of the footplate at low acoustic pressures.

The kidney-shaped footplate of the stapes is set in an annular ligament about 3 mm thick which connects its margin with the adjacent wall of the oval window (*fenestra vestibuli*). The elastic ligaments bridging the gap, according to Wrightson and Keith, have the average dimensions shown in Fig. VII–14. Of special significance is the fact that the anterior ligaments are about ten times longer than the less active posterior ligaments.

Movements of the Stapes

In its rest position, with no tension on the stapedius tensor, the footplate is held by its ligaments in a nearly vertical plane with the convex edge of the plate in the superior position. Under contractile action of the stapedius tensor the inferior and posterior margins are pushed into the window, while the superior and anterior margins are pulled out to the limits set by the width of the annular ligament. These movements are illustrated in Fig. VII–15. The resultant diagonal motion of the capitulum carries the attached lenticular process of the incus with it and pushes the posterior end of the short crus of the incus into a shallow depression (*fossa incudis*) where a fan-shaped ligament anchors this end of the incus to the fossa in the posterior wall. This motion puts the ligaments of the malleus-incus articulation under tension, producing the previously discussed loose-coupled malleus-incus joint.

On inward motion of the lenticular process, the capitulum is put under compression, raising and pushing the stapes in the anterior direction. This compression pushes the superior and anterior edge of the footplate into the oval window. To resist the stresses of this complex motion, the inner surface of the footplate has developed, where it makes contact with the cochlear fluid, compensating surface reinforcements. The shading (Fig. VII–16) shows the thickened parts where the bone structure possesses these reinforcements.

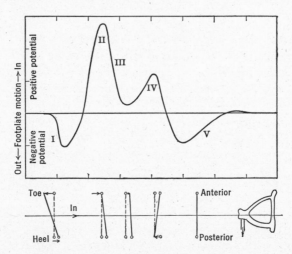

Fɪɢ. VII–15.   This graph shows the changes in potential at the apex of the cochlea from data by Wiggers [1937].   The lower diagram shows the correlated positions of the footplate proposed to account for the successive changes in potential observed by Wiggers.

Cochlear Microphonics

That the compressional waves communicated by the moving footplate to the vestibular fluid excite the aural membrane to set up an electric potential, which may be detected in the acoustic nerve, was first discovered by Wever and Bray [1930].   That the cochlea develops an independent electrical potential synchronized with the pressure gradient set up by the motion of the footplate was discovered by Saul and Davis [1932].

Of special importance in the interpretation of the cochlear microphonics is the discovery by Davis et al. [1934] that the inward movement of the stapedial footplate created a positive change of potential and the outward movement a negative potential at the cochlear apex.   This discovery led Wiggers [1937] to follow experimentally the changes in potential that took place at the apex of the cochlea as the motion of the footplate slowly executed a complete cycle of positional changes.   He found, for example, that when the acoustic wave arrived at the eardrum the stapedius muscle contracted.   This contraction caused an outward movement of the footplate, cocking the stapes for action.   Fifty milliseconds later the tympanic tensor contracted, overpowering the stapedius contraction and forcing the footplate inward. This subjected the interscalar fluid to a steep pressure gradient at the footplate. The stapedius then relaxed, permitting the tympanic tensor to push the footplate further inward. The tympanic tensor then relaxed, and finally the elastic recoil of the supporting structure shifted the footplate back into its normal position.

If Wiggers' interpretation of the electrical response data is correct, it should be borne out by the structural characteristic of the stapes and its possible degrees of freedom of motion under the action of the interaural muscles as shown in Fig. VII-15.

I. The stapedius tensor contracts. The footplate moves outward, and as a result a small increase in negative potential is developed at the apex of the cochlea.

Mechanically, when the stapedius tensor contracts, the heel (posterior margin) of the footplate is pushed in, and the toe (anterior margin), suspended by longer ligaments than those attached to the heel, is pulled out further. Since the structure of the arch is not symmetrical, the stapedius contraction forces the superior margin out and the inferior margin in. This diagonal thrust produces an effective outward excursion of the footplate. All these movements are shown diagrammatically in Fig. VII-15.

II. The tympanic tensor contracts and overpowers the sustained stapedius contraction. The footplate is forced inward. A positive potential is generated.

Mechanically, when the tympanic tensor contracts and overpowers the stapedius contraction, it pushes the footplate in. The heel, set for maximum displacement, cannot move further in, but the toe can be pushed in with the accompanying production of a positive electrical potential at the cochlear apex.

III. The high positive potential rapidly drops to zero after the footplate has attained its initial inward displacement. The fluid in the cochlea must adjust itself via the helicotrema, reducing the electrical potential to zero.

IV. The stapedius tensor relaxes. The tympanic tensor continues to contract and thrusts the anterior edge of the footplate as far inward as the length of the annular ligaments permit, thus creating a second positive potential at the apex.

After the tension of the stapedius tensor has fallen to zero, the toe of the footplate is displaced farther inward until it reaches its elastically limiting position. This excursion is not so great as the previous positive one and will, therefore, produce a smaller positive potential.

V. The tympanic tensor relaxes and the footplate shifts to its normal position, producing a negative potential.

Mechanically, the plate returns to its normal position in two steps. The tympanic tensor relaxes, and the toe of the plate returns to its normal position. Then the restoring forces of the ligaments pull the heel back to its normal position. The negative potential generated by this double movement of the fluid in the cochlea should be electrically separable, and it may account for the complexity of the fifth phase of Wiggers' electrical response curve.

The conclusion is that Wiggers' cochlear microphonic action data parallel the possible motions of the stapes without violating any of the mechanical degrees of freedom of its structural characteristics.

INTERNAL EAR

The petrous portion of the temporal bone contains two mechanisms, the vestibule and the cochlea. The vestibule consists of a series of organs which concern the maintenance of positional equilibrium. The anatomically closely related, though physiologically entirely separate, bony cochlea is a two-and-one-half-turn hollow canal having a spirally converging radius. This hollow spiral bony coil has a base whose diameter is about 6 mm (Keen [1939]); its second turn is about 4 mm in diameter, and the diagonal distance from its apex to the upper margin of the oval window is about 6 mm; its altitude is about 5.5 mm. The spiral is wound around a hollow cone of bone called the *modiolus*, along the axis of which runs the auditory nerve. An inner spiral shelf of bone extends about two thirds the way across the canal, dividing it nearly equally into an upper and a lower portion (Fig. VII–16). Attached to the edge of this bony shelf are two membranes connected to the outer wall of the canal so that the upper canal is divided throughout its length into two ducts. The duct nearest to the apex is called the *scala vestibuli*; the triangular middle duct, limited by the two membranes and the outer wall, is known as the *scala media*. The canal nearest to the base is called the *scala tympani*.

The gap between the inner spiral shelf and the outer wall is bridged by the firm, fibrous *basilar membrane*. The very delicate non-vascular membrane stretching from the spiral shelf obliquely outward to the bony wall of the cochlea is called *Reissner's membrane*. The scala media has for its diagonal ceiling the Reissner membrane and for its floor the acoustic membrane supporting the cells of Hensen and the organ of Corti.

The scala tympani below, and the scala vestibuli above, the scala media extend spirally from the base to the apex of the cochlea. At the apex they are united by the *helicotrema*, a small hole about 0.4 sq mm in area.   From this apex the two canals diverge with an approximate constant increase in diameter, as shown in Fig. VII–9.   The scala tympani ends abruptly in a pocket just below the oval window.   A round hole, covered by a fibrous membrane, the *round window*, separates this terminus of the scala tympani and the cavity of the middle ear.

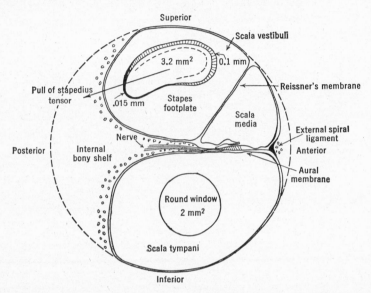

FIG. VII–16.   Diagrammatic section of the cochlea showing the relative positions of the footplate of the stapes and the round window with respect to the scala media and aural membrane.   Note relative width of ligaments of superior-anterior edge of footplate and relative size of footplate and round window with respect to position of the scala media.

The scala vestibuli is connected at its base to the saccule and utricle. In the outer wall of the bony vestibule is inserted the fenestra vestibuli (oval window) closed by the footplate of the stapes, whose annular membrane permits motion of the footplate without allowing the escape of the perilymph filling these canals (Fig. VII–16).

The scala media is an endolymphatic tubular sac.   At the apex of the cochlea it ends in a blind extremity: its basal end forms a blind pouch between the oval window and the round window.   It is connected with saccule and utricle by a small canal through which its hydrostatic pressure is adjustable.   The density of its fluid is 1.034 grams/cc at 37° C and its viscosity 0.0197 cgs units (Békésy [1933]).

The floor of the scala media is the acoustic membrane.   It is composed of the basilar membrane, the cells of Hensen, the organ of Corti, and the tectorial membrane.

TECTORIAL MEMBRANE

The tectorial membrane extends the whole length of the scala media. It is described by Hardesty [1908] as consisting of a hyaline matrix, probably keratin, in gelatinous form, in which are embedded numerous fine fibers or threads of uniform size. It is slightly elastic and semi-

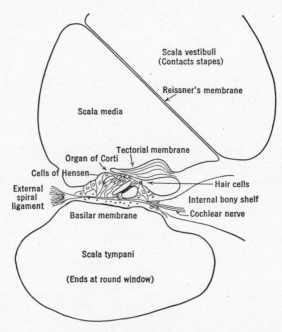

FIG. VII–17. A section through the cochlea showing how the tectorial membrane rests with its lower surface on the hair cells protruding above the surface of the organ of Corti. The basilar membrane is under tension. Its fibers extend from the internal bony shelf to the external spiral ligament. Note how the lower surface of the basilar membrane is reinforced to resist distortion. This composite group of tissues is referred to as the aural membrane.

solid, and possesses marked adhesiveness. Its density is only slightly greater than that of the endolymph in which it is submerged. In the pig it is about five times as wide and five times as thick in the apical turn as at the basal end. Its apical section has an area about twenty-one times and a volume ninety-five times the area and volume at its basal end. Its free liplike margin (Fig. VII–17) rests lightly upon the hair cells of the organ of Corti.

ORGAN OF CORTI

The end organ of the auditory nerve is represented by the organ of Corti. It consists of highly differentiated neuroepithelium whose specialized cells are arranged in an invariable pattern extending from its base to the apex of the cochlea.

The superficial area of the organ has projecting above its surface an inner row and three to five outer rows of auditory cells terminating in a brush of cilia (hair cells) presumably projecting through a cuticular membrane. There are about 3600 inner and about 18,000 outer hair cells. The free margin of the tectorial membrane overhangs and rests upon these hair cells. Presumably, any movement of the tectorial membrane can be transmitted to the hair cells. An adequate stimulus for their tactile nerve endings is not so much a change in pressure as a deformation of the surface in which they are embedded.

In evaluating the sensibility of any tactile area it is important to remember that the hairs themselves form very effective tactile organs, for there is a dense group of nerve fibers around the root of each hair. A force applied to the free end of a hair acts on the long end of a lever with the fulcrum at the surface of the membrane, so that a much greater force can be developed at the root of the hair to distort the tissues in which the ends of the acoustic nerve fibers are embedded.

BASILAR MEMBRANE

The basilar membrane is the membranous structure upon which rests the epithelium of Corti's organ. Hardesty [1908] describes it as a flat tendon strengthening the floor of the scala media. Its lower surface is covered by a continuation of the lining membrane of the scala tympani. Its intermediate layer is made up of tendinous bands which span the gap between the inner margin of the bony spiral lamina and the margin of the external spiral ligament.

The internal bony shelf (modiolus) has its greatest width at the beginning of the basal turn, from which point its width rapidly diminishes towards the apex of the cochlea. The gap to be spanned by the basilar membrane (Fig. VII–18) is relatively small at the beginning of the basal turn of the scala media but progressively widens as the apex of the cochlea is approached. The shortest and thickest fibers bridging the gap to form the basilar membrane are consequently located at the base of the cochlea near the fenestra ovalis. The average length of the fibers in the basal turn is 0.21 mm, increasing to 0.34 mm in the middle and to 0.36 in the apical turn. The total spiral length of the organ of Corti and its

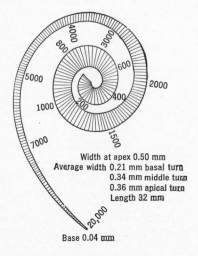

Width at apex 0.50 mm
Average width 0.21 mm basal turn
0.34 mm middle turn
0.36 mm apical turn
Length 32 mm

Base 0.04 mm

FIG. VII–18. The basilar membrane as it ascends the cochlea widens from 0.04 mm at its base to about 0.50 mm at the apex. This scale diagram shows the membrane projected into the plane of the paper. The numbers show the positions of maximum response at the frequencies indicated.

supporting membrane is about 30 mm. Figure VII–18 shows the average dimensions and shape of the human basilar membrane.

The outer spiral ligament which maintains the tension on these fibers is stronger and heavier at the base and thins away to a few strands at the apex. The fibers of the basilar membrane stretched between this ligament and the inner edge of the spiral bony shelf are straight, smooth and without branches, forming a tough elastic base upon which the arches of the Corti organ rest. It is supposed that when this membrane yields the arches of Corti rock to and fro, thus causing the hairlets to bend with the torque applied by the lightly touching tectorial membrane. From this point of view, the arches of Corti must act as levers magnifying the motion of the tectorial hairs, which in turn probably excite a mediator to initiate the nerve impulses which are conveyed by the acoustic nerve to the brain.

MECHANICS OF THE COCHLEA

Broadly speaking, the incompressible fluids filling the membranous labyrinth are bounded by the rigid bony walls of the cavity. A gradual pressure applied by the footplate, at the base of the scala vestibuli, to the cochlear fluid must displace the perilymph through the helicotrema into the scala tympani. This fluid displacement causes the membrane of the round window to bulge into the middle-ear cavity. The very small diameter of the helicotrema prevents a volume displacement of the fluid for all pressure changes except the slowest.

An impulsive force impressed by the footplate upon the fluid at the basal end of the scala vestibuli must travel across the membrane of Reissner and the endolymph in the scala media to reach the aural membrane. After crossing this membrane, and the basilar membrane which supports this structure, the impulse must travel down the perilymph of the scala tympani and out at the round window. The resulting pressure gradient across the scala media may cause the tectorial membrane and organs of Corti to bend about their inward edges where they are supported by the inward edge of the internal cochlear bony shelf.

The aural membrane, composed of the supporting basilar membrane, loaded at its upper surface by the Corti organ and tectorial membrane, and bounded at its lower surface by the tissue lining of the scala tympani, contains the necessary mechanical elements to act as a highly damped mechanism responding to the impulsive forces passing over it.

THE HELMHOLTZ RESONANCE THEORY OF HEARING

The conception of the cochlea as a resonating response mechanism will always be identified with the name of Hermann von Helmholtz. Helmholtz states definitely in the third edition (1870) of his work, *Die Lehre von den Tonempfindungen,* that " any exciting tone would set that part of the membrane into sympathetic vibration, for which the proper tone of one of its radial fibers, that are loaded with the various appendages already described, corresponds most nearly with the exciting tone; and thence the vibrations will extend with rapidly diminishing strength on to the adjacent parts of the membrane."

This statement indicates that what Helmholtz pictured was the division of the basilar membrane into vibrating areas, with regions of maximum intensity of vibration at their centers, and not the selective vibration of independent fibers of the basilar membrane. Before an adequate theory of hearing can be developed, the contributions of the aural mechanism to the subjective phenomena of loudness and pitch must be explained.

The counterpart of loudness is the intensity or pressure presented to the ear by the medium in which the ear is immersed. Loudness to intensity is not a 1-to-1 relation; it is an approximate logarithmic relation. A *decibel notation* has been adopted to express these logarithmic magnitudes.

DECIBEL SCALE

In the study of the relation between the strength of a stimulus and the amount of the experienced sensation, it is found within restricted limits, that an appreciable change of the sensation is brought about by a corresponding change in the stimulus. Thus an increase in the experienced sensation (ΔS) is proportional to the increase in stimulus (ΔI). If the just-perceptible differences in sensation are assumed to represent equal amounts of sensation, it is found that it takes less stimulus to produce this increment in sensation at low than at high sensation levels, so that the experienced increment in sensation (ΔS) is inversely proportional to the stimulus (I). Combining these two into a mathematical statement, we may write

$$\Delta S = k \frac{\Delta I}{I}$$

where k is the constant of proportionality. In consequence of this statement we deduce, by summing both the sensation and the stimulus from their minimum threshold values to the maximum values attained by each, that

$$\sum_{S_0}^{S} \Delta S = k \sum_{I_0}^{I} \frac{\Delta I}{I}$$

so that

$$S - S_0 = k \,(\log I - \log I_0)$$

When the stimulus I is I_0, the experienced sensation is (minimum) threshold; i.e., $S_0 = 0$. Then

$$S = k \,\log_e \left(\frac{I}{I_0}\right)$$

where k is a constant whose magnitude depends on the kind of stimulus and also upon the kind of receptor used to measure the stimulus. In the case of sound the value of k varies only with the frequency of the source for a normal ear excited at moderate intensities.

The above statement is known as the psychophysical law of Weber-Fechner. It states that when the experienced sensation is increased by equal amounts (in arithmetic progression) the stimulus must vary in a geometric progression. The experienced sensation must therefore vary as the natural logarithm of the stimulus.

Except in precision work or at great intensities it is assumed that the response of the aural mechanism follows very closely such a logarithmic scale. Thus, as the intensity level of the sound field rises, the amount of power required to develop successive aural responses becomes increasingly greater. Such a scale is started at the intensity level I_0, where the ear first experiences a sound sensation, i.e., the " threshold of audibility " identified by the contour marked 0 in Fig. VII–19.

As the intensity rises, an upper limit of loudness is eventually reached where the experienced loudness is replaced by a tickling sensation in the middle ear which sensation is rapidly followed by pain. This limit is called the " threshold of feeling." Intensities producing the sensations of pain, if maintained over too long a period of time, may cause injury to the aural membrane of the cochlea.

The experienced loudness sensation depends on the power in the acoustic waves presented to the ear, the frequency of these waves, and the sensibility of the ear. The relation between these determining factors is represented graphically in Fig. VII–19. The lower curve

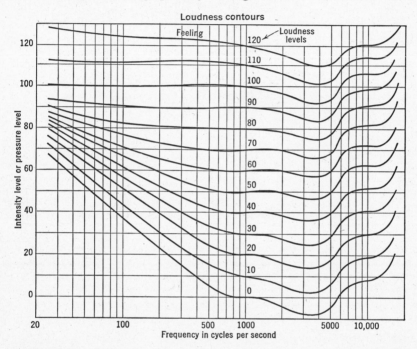

FIG. VII–19. Loudness contours of pure tones as adopted by the American Standards Association, February, 1936. (By courtesy of the American Standards Association, New York.)

represents the threshold of audibility of a normal ear; the upper curve, the threshold of feeling. The sensation level of a sound presented to the ear is the number of sensation units it is above the threshold level or threshold of audibility.

Suppose that a 1000-cycle acoustic vibration reaches a normal ear at an intensity level below the threshold of audibility. As the intensity of the acoustic waves is gradually increased, the threshold of audibility is reached. At this point the intensity level is I_0, and the experienced loudness $L = 0$. The intensity is progressively increased so as to produce successive equal increments (ΔL) in loudness. It is found that at first the change in intensity to produce this increase is very small, but that at greater loudness levels the intensity must get progressively larger and eventually increase enormously to produce the same change in loudness. The change in intensity to produce these equal increments in loudness may be written

$$\Delta L = L_1 - L_2 = k \log_e \left(\frac{I_1}{I_2} \right)$$

Unfortunately, logarithmic tables to the base e are not as convenient to use as logarithmic tables to the base 10; therefore for convenience we write

$$\Delta L = k' \log_{10} \left(\frac{I_1}{I_2} \right)$$

where k' includes k and the conversion factor which changes base e to base 10. Since the intensity is proportional to the square of the pressure, we may write

$$\Delta L = 2k' \log \frac{p_1}{p_2}$$

where the root-mean-square pressure variation corresponding with the threshold of audibility at 1000 cycles is taken as 0.0002 dyne/cm^2 ($p_0 = 2.8 \times 10^{-4}$ dyne/cm^2), or in power units as 10^{-16} watt/cm^2 as in Fig. VII–6.

The most convenient choice of the intensity or pressure that may be used as a standard for comparison depends on the problem under consideration. In the auditory sensation area of Fig. VII–6, the intensity line corresponding with 1 dyne/cm^2 was used in the literature before 1936 as the zero level; i.e., both p_2 and the constant were chosen as unity.

If, however, I_1 and I_2 are the two different amounts of power to be compared, then the logarithm of the ratio (to the base 10) is a dimensionless unit designated as a " bel," a name adopted in honor of Alexander Graham Bell. Its origin is traced to the telephone engineer's use of a " mile of standard cable " or the actual level of sound which existed after signals from a telephone transmitter had passed through a mile of telephone cable. Subsequently, when a unit was needed to express the rates of the smaller acoustical quantities, the " decibel," which is $\frac{1}{10}$ of 1 bel, was used. The decibel notation is now simply a convenient means of expressing a gain or loss ratio and does not signify any definite physical unit. It has no meaning unless a reference level and the units in which the reference level is measured are designated.

As an illustration of its use, let us examine what happens to a culture of some germs which has multiplied itself 100,000 times. We may say that its mass has increased in the ratio of 100,000 to 1 or 100,000 times. Instead of expressing this ratio increase in such large numbers, we will apply the decibel system of notation. The "germ gain" can be expressed as follows:

$$\text{Germ gain} = \log_{10} \frac{\text{Total germs at the finish}}{\text{Total germs at the start}}$$

$$= \log_{10} \left(\frac{100,000}{1}\right)$$

$$= 5$$

In this notation we say that we have a germ gain of 5 bels or 50 db above total germs at the start instead of a 100,000 ratio gain.

If the group of germs continues to increase until a quantity 1,000,000 has been reached, the germ gain in decibels is $10 \times \log (1,000,000) = 60$ db. Thus, the mass of germs has increased 900,000 units, while in the decibel notation it has increased from 50 db above threshold to 60 db above threshold, or a 10-db germ gain. In other words, as the level of the germ mass rises, the additional germs needed to effect equal germ gain increase is not the same, and an increasingly greater quantity of germs is required to cause an equal germ gain increase.

The American Standards Association [1936] adopted 10^{-16} watt/cm^2 as representing the lowest intensity that a 1000-cycle sound may have and yet be just audible by a normal ear. This value is used as a standard reference level of acoustic power.

If the intensity of an acoustic disturbance of 1000-cycle frequency (Fig. VII–6) increases from 10^{-12} watt/cm^2 to 10^{-6} watt/cm^2 above threshold, then in the decibel notation it has increased from an intensity level of 40 db above threshold to an intensity level of 100 db above threshold, or an intensity gain of 60 db has taken place.

If the acoustic waves presented to the ear had a 100-cycle frequency, the examination of Fig. VII–19 would reveal that the above intensity gain would have carried the tone from threshold to the 97-db loudness level.

The decibel notation uses the average speech power as the zero decibel level. The level of very loud speech would then be designated as +20 db, of weak speech as −20 db, and of a just audible whisper as −40 db from this average speech power level. The speech power gain from a whisper to very loud speech is therefore about 60 db.

A change in power level of a sound by 1 db is approximately the smallest that the ear can detect. This is known as the "sensation unit."

The sensation level of any identified sound is the number of sensation units above its threshold level for audition. The sensation units are not expressed in the decibel notation, but the sensation level is.

TABLE VII–2

Intensity Level decibels above 10^{-16} watt/cm^2	Power Ratio	RMS Sound Pressure dynes/cm^2	Intensity microwatts/cm^2
120 Thunder	10^{12}	$2 \times 10^{2.0}$	10^{+2}
Artillery gunfire			
110 Airplane engine	10^{11}	$2 \times 10^{1.5}$	10^{+1}
100 Riveters 35 ft away	10^{10}	$2 \times 10^{1.0}$	10^{0}
90 Elevated train on open	10^{9}	$2 \times 10^{0.5}$	10^{-1}
structure			
80 Heavy street traffic	10^{8}	2×10^{0}	10^{-2}
Full orchestral music			
70 Busy street	10^{7}	$2 \times 10^{-0.5}$	10^{-3}
60 Very loud speech	10^{6}	$2 \times 10^{-1.0}$	10^{-4}
50 Quiet automobile	10^{5}	$2 \times 10^{-1.5}$	10^{-5}
40 Average speech	10^{4}	$2 \times 10^{-2.0}$	10^{-6}
Average office			
30 Average dwelling	10^{3}	$2 \times 10^{-2.5}$	10^{-7}
Cough			
20 Weak speech	10^{2}	$2 \times 10^{-3.0}$	10^{-8}
10 Whisper	10^{1}	$2 \times 10^{-3.5}$	10^{-9}
0 Heart murmurs	10^{0}	$2 \times 10^{-4.0}$	10^{-10}

The measurement of sound intensity in the decibel notation, it must be emphasized, presupposes a standard of reference intensity since the decibel scale must always represent the relation of one intensity (power, pressure) to another. This standard level of reference is the threshold of hearing of a 1000-cycle pure tone taken as 10^{-16} watt/cm^2 comparable to a root-mean-square pressure of 2×10^{-4} dyne/cm^2.

Some typical noises and sounds evaluated in terms of a decibel notation are shown in Table VII–2.

LOUDNESS

One of the attributes of the sensation experienced by listening to a source of sound which is changing in amplitude is a change in loudness. The experienced loudness of a pure tone, a subjective phenomenon, may be altered also by changing the frequency of the vibrating source. The experienced loudness is therefore a function of two physical variables, intensity and frequency.

Loudness may be defined as that attribute of the experienced auditory sensation in terms of which sounds may be ordered on a scale from " very faint " to " very loud." Using such a scale, a listener experiences great difficulty in deciding exactly how much louder one sound is than another. Fletcher and Munson [1933] suggested a method of obtaining a rational loudness scale on the idea that the experienced loudness " is cut in half " when only one ear is used for listening to a sound.

In order to establish a base for a loudness scale a standard simple harmonic source, having a frequency of 1000 cycles, excited at an intensity level of 40 db above threshold, and listened to with both (normal) ears, was chosen, and to it was assigned an arbitrary basic loudness of 1000 phons. That the loudness range above this level is sufficiently extensive may be judged from the fact that the loudness experienced from the 40-db source is equal to about $\frac{1}{3}$ of 1 per cent of the maximum loudness the human ear can withstand.

SCALE OF LOUDNESS

An observer is asked to listen to the 1000-cycle, 40-db-above-threshold reference tone with the aid of earphones, using one ear. He is then asked to use earphones over both ears and adjust the intensity level of the reference tone until the loudness is the same as that experienced with one ear. It will be found, for instance, that an intensity level of 33 db, when heard with both ears, matches the loudness experienced by the observer when listening to the 40-db intensity level when one ear was used.

If listening with one ear cuts the loudness in half, then it follows that an intensity level of 33 db is subjectively experienced as one half as loud as an intensity level of 40 db. Consequently, if a loudness unit of 1000 phons is assigned to an intensity of 40 db, then 33 db must be assigned to a loudness level of 500 phons. In a similar way it is found that an intensity level of 49 db is experienced as a loudness of 2000 phons and a 73-db intensity level as a loudness of 10,000 phons. Therefore the standard sound is judged ten times louder at the 73-db than at the 40-db level. Comparable data are then developed similarly for other loudness levels.

THE LOUDNESS FUNCTION

The above data are used to construct a graph representing the loudness function. In Fig. VII–20 are shown results of how the loudness of the 1000-cycle reference tone changes with its intensity level. In a similar way other frequencies may be explored, giving an essentially different, though analogous, graphical relation. These data unquestionably prove that the normal ear is a reliable loudness meter.

It has been found by Stevens and Davis [1938] that the data representing the 1000-cycle loudness function quite accurately expresses the

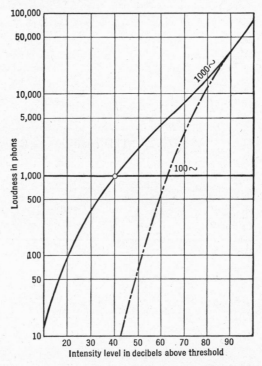

FIG. VII–20. The loudness function. This shows how the experienced loudness varies with the intensity of the stimulus at the frequencies indicated. These standard curves were adopted from data by Fletcher and Munson [1933]. (By courtesy of the American Standards Association, New York.)

data for the frequency range 700 to 4000 cycles. In general, at lower frequencies loudness increases faster than in the higher range of audible frequencies for the same change in intensity. Thus an increase in intensity of 20 db (50 to 70 db), i.e., a tenfold increase in pressure amplitude of the sound stimulus of a 100-cycle tone (Fig. VII–20), will increase the loudness fifty fold, but for the 1000-cycle tone this change produces only a fourfold increase in loudness. In general, in the 100- to 4000-cycle frequency band (vowel sounds 300 to 2500 cycles) at an intensity level of about 60 db, the high-frequency tones are heard as much as ten times louder than the low-frequency tones.

These results have an important bearing on the electrical reproduction of musical and vocal selections from phonograph records and the loudness levels at which loud speakers should be used. It is well recognized that in the reproduction of music by electrical devices the original quality of the selection can be duplicated only if the reproduction is made at the same intensity level as the rendition. If reproduction is made at an intensity below the intensity level of rendition, the selection heard appears to have lost its low-frequency tones, and the selection sounds thin and unimpressive. Reproduction at too high an intensity level is experienced as a dull rendition because of the overemphasized low tones.

Equal-Loudness Contours

The experienced loudness varies not only with the intensity but also with the frequency of the source. This condition was first mentioned in connection with the threshold of audibility curve. To show how the intensity level varies with frequency when the loudness level is maintained constant, the results of experiments obtained by Fletcher and Munson [1933] must be examined. They found that two tones of different frequencies are not heard equally loud unless they are presented to the ear at different intensity levels. The precise relation between loudness and frequency was discovered by plotting what are called equal-loudness contours, that is to say, by determining at what intensities tones of different frequencies are experienced as equal in loudness to a standard tone (1000 cycles) at various intensities. These contours are shown in Fig. VII–19.

The lowest contour, marked zero, is the same as the threshold curve for minimum audible pressure shown in Fig. VII–6. The curve marked 40 indicates the loudness level (not loudness) in decibels of the 1000-cycle tone above threshold. All frequencies lying on this curve must be raised to intensity levels indicated by the magnitudes of the ordinates, so that they are experienced as having the same loudness as the 1000-cycle reference tone.

Effect of Masking on Loudness

The loudness of a tone of constant intensity and frequency is modified by the presence or absence of other tones. The natural inclination of a person is to raise the pitch of his conversation and shout when surrounded by the noise of a machine shop or of a running airplane engine, or when conversing in large indoor social gatherings.

In these situations the low frequencies of the general noise mask the high frequencies of the voice very effectively. To compensate for this masking effect the person wrongly increases the intensity and often raises the frequency level of the shouted conversation. To make the best of the situation the voice should be pitched below the predominant frequencies of the masking noise because low tones are not effectively masked by the high-frequency content of the general background or masking noise.

In general, it has been found that if an observer is surrounded by a constant source of noise the noise does not mask all frequencies the same amount. Low-frequency tones mask high-frequency tones far more effectively than high tones mask low ones.

Masking is also very pronounced when two tones lie close together in frequency. If their frequencies are only slightly different, the masking is so pronounced that only beats are heard.

Pitch

The attribute of a sustained simple harmonic vibration of changing frequency incident on the eardrum is experienced as a change in pitch.

The words frequency and pitch are not interchangeable, because pitch is not uniquely determined by the frequency of the stimulus. The human auditory mechanism possesses a frequency characteristic which is a function of the magnitude of the driving force.

That the pitch of a pure tone depends on its intensity can be verified by asking an observer to reproduce vocally the pitch of a tuning fork, middle C, when the fork is held at various distances from the ear. It will be found that when the fork is held close to the ear the pitch of the voice reproducing the tone is slightly lower than when the fork is held at some distance from the ear. Apparently, the observer hears the louder tone as lower in pitch.

Pure tones of low frequency decrease in pitch as the intensity increases, whereas high-frequency tones increase in pitch with increase in intensity. Experimental results (Stevens [1935]) show that the frequencies at which the perceived change in pitch with change in intensity is least lie in the band to which the ear is most sensitive, i.e., around 2000 cycles.

According to Békésy [1936], an observer experiences his first sensation of pitch at a frequency of excitation of 18 cycles. At this frequency one suddenly passes from the perception of a succession of impulses to a single fused sensation which may be designated as a tone. This may be called the fusion frequency of pitch perception. The upper limit of pitch perception cannot be determined with great precision on account of the marked variation with age of the individual ear. The upper limit is usually set at 20,000 cycles.

Numerical Scale of Pitch

The " mel " is the subjective unit of pitch adopted from the root of the word *melody*. A pitch of 1000 mels is arbitrarily assigned to a pure 1000-cycle tone of 40-db intensity above threshold; to the pitch of a tone sounding half as high as 1000 mels a pitch of 500 mels is assigned. To a tone sounding half as high as 500 mels a pitch of 250 mels is assigned, etc.

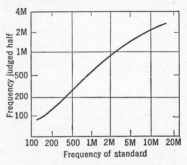

On the assumption that it is possible quantitatively to judge that " this pitch is half as high as the former one," a numerical scale of pitch has been constructed by Stevens, Volkmann, and Newman [1937]. The change in pitch was measured by allowing the observer to identify alternately the pitch of two pure tones maintained at a fixed loudness level. One was maintained at a fixed frequency, and the second could be varied

FIG. VII–21. This shows the frequency of a tone which sounds half as high in pitch as a standard tone of another frequency (Stevens, Volkmann, and Newman [1937]). (By courtesy of Stevens and Davis, *Hearing*, John Wiley & Sons, New York.)

in frequency by the observer until its pitch was identified as half the pitch of the fixed-frequency source. The results showed, for instance, that a tone whose pitch sounded half as high as the standard 1000-cycle frequency was adjusted by the observer to a frequency of 440 cycles. Figure VII–21 shows how an observer adjusts the frequencies of the variable tones so that they may be experienced as half the pitch of the standard tones. With the aid of this curve the pitch function can be constructed.

Pitch Function

To the standard 1000-cycle source sounded at 40 db above threshold was assigned a pitch of 1000 mels. To the 440-cycle source was assigned a pitch of 500 mels, and similarly to all other values of the invariable frequencies may be assigned pitches comparable to the experiences of the observer. The relation between frequency and pitch may therefore be obtained by plotting at an assigned loudness level these two quantities in a coordinate system giving the pitch function shown in Fig. VII–22.

This curve very definitely shows that the frequency-pitch reaction is not a 1-to-1 correspondence. Of particular value is the fact that below a frequency of 1000 cycles the rise in the experienced pitch with increased frequency of the source is less marked than at high frequencies; therefore, the range of any experienced musical interval is greater at higher than at lower pitches. For example, the octave 256 to 512 cycles is experienced as a pitch range varying from 250 to 400 mels, but the high-frequency-range octave 1024 to 2048 cycles extends from a pitch of 700 to one of 1000 mels.

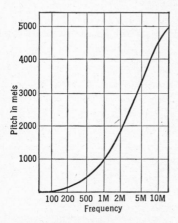

FIG. VII–22. The pitch function. This shows how the experienced pitch of a tone (mels) changes as a function of the frequency of the stimulus. This graph was developed at a loudness level of 60 db. (Stevens, Volkmann, and Newman [1937].) (By courtesy of Stevens and Davis, *Hearing*, John Wiley & Sons, New York.)

RESOLVING POWER OF THE EAR

If two equally intense tones are sufficiently close together in frequency so that the ear is able to experience them as two just-differentiable pitches, the limits of pitch resolution of the ear is attained. The sensitivity of the ear to small changes in pitch at very low intensities of stimulation (just above the threshold of sensitivity) is comparatively small. As the intensity increases, the ear becomes more sensitive to small changes in frequency until, at 80 db, a 1000-cycle stimulus (Shower and Biddulph [1931]) can be distinguished from an equally intense source of 1003 cycles as a difference in pitch.

Such a minimum detectable change in frequency is called by psychologists the difference limen (DL). The size of a difference limen not only is a function of the frequency of the tone presented to the ear but also depends on its intensity. The difference limens have been found to differ greatly not only among different observers but also under different experimental conditions for the same observer.

The ability to resolve two neighboring pitches, or the resolving power, is equal to the reciprocal of the difference limen. It has been found that the resolving power increases with increase in intensity. It should follow that for binaural listening, through which the loudness is doubled, the resolving power should be greater than for monaural listening processes. This difference is verifiable from the experiments by Shower and Biddulph [1931], who also found that at frequencies below 500 cycles the difference limens are approximately constant except for frequencies below 45 cycles, where aural subjective harmonics are introduced, especially at the larger excitation intensities. In the whole audible frequency range of 20 to 20,000 cycles, at the loudness level excited by 40 db above threshold, 1500 different pitches are distinguishable. The maximum number of changes in pitch, amounting to 1800, are experienced along the 60-db loudness contour. The resolving power of the ear at a conversational loudness level of about 40 db is about three times as great as at the loudness level of whispered conversation.

DURATION OF STIMULUS TO PRODUCE PITCH SENSATION

It has been shown experimentally that when the sounding stimulus has a frequency of 1000 cycles at least 12 cycles are necessary to produce a sensation of pitch and at 10,000 cycles not less than 250 cycles are needed. At 1000 cycles the tone must persist for at least 0.012 second, and at 10,000 cycles for 0.025 second, before the pitch sensation is built up.

TABLE VII-3

These data show how many seconds a tone of a given frequency must last to produce its pitch sensation.

Frequency of Source	Duration in Seconds	Number of Waves Required to Give Pitch Sensation
50	0.060	3
200	0.022	4.4
500	0.014	7
1,000	0.012	12
2,000	0.012	24
5,000	0.015	75
10,000	0.025	250

Bürck, Kotowski, and Lichte [1935].

The experiments of Bürck, Kotowski, and Lichte [1935] show to what extent a time element is involved for the identification of pitch. This time element (Table VII-3) is smallest in the frequency range 1000 to 3000 cycles, where it is about 0.01 second. During this time a minimum number of compressional disturbances must impinge on the eardrum before the pitch of the incident frequency can be identified. The time of adjustment of the interaural mechanism to frequency response is apparently a minimum in the range of greatest aural sensitivity and takes place more rapidly for high than for low frequencies. This may be attributed to the variation of pitch response in time to the reflex of the interaural muscles. As pointed out in a previous section, muscular tensile equilibrium is attained in 0.010 to 0.016 second with the tympanic muscular contraction predominating at high frequencies and high intensities. Under these conditions the coupling action of the aural mechanism is small and will as a result exclude any surges in the transmitted energy. If the coupling is large because of loose ossicle connections, and if the time of adjustment is long, the surges set up in the system may produce aural harmonics.

AURAL HARMONICS

A harmonic is a component of a complex periodic disturbance possessing a frequency which is an integral multiple of the fundamental frequency. Aural harmonics are subjective tones. They are heard when very loud tones are impressed on the eardrum. They are introduced as a result of the nonlinear and asymmetric transmission characteristics of the mechanism of the middle ear and cochlea.

When, for example, the source of sound is a 200-cycle pure sinusoidal wave of sufficient intensity (30 db), a careful observer can, in addition to the fundamental pitch, identify the pitches corresponding with the harmonic frequencies 400 and 600 cycles. When two simple harmonic frequencies excite the aural mechanism simultaneously, it is possible to experience a group of subjective combination tones in addition to the two fundamental tones. They are the aural harmonics called summation and difference tones.

AURAL HARMONICS AS CONDITIONED BY INTENSITY

It was shown by Fletcher [1929] that when a pure tone of 256 cycles was presented to the ear the second harmonic was identified when the intensity of the fundamental reached a sensation level of 30 db, the fourth at about 48 db, and the fifth at about 60 db above threshold. For frequencies above 1000 cycles no harmonics were heard until the sensation level had reached 50 db above threshold.

Owing to the fact that the threshold-of-hearing curve (Fig. VII–19) is concave upward, a constant physical intensity level at different frequencies represents different sensory loudness levels, so that at low frequencies the higher harmonics are heard relatively more pronounced because the ear is more sensitive to them than to the lower fundamental. If the fundamental has a high frequency, the aural harmonics accompanying it fall in the very high-pitch range where the ear is less sensitive; hence, one hears them less loud than the fundamental.

Direct measurements of the magnitude of the aural harmonics were obtained by Stevens and Newman [1936] by observing the microphonics produced in the cochleas of cats' and guinea pigs' ears. These experiments indicate that the pressure disturbances which cause the eardrum and ossicle chain to move and impress these motions on the cochlear fluids generate a fluctuating electrical potential in the cochlea, simulating the mechanical wave disturbance in intensity and frequency.

The cochlear potentials can be detected by observing the change in potential of a pair of electrodes, one of which is placed on the round window and the other in contact with some other part of the animal. These cochlear potentials are amplified so that their amplitudes may be measured and their frequencies determined by means of a vacuum-tube wave analyzer, tuned to respond to any component of the generated electrical potential wave form. The cochlear potential has now been found to be only a rough measure of the sensation level of the stimulus.

Figure VII–23 shows the results of an analysis of the cochlear microphonics obtained by Stevens and Newman [1936] from a cat's ear when stimulated by a pure tone of 1000 cycles at successive higher intensities. Of special interest is the fact that, as the intensity of the stimulus increases, the fundamental (first harmonic) and the third and fifth harmonics maintain their relative response magnitudes with respect to each other throughout the range of intensity, but the second and fourth harmonics decrease after passing through a maximum of response at the higher intensities of stimulation.

The fundamental was found to possess the greatest magnitude at all stimulus intensities. It increases almost linearly until a maximum saturation value is reached, where an increase in stimulus produces no further increase in response.

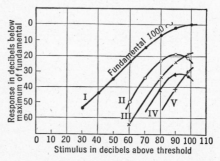

FIG. VII–23. Analysis of the cochlear microphonics obtained from a cat's ear. Stimulating tone 1000 cycles. Horizontal axis represents intensity of stimulus above average human threshold. The upper curve is the response to the fundamental, and the lower curves are higher harmonics which appear as the intensity increases. (Stevens and Newman [1936].) (By courtesy of Stevens and Davis, *Hearing*, John Wiley & Sons, New York.)

When the potential generated in the cochlea was analyzed at a sensation level of 60 db, it was found that the second harmonic had a magnitude about 20 db smaller than the fundamental, the third harmonic possessed a magnitude as much as 35 db below the fundamental, and the fourth and fifth harmonics were negligibly small.

Stevens and Newman attribute the change in even harmonic content to changes in the tension of the muscles of the middle ear, and they suggested that this change in tension does not appreciably change the magnitude of the odd harmonics. They found that, when the tendinous attachment of the tympanic tensor muscle of a cat was cut at a point near the eardrum, the second-harmonic content was increased without an appreciable change in the third-harmonic content.

Since the two interaural muscles control the degree of coupling of the malleus-incus joint, it should follow that when the tensor tympanic attachment is severed the resulting malleus-incus coupling depends exclusively on the tension of the stapedius tensor. This tension produces a loose connection between the malleus and incus, resulting in large coupling which would allow the coupling mechanism to pass any generated surges. Among these the low-frequency harmonics (the second harmonic) are therefore enhanced.

Beat Frequencies are Aural Harmonics

The sum and difference frequencies are often called beat frequencies. Thus, if frequencies of 2000 and 3000 cycles simultaneously excite the eardrum and then pass through the non-linear aural mechanism, there will be present in the output not only the two original frequencies but also frequencies of 1000 (3000 − 2000) and 5000 (3000 + 2000) cycles.

The presence of these tones is a necessary consequence of the type of characteristic operating curve attributed to the ear by Stevens and Newman (Fig. VII–12) and subsequently verified experimentally by Stuhlman (Fig. VII–11).

The Response Characteristics of the Aural Membrane

The aural membrane was defined as the elastic structure separating the scala media above from the scala tympani below the basilar membrane. It is a highly damped structure in which the acoustic nerves terminate. Its upper structure is composed of the tectorial membrane resting on the organ of Corti, which in turn is supported by the basilar membrane lined on its lower side with the epithelium of the tympanic mucosa.

An important aspect of the aural membrane as a resonating structure is its damping factor. This membrane is closely coupled to the fluids which cover its anterior and posterior surface. Since the damping factor of the overall auditory mechanism is about 50 milliseconds, the amplitude of a wave traveling through the ear as a whole, after the cessation of the incident vibration, falls to $1/e = 1/2.718$ of its initial value in

50 milliseconds. As pointed out previously, the transmission mechanism possesses inertia and resistance. Measurement of the damping factor of the aural membrane itself is, of course, practically impossible since the membrane is closely coupled to the organ of Corti, the attached tectorial membrane, and the tissues lining the scala tympani. If the aural membrane is considered as a whole, the viscosity of the adjoining fluids must produce a high degree of damping, and evidence from the cochlear microphonic measurements of Saul and Davis [1932] leads to the belief that it is very highly damped.

To produce a sharp resonance of the aural membrane it is necessary that the resistance of the membrane be small and the damping negligible. If the resonance is poor because of a large resistance, the system is said to be highly damped, so that the peak of resonance is less sharp.   In consequence, this poor resonance does not lead to a high degree of selectivity on the part of the resonance mechanism. On the other hand, with small damping and its accompanying high degree of selectivity, time is required for a resonance system to come to a steady state in response to an applied force.

A person is not conscious of appreciable sensations of sound which persist after the external wave has ceased to function. The fact that a discontinued sound is heard to last only about 50 milliseconds is proof of the great damping undergone. This leads one to discount the popular idea sometimes attributed to Helmholtz that the aural membrane acts like a set of tuned resonators strung out in series on the basilar membrane.

REBOUL'S HYDRODYNAMIC THEORY

If the cochlea is treated as a hydraulic tunnel in which a strip of longitudinal wall is elastic, simulating the aural membrane, then the necessary conditions for a selective response mechanism with a large damping factor, are present.

Reboul [1938] suggested that the response of such a hydrodynamic system could be assumed to follow the mathematical analysis of a hydraulic system contained in a cylindrical vessel with elastic walls along which a pressure disturbance is propagated.

The response mechanism of the cochlea tube can then be pictured as follows. The compressional wave starting at the oval window, caused by an inward movement of the stapes, travels up the scala vestibuli towards the helicotrema. The scala media and its aural membrane may be considered as an elastic floorplate having a high damping factor.

According to Reboul's analysis, which contains reasonable assumptions about the property of the liquid, the elastic membrane can undergo maximal displacements at positions on its surface governed by the frequency of the pulses traveling up the canal. Pressure gradients can be produced across the membrane, the locations of which are also determined by the frequency. Reboul showed that if the compressional wave starting at the stapes had a steep wave front, such as is associated with high-frequency excitation, then the greatest pressure distortions of the membrane took place in the basal turn of the cochlea. At low frequencies it took place in the apical turn. Samples of the calculated pressure distribution in these wave forms are shown in Fig. VII–24.

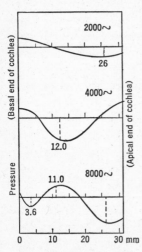

FIG. VII–24. Reboul's [1938] calculated curves showing the positions of maximum pressure gradient in the cochlea. The positions on the aural membrane of the maximum pressure gradients are indicated by the dotted lines.

An important item in the analysis is the speed of propagation of the pressure pulse distorting the elastic and highly damped floorplate. The calculated speed of propagation was found to be approximately 50 meters per second. This low velocity is possible because of the wall effects which enter the calculations in the form of frictional factors introduced by the rapidly decreasing dimensions of the tube and the drag of the elastic membranes, which become progressively thicker and wider as the apex of the cochlea is approached.

That such a low velocity can exist is supported by experimental evidence. The existence of a slow-traveling cochlear wave was verified by Békésy [1933]. From his data one may conclude that a wave pulse introduced at the basal end of the cochlea travels to the apical end with a speed of 20 to 30 meters per second. The speed is larger at the stapes and smaller at the helicotrema. The experimental time interval between the arrival of a sound at the eardrum and its arrival at the round window was found to be not greater than 0.1 millisecond. If the impulse had traveled via the helicotrema with a speed of 25 meters per second, it would have taken 2.4 milliseconds to pass through the 60-mm path of fluid. Since it took only 0.1 millisecond, it must have short-circuited across the aural membrane at a point lying 0.12 mm from the basilar end. This evidence indicates that the pressure gradient of the hydraulic impulse short-circuits across the aural membrane to reach the round window.

In this way a response area due to an 800-cycle frequency was located at a point one and one half turns from the base of the cochlea while the response area due to a very low frequency was localized at the apex of the cochlea. A composite picture of the location of various frequency response areas on the aural membrane is given in Fig. VII–18 with an indication of the width of the basilar membrane.

That the aural membrane is subjected to intense localized stresses as the impulse travels across the scala media is also supported by Reboul's data shown in Fig. VII–24. The calculated positions of maximum pressure disturbances are compared with the experimental positions on the basilar membrane, located by lesions which were produced by long-continued acoustical stimulations. Various experimenters agree that lesions can be found at 5, 11, and 17 mm, respectively, from the basilar end of the cochlea, for frequencies 8192, 4096, and 2048 cycles. The calculated values are found at 3.6, 12, and 26 mm for frequencies 8000, 4000, and 2000 cycles. These are in good enough agreement with the experimental results to justify the hope that a place theory of frequency reception due to localized stresses produced by pressure gradients may eventually be supported by further experimental evidence.

NERVE RESPONSE AS RELATED TO LOUDNESS AND PITCH

The average experienced pitch ranges from 20 to 20,000 cycles per second. There are approximately 3500 hair cells in the inner row of the organ of Corti and about 20,000 divided among the three outer rows. They are quite evenly spaced along the aural membrane. Each inner hair cell is innervated by one or two nerve fibers, and each nerve fiber makes connections with one or two hair cells (Lorente, de Nó [1933]). The maximum number of impulses per second that a nerve fiber can carry is nearly 1000. This maximum frequency response is imposed, as was shown in the previous chapter, by what is called the " refractory period " of the nerve fibers. After a nervous impulse has passed along a nerve, there is an absolute refractory phase, or short period of time, during which the nerve is unable to transmit an impulse. If a single nerve fiber cannot transmit more than 1000 impulses per second, how can the identification of a 20,000-cycle tone be explained? To explain this high pitch the idea of a group of cooperating fibers was introduced, each able to conduct in rotation, so that while one fiber is in its active state a second may be passing through its inactive or refractory phase. Thus, if three nerve fibers end in a very small stimulated patch of the aural membrane, a series of three out-of-phase discharges may travel to a common terminal, arriving as a frequency pattern. The sensation of pitch is determined by the position of the stimulated patch on the aural membrane and not by the frequency of nerve impulses in the auditory nerve.

The resolving power of the asymmetrical aural membrane is thus limited by the distance between the maxima of two adjacent stimulated patches to which two hair cells can respond. Thus a just-noticeable change in pitch represents a minimum shift of the region of activity along the aural membrane, which in the 1000-to-2000 pitch region corresponds very closely with the distance between two internal hair cells.

Loudness, which is the experience of the intensity of the acoustic disturbance, is probably directly related to the total number of nerve impulses reaching the brain from a stimulated patch of the aural membrane.

Evidence for this hypothesis may be obtained from the work of Derbyshire and Davis [1935]. They have shown that the voltage of the action potential recorded from the auditory nerve increases as the intensity of the stimulating tone is increased. As the intensity is increased, it is found that the number of nerve impulses passing along a nerve per unit of time also increases. Since the nerve-fiber impulses are of an all-or-none nature, an increase in voltage of the overall action potential of the acoustic nerve must be due to an increase in the number of fibers activated. A reasonable conclusion is that an increase of activity in the auditory nerve is correlated best with an increase of active fibers as a physiological basis of loudness. However, there is need for more extensive experimental data to determine the functional relation between loudness and the activity of the fibers in the auditory nerve.

In the meantime, the response to intensity increases can be pictured as an increased distortion of a narrow strip of aural membrane, which at high intensities spreads enough to produce the experienced change in pitch. The nerve endings lying at the position of maximal pressure gradient stimulate the nerve fibers to discharge impulses oftener than those farther away. As the distortion increases, the patch of excitation spreads both laterally and across the aural membrane, thus increasing the number of hair cells and associated nerve endings responding to the mechanical distortion. Owing to the asymmetrical structure of the aural mechanism and aural membrane, the change in the experienced loudness does not duplicate the change in intensity but has a functional relation to the intensity, thus probably accounting for the form of the loudness function shown in Fig. VII–20.

AUDITORY PATTERNS OF THE AURAL MEMBRANE

Electrical response studies (aural microphonics) have demonstrated that the sensation of pitch is determined by the position of the pressure-gradient pattern on the aural membrane. By a method of localized measurements along the cochlea, Culler [1935] and later Kemp and Johnson [1939] were able to map the various maximal positions of pitch responsiveness in the cochlea in terms of distances from the apical end. Figure VII–25 shows such an auditory map, in which the spiral represents the cochlea to scale with its length divided into 100 units.

Further evidence to support this map of positions of maximum response to pure tones is offered by Fletcher [1940], who carried out two sets of calculations, the first based on the width of the band of frequencies that a noise must contain in order to mask a pure tone, and the second upon the ratio of the intensity of the necessary noise to the intensity of the masked tones.

On the basis of these independent supporting data we can now accept with confidence the pitch maps of the cochlea. In Fig. VII–25 the height of the dark portion is drawn proportional to the response of the nerves at the positions indicated. The pattern is that produced in a typical normal cochlea when a 700–cycle tone is heard at an intensity level 90 db above threshold. Most of the experienced loudness is seen to come from position 20. A considerable part of the loudness is shown to originate near positions 36, 48, and 56. These last are the aural harmonics probably introduced by the asymmetrical characteristics of the ear at this loudness level. The total loudness is represented as corresponding with the total area of the darkened part. As the intensity increases the amplitude of the loudness pattern increases, spreads, and additional higher harmonics appear further down the aural membrane.

An important application of pitch localization, as used by Fletcher, is illustrated in an audiogram of a case of nerve deafness (Fig. VII–26). The breadth of the cross-hatched portion is supposed to indicate the amount of damage to the nerve endings at the various positions along the basilar membrane. In order to hear any sound, the deaf person must have the normal auditory pattern (solid black) projecting above his nerve-deafness pattern. The 6900- and 4600-cycle tones will not be heard, for their auditory pattern does not project through the deafness pattern.

The 2300-cycle tone, however, will be heard only in proportion to the amount of the loudness pattern projecting above the deafness pattern at that frequency.

The above evidence strongly favors a " place-resonance " theory of pitch perception, in which loudness correlates best with the total number of active nerve fibers rather than with any simple function of the number or frequency of nerve impulses.

The above general principles are basic to any understanding of the relations between the objective phenomena in the form of the acoustic impulses, and the complexities introduced by the transmission mechanism of the ear into the mechanical vibrations which are translated via nerve impulses into pitch and loudness perceptions. The above interpretations of the data appear to be consistent with a place theory of hearing that does not employ the principle of simple resonance.

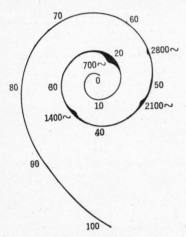

FIG. VII–25. The auditory cochlear pattern of a 700-cycle tone at 90 db. Numbers 0 to 100 indicate linear distances from the apex. The length of the aural membrane is taken as 100 units. Note the positions and intensities of the aural harmonics. (By courtesy of H. Fletcher [1940].)

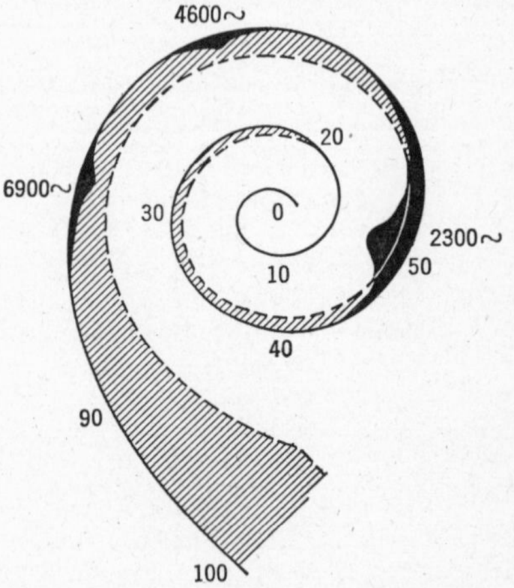

FIG. VII–26. A nerve-deafness pattern. The breadth of the cross hatching indicates the degree of deafness. This person can hear 2300 cycles because his auditory pattern at 2300 cycles protrudes through his deafness pattern. He does not hear the aural harmonics at this intensity level. (By courtesy of H. Fletcher [1940].)

A more systematic and consistent picture of the auditory processes is presented by S. S. Stevens and Hallowell Davis in their monograph, *Hearing, Its Psychology and Physiology* (John Wiley & Sons, 1938), which the thoughtful student will enjoy reading to supplement the above elementary presentation of an important field of research in biophysics.

BIBLIOGRAPHY

1862 HELMHOLTZ, H. v., *Die Lehre von den Tonempfindungen*, 1st Ed., Braunschweig.
1905 SHAW, P. E., *Proc. Roy. Soc. London*, **A76**, 360.
1908 HARDESTY, I., *Am. J. Anat.*, **8**, 109.
1910 KÖHLER, W., *Z. Psychol.*, **54**, 241.

1918 WRIGHTSON, T., and A. KEITH, *An Enquiry into the Analytical Mechanism of the Internal Ear*, Macmillan and Company, London.

1923 FRANK, O., *Münch. Bay. Akad. Wiss.*, **53**, 11.

1924 WILKINSON, G., and A. A. GRAY, *The Mechanism of the Cochlea. A Restatement of the Resonance Theory of Hearing*, Macmillan and Company, London.

1925 LAMB, H., *The Dynamical Theory of Sound*, E. Arnold and Company, London.

1929 BUNCH, C. C., *Arch. Otolaryngol.*, **9**, 625.

1929 FLETCHER, H., *Speech and Hearing*, D. Van Nostrand Company, New York.

1930 STEWART, G. W., and R. B. LINDSAY, *Acoustics*, D. Van Nostrand Company, New York.

1930 TRÖGER, J., *Physik. Z.*, **31**, 26.

1930 WEVER, E. G., and C. W. BRAY, *Proc. Nat. Acad. Sci.*, **16**, 344.

1931 BUNCH, C. C., and T. S. RAIFORD, *Arch. Otolaryngol.*, **13**, 423.

1931 SHOWER, E. G., and R. BIDDULPH, *J. Acous. Soc. Am.*, **3**, 275.

1932 BEATY, R. T., *Hearing in Man and Animals*, Bell and Sons, London.

1932 BÉKÉSY, G. v., *Ann. Physik*, **13**, 111; **14**, 51.

1932 CROWE, S. J., *Harvey Lectures*, **27**, 100.

1932 MONTGOMERY, H. C., *Bell. Lab. Rec.*, **10**, 311.

1932 SAUL, L. J., and H. DAVIS, *Arch. Neurol. Psychiat.*, **28**, 1104.

1932 WEST, W., *Acoustical Engineering*, I. Putnam & Son, London.

1933 BÉKÉSY, G. v., *Physik. Z.*, **34**, 577.

1933 FLETCHER, H., and W. A. MUNSON, *J. Acous. Soc. Am.*, **5**, 82.

1933 LORENT, DE NO, R., *Trans. Am. Laryngol. Rhin. Otol. Soc.*, **39**, 26

1933 LORENT, DE NO, R., and A. S. HARRIS, *Laryngoscope*, **43**, 315.

1933 SIVIAN, L. T., and S. D. WHITE, *J. Acous. Soc. Am.*, **4**, 306.

1933 WEVER, E. G., " The Physiology of Hearing," *Physiol. Rev.*, **13**, 400.

1934 DAVIS, H., A. J. DERBYSHIRE, M. H. LURIE, and L. T. SAUL, *Am. J. Physiol.*, **107**, 311.

1934 FLETCHER, H., *Bell System Tech. J.*, **13**, 239; *J. Acous. Soc. Am.*, **5**, 6.

1934 GEFFCKEN, W., *Ann. Physik*, **19**, 829.

1935 BÜRCK, W., P. KOTOWSKI, and H. LICHTE, *Elek. Nachr.-Tech.*, **12**, 326.

1935 CULLER, E. A., *Ann. Otol. Rhin. Laryng.*, **44**, 807.

1935 DERBYSHIRE, A. J., and H. DAVIS, *Am. J. Physiol.*, **113**, 476.

1935 STEVENS, S. S., *J. Acous. Soc. Am.*, **6**, 150.

1935 STEVENS, S. S., H. DAVIS, and H. H. LURIE, *Am. Otol. Rhin. Laryng.*, **44**, 776.

1935 WILSKA, A., *Skand. Arch. Physiol.*, **72**, 161.

1936 AMERICAN STANDARDS ASSOCIATION, Acoustical Terminology, Z24.1, 29 W. 39th St., New York.

1936 BÉKÉSY, G. v., *Akust. Z.*, **1**, 13.

1936 MCLACHLAN, M. W., *The New Acoustics*, Oxford University Press, London.

1936 MORSE, P. M., *Vibrations and Sound*, McGraw-Hill Book Company, New York.

1936 STEVENS, S. S., and E. B. NEWMAN, *Proc. Natl. Acad. Sci.*, **22**, 668.

1937 COLBY, M. Y., *Sound Waves and Acoustics*, Henry Holt and Company, New York.

1937 STEVENS, S. S., J. VOLKMANN, and E. B. NEWMAN, *J. Acous. Soc. Am.*, **8**, 185.

1937 STUHLMAN, O., JR., *J. Acous. Soc. Am.*, **9**, 119.

1937 WIGGERS, H. C., *Am. J. Physiol.*, **120**, 771.

1938 REBOUL, J. A., *J. phys. et le Radium*, **9**, 185.

1938　Stevens, S. S., and H. Davis, *Hearing*, John Wiley & Sons, New York.
1939　Keen, J. A., *J. Anat.*, **73**, 592.
1939　Kemp, E. H., and P. Johnson, *Science*, **90**, 405.
1940　Fletcher, H., " Auditory Patterns," *Rev. Modern Phys.*, **12**, 47.
1941　Bárány, E., A review of recent articles, *Ann. Rev. Physiol.*, **3**, 449.
1941　Wood, A. B., *A Textbook of Sound*, 2nd Ed., Macmillan Company, New York.

Chapter VIII

THE COMPOUND MICROSCOPE; THE ELECTRON MICROSCOPE

THE COMPOUND MICROSCOPE

In the chapter on the biophysical aspects of the eye the size of the visual receptors in the retina of the human eye were discussed, and it was shown that, in the region of greatest visual acuity, which lies at the fovea centralis of the macula lutea, only very slender cones are found. These cones are hexagonally packed with centers about 3 microns apart. The retinal image must of necessity be at least 3 microns long in order to excite two cones, from which we concluded that this distance subtended an angle of 1 minute of arc, whose center of curvature was a nodal point of the lens. The object producing the image must, therefore, also subtend an angle of 1 minute of arc no matter how great the visual distance. In a like manner any two details must subtend at least an arc of 1 minute for them to be just separable.

RESOLVING POWER OF THE EYE

The eye, at the distance of distinct vision (25 cm), can resolve two points lying as close as 0.074 mm. At a distance of 1 meter from the eye these two points may not be closer than 0.29 mm, for otherwise they would fuse into one image.

If the object is of constant size but at varying distances from the eye, the visual angle in which the object is seen grows larger as the object approaches the eye. Since the power of accommodation of the eye is limited, there is a practical limit to which an object may approach an eye and still maintain a focused image on the retina. By interposing a simple converging lens between the eye and object the visual angle subtended by the object is increased and therefore the angle subtended by the retinal image is increased; this allows the eye to approach the object very close and still retain the sharpness of its retinal image. The lens aids the eye to produce a larger retinal image so as to make adjoining details spread out enough to fall on more than one retinal element, thus making resolution possible.

The microscopist uses a train of lenses to aid him to produce a high resolution. He is not essentially interested in how big he can make his material under examination appear, but in how much of the actual structure he can render clearly visible. This is determined by the resolving power of his instrument, not by its magnifying power.

MAGNIFYING POWER

The total magnification of a microscope must be sufficient to make the closest detail one hopes to see in the virtual image appear separated at the distance of distinct vision, at least 0.074 mm. By examining Fig. VIII–1 it is seen how this magnification is obtained.

The magnifying power of a compound microscope is the relative size of the virtual image to object.

There are five ways of varying the magnifying power of a compound microscope:

1. By using a higher- or lower-power objective.
2. By using a higher- or lower-power ocular.
3. By lengthening or shortening the draw tube. (Normal length 160 mm.)
4. By increasing or diminishing the distance at which the virtual image is projected. (Normal or distance of distinct vision, 250 mm.)
5. By the use of an optical amplifier, i.e., a diverging lens placed between objective and ocular.

STRUCTURE OF THE COMPOUND MICROSCOPE

In its simplest form (Fig. VIII–1) the microscope consists of an objective (11), which forms a real, magnified, and inverted image of an object placed just below the principal focus of the objective. The magnified image is viewed by the aid of the ocular (1). This real image lies in the eyepiece aperture below the eyepoint and hence must be spread sufficiently by the eye lens of the ocular so that the retinal image has two adjoining structures fall on at least two retinal elements. It thus becomes apparent that a compound microscope must comprise a short-focus objective and a short-focus eye lens.

NUMERICAL APERTURE OR N.A.

The term numerical aperture was introduced by Professor Abbe to allow a precise comparison to be made of the resolving power of one lens or train of lenses with another.

It must be remembered that the numerical aperture is the measure of the resolving power of a microscope objective. Numerical aperture is not a direct expression of the resolving power, though from it one may be able to calculate the resolving power.

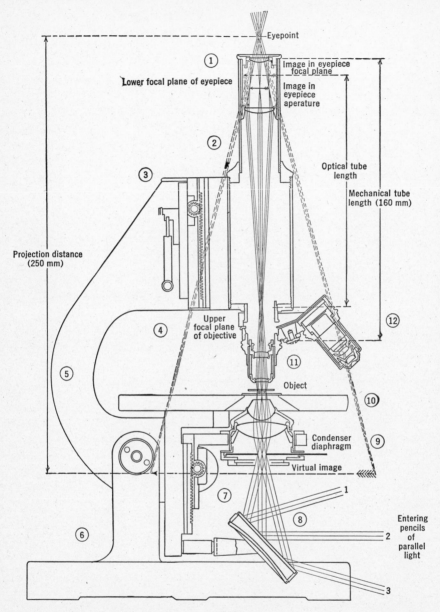

Eyepoint

Image in eyepiece focal plane

Lower focal plane of eyepiece

Image in eyepiece aperature

Optical tube length

Mechanical tube length (160 mm)

Projection distance (250 mm)

Upper focal plane of objective

Object

Condenser diaphragm

Virtual image

Entering pencils of parallel light

1

2

3

FIG. VIII–1. Section through the optical axis of a standard laboratory-type microscope, showing construction of objectives, eyepiece, and condenser. Since the condenser is in place note how the plane mirror is used in connection with the condenser diaphragm to illuminate the object. 1, eyepiece. 2, tube. 3, coarse focusing adjustment. 4, fine adjustment. 5, curved arm. 6, base. 7, substage. 8, mirror. 9, condenser. 10, stage. 11, objective. 12, nosepiece. By courtesy of Bausch and Lomb Optical Company, Rochester, New York.

Numerical aperture is the sine of half the angle of the cone of light entering an objective, multiplied by the refractive index (n) of the medium between the object and the front lens of the objective, which may be air, water, glycerine, or an oil. Thus

$$N.A. = n \sin a$$

where a is the half angle of the cone of light entering the objective as seen in Fig. VIII–2.

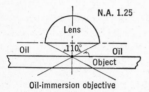

Oil-immersion objective

Thus, if air is the medium between the object and the lens, the widest possible angle of light that can enter a 16-mm objective of 0.25 N.A. is, as illustrated in Fig. VIII–2, equal to 29°.

$$N.A. = n \sin a$$

$$0.25 = 1.000 \times \sin a$$

$$a = 14° 30'$$

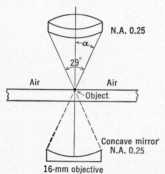

16-mm objective

Fig. VIII–2. N.A. $= n \sin a$.

If the medium between the object and the lens is some liquid like water, cedar oil, or Canada balsam, the focal length of the lens is shortened. This type of objective is called an immersion objective. Thus, for instance, a cedar-oil-immersion objective of N.A. 1.25 is used where object and lens are immersed in cedar oil of index of refraction 1.52. The widest possible cone of light entering this lens is about 110°, since

$$1.25 = 1.52 \sin a$$

$$a = 55° 20'$$

A solid angle subtending 110° in air works out to a numerical aperture of 0.82. Thus the insertion of oil increases its numerical aperture from 0.82 to 1.25, which we shall see increases the resolving power of the lens.

LIMIT OF RESOLUTION

By resolution we mean the measure of the smallest distance of approach of two luminous points so that they may be identified as two entities. The geometric shadow cast by a very narrow slit, having sharp parallel edges, when illuminated by a parallel beam of monochromatic light, will be examined first. As the beam of light passes through the slit it spreads out to a certain extent, producing a fuzzy-edged outline caused by the diffracted light which spreads into the geometrical shadow. If the geometrical pattern is focused on a photographic plate by means of a lens it will be found that the developed photographic image is

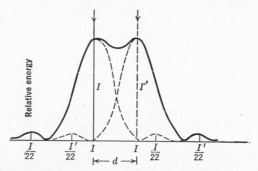

Fig. VIII–3. A photometric analysis of the Fraunhofer diffraction patterns of two identical sources. The distance of nearest approach d has been reached where I is still distinguishable from I'. The intensity of the secondary maximum is not shown. It is $I/62$.

edged with a series of dark and bright diffraction bands. The intensity distribution I across such a photographed slit is shown as a broken line in Fig. VIII–3, provided that the exposure is not too long to bring out the diffraction bands of lower intensity than the first. Note that the intensity I at the center of the slit rapidly drops to zero at the distance d and then passes through a secondary maximum of intensity $I/22$ which is the first diffraction fringe.

If two such slits separated by a distance d are simultaneously photographed, the two image patterns I and I' will overlap as shown in Fig. VIII–3.

The distance d between the maxima of these two diffraction patterns is the measure of the resolution.

The *limit of resolution* is defined by the distance d of nearest approach of two sources emitting monochromatic light such that, in the maximum intensity curves, the foot of one and the maximum of the other coincide.

Whereas a single slit aperture forms a series of fine dark and bright bands, a square aperture forms bright and dark bands in two directions crossing each other at right angles. If the aperture is circular the pattern is in the form of a central bright disk surrounded by bright rings rapidly decreasing in intensity.

The mathematical analysis of the angular separation of the diffraction circles is a problem of considerable mathematical difficulty. The angular separation θ of the first dark ring from its center is

$$\theta = \frac{1.220\lambda}{d}$$

in which d is identified as the distance of the foot of the intensity curve (Fig. VIII–3) from the central maximum, and λ is the wavelength of the light forming the diffraction pattern.

According to Rayleigh's criterion, the *limit of resolution* is reached when two circular-aperture images are separated by the distance d as given by the above relation.

The resolution of two point sources of an object, that is obtainable with the aid of a lens, depends on the angle of the cone of light which subtends the lens and not on that which subtends the image, because the lens has the properties of an aperture. The margin of the lens acts as an edge of a circular aperture. If the lens forms a point image by means of a wide-angle cone of light the diffraction disk is large. When two adjoining diffraction disks are observed to be far apart, then according to the Rayleigh criterion the resolution is large.

The angular separation, θ, in the above formula is half the angle of the cone of light forming the image and not of the light as it enters the object lens. For a microscope, it is necessary to convert the above formula into a form that expresses the distance of closest approach of the diffraction disks in terms of the aperture of the lens.

A point source placed close to the objective of a microscope is examined. Such a source subtends an angle $2a$ in the object space, of index of refraction n. The separation of two such points O and O' in the object plane will produce images I and I' in the image plane that are just resolvable. From simple geometrical considerations this separation S can be shown to be

$$S = \frac{1.22\lambda}{2n \sin a} \equiv \frac{\lambda}{2\ \text{N.A.}}$$

Abbe investigated this problem in detail and concluded that good working results for the resolution were obtainable by assuming the factor 1.22 to be equal to unity.

Resolving Power

The resolving power (R.P.) is defined as

$$\text{R.P.} = \frac{2\ \text{N.A.}}{\lambda}\ \text{cm}^{-1}$$

Everything else being equal, the resolving power is inversely proportional to the wavelength of the visible light used to illuminate the details of the object. Blue-light illumination produces a greater resolving power than red light, under identical circumstances. For white light the average value of λ is taken as 5300 Å. Cone vision attains its maximum visibility at 5560 Å.

A microscope objective having a 1.6 N.A. with the cone of illumination filling the whole aperture will resolve two elementary lines on an object separated by a distance of $5560 \times 10^{-8}/2 \times 1.6 = 1.74 \times 10^{-5}$ cm, a resolving power of about 6000 lines per millimeter. This resolving power is the practical limit attainable using this wavelength. A 4-mm 0.85-N.A. objective will resolve lines separated by distances ranging between 0.00062 and 0.00031 mm, depending upon the angular aperture and wavelength employed.

By *angular aperture* is meant the size of the cone of light which passes from the object to the objective and becomes effective in producing the image.

In the eye the greatest acuity is attained for a pupilar diameter of 2 mm. The resolution obtainable with the eye, as we have seen, is limited to a visual angle of 1 minute of arc. The resolving power is then 14 lines per millimeter. Its numerical aperture is therefore very small.

In round numbers an objective of N.A. 1.00 will resolve 100,000 lines per inch, and, since R.P. is proportional to N.A., a 0.25-N.A. will then resolve 25,000 lines per inch and 1.30-N.A. will resolve about 130,000 lines per inch. If a structure is known to be of the order of 35,000 lines per inch, for example, it is impossible to resolve that detail with an objective of N.A. 0.25, no matter how much magnification may be employed.

An ideal objective of N.A. 1.00, used with white light $(\lambda = 5300$ Å$)$ should resolve lines separated by 0.000265 mm. If these spaces are magnified about 300 times they should become visible. That is, 300 times the numerical aperture suffices to disclose all details resolvable by the corresponding objective, although many eyes would require as much as 500 times the numerical aperture.

Using 500 times the numerical aperture as required to resolve any detail, so as to make the detail comfortably visible to the average eye, what combination of eyepiece and objective is necessary to resolve details in a specimen separated by 0.000075 cm, illuminated by white light of average wavelength 5300 Å?

If N.A. 1.00 resolves 0.000265 mm, N.A. 0.35 will resolve 0.00075 mm. Since we have stated above that a total magnification equal to 500 times the numerical aperture is more than enough for the eye to resolve the detail, the total magnification required for the specimen will be 165×.

TABLE VIII–1

ACHROMATIC OBJECTIVES — HUYGENIAN EYEPIECES
MAGNIFICATIONS AND REAL FIELDS

Microscope tube length 160 mm.   Image distance 250 mm.   Real fields (italics) in mm.

Objectives		Eyepieces						
Equivalent Focus Numerical Aperture	Magnification	5×	6.4×	7.5×	10×	Micrometer Value with 10× Eyepiece	12.5×	15×
48 mm	2×	10×	12.8×	15×	20×	0.076	25×	30×
0.08 N.A.		*10.2*	*9.6*	*9.2*	*7.8*		*6.9*	*5.65*
40 mm	2.6×	13×	16.6×	19.5×	26×	0.058	32.5×	39×
0.08 N.A.		*8.0*	*7.25*	*7.1*	*5.9*		*5.25*	*4.25*
32 mm	4×	20×	25.6×	30×	40×	0.038	50×	60×
0.10 N.A.		*5.25*	*4.80*	*4.63*	*3.87*		*3.43*	*2.82*
22.7 mm	6×	30×	38.4×	45×	60×	0.024	75×	90×
0.17 N.A.		*3.48*	*3.20*	*3.08*	*2.56*		*2.26*	*1.87*
16 mm	10×	50×	64×	75×	100×	0.0145	125×	150×
0.25 N.A.		*2.05*	*1.90*	*1.80*	*1.50*		*1.33*	*1.10*
8 mm	21×	105×	134×	157×	210×	0.0072	262×	315×
0.50 N.A.		*1.01*	*0.93*	*0.89*	*0.74*		*0.65*	*0.55*
4 mm	43×	215×	275×	322×	430×	0.0034	537×	645×
0.65 N.A.		*0.48*	*0.44*	*0.42*	*0.35*		*0.31*	*0.26*
4 mm	45×	225×	288×	337×	450×	0.0033	562×	675×
0.85 N.A.		*0.47*	*0.43*	*0.41*	*0.35*		*0.31*	*0.26*
3 mm	60×	300×	384×	450×	600×	0.0025	750×	900×
0.85 N.A.		*0.35*	*0.32*	*0.30*	*0.25*		*0.225*	*0.185*

Since a 0.35-N.A. objective may not be commercially available (see Table VIII–1), we choose the next larger, 0.50-N.A., having a magnification number 21×; using this in connection with a 7.5× eyepiece gives a total magnification of 157 diameters.

It is recommended that the lowest-power eyepiece be used that will disclose the detail desired in order to assure getting the best definition and illumination, and a comfortable high eyepoint.

OBJECTIVES OF NUMERICAL APERTURE GREATER THAN 1.00

The higher the numerical aperture, the greater the resolving power of the objective.   The definition

$$\text{N.A.} = n \sin a$$

includes the index of refraction (n) of the medium from which the light passes into the objective.   If this index is greater than unity, like that of water (1.33), oil of cedar (1.52), or Canada balsam (1.53), an objective having a 1.25 N.A. immersed in oil of cedar (Fig. VIII–4) has an angular aperture of 110.5°.   An immersion objective with numerical aperture greater than unity will therefore have an aperture which will

TABLE VIII–1 Cont.

Magnification Table

Apochromatic Objectives — Compensating Eyepieces
Magnifications and Real Fields

Microscope tube length 160 mm.   Image distance 250 mm.   Real fields (italics) in mm.

Objectives		Eyepieces						
Equivalent Focus Numerical Aperture	Objective Magnification	5 ×	7.5×	10 ×	Micrometer Value with 10× Eyepiece	12.5×	15×	25×
16 mm	10×	50×	75×	100×	0.0132	125×	150×	250×
0.30 N.A.		*2.13*	*1.80*	*1.50*		*1.33*	*1.15*	*0.65*
8.3 mm	20×	100×	150×	200×	0.0067	250×	300×	500×
0.65 N.A.		*1.08*	*0.91*	*0.76*		*0.68*	*0.59*	*0.33*
4 mm	47.5×	237.5×	356.3×	475×	0.00275	5938×	712.5×	1187.5×
0.95 N.A.		*0.44*	*0.37*	*0.31*		*0.275*	*0.235*	*0.135*
3 mm	67×	335×	502.5×	670×	0.00205	837×	1005×	1678×
0.95 N.A.		*0.33*	*0.28*	*0.23*		*0.21*	*0.18*	*0.10*
3 mm	61×	305×	457.5×	610×	0.0022	762.5×	915×	1525×
1.40 N.A.		*0.355*	*0.295*	*0.25*		*0.22*	*0.19*	*0.108*
2.2 mm	78×	390×	585×	780×	0.0017	975×	1170×	1950×
1.00 N.A.		*0.26*	*0.22*	*0.185*		*0.165*	*0.14*	*0.080*
2 mm	90×	450×	675×	900×	0.00142	1125×	1350×	2250×
1.30 N.A.		*0.23*	*0.195*	*0.16*		*0.145*	*0.125*	*0.070*
2 mm	90×	450×	675×	900×	0.00142	1125×	1350×	2250×
1.40 N.A.		*0.23*	*0.195*	*0.16*		*0.145*	*0.125*	*0.070*
1.5 mm	120×	600×	900×	1200×	0.00107	.1500×	1800×	3000×
1.30 N.A.		*0.175*	*0.145*	*0.122*		*0.110*	*0.095*	*0.055*

exceed 180° of light in air. By referring to Fig. VIII–4 it becomes apparent that a given lens has greater light-gathering power when immersed in oil than when immersed in air.

Since the brightness of an image is proportional to the square of the numerical aperture, there is a definite additional advantage in the use of an oil-immersion objective.

Depth of Focus

With objectives of low numerical aperture it is possible to change the focus markedly up or down without loss in sharpness of detail. In objectives of large numerical aperture a sharp focus is almost immediately lost for a slight shift in vertical motion of the objective. It will be noticed by referring to Fig. VIII–5 that the same slight shift above or below the focal point produces very large circles of diffusion in the large-numerical-aperture objective but only small circles of diffusion in the low-numerical-aperture one. Thus the appearance is only slightly changed in the low-numerical-aperture objective by a slight vertical displacement.

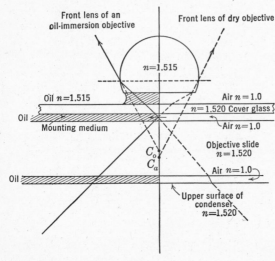

FIG. VIII-4. The relative size of a cone of light originating at the virtual source C_o when oil is used as compared with the virtual source C_a when air is used between all mountings. The numerical aperture of the oil cone is larger than that of the air cone. Note how much larger the angular aperture of the lens becomes as the result of its oil immersion.

MICROSCOPE OBJECTIVES

Objectives (Fig. VIII-6) may be designated by their equivalent focal lengths. These numbers (0.25 N.A., 16 mm) indicate that the objective produces a real image of approximately the same size as that produced by a simple convex lens whose principal focus lies at the distance marked upon the objective.

FIG. VIII-5. The circles of diffusion at equal distances from the focal point F are shown as black disks. 1. Lens with large aperture. 2. Lens with small aperture. In (2) circles of diffusion as large as in (1) can be found further to the right and left of F. Depth of focus (2) > (1).

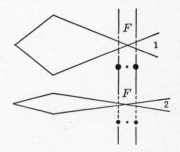

MICROSCOPE OBJECTIVE CORRECTIONS

The purpose of the microscope is to give the best possible image of the detail in the object, and faithfully reproduce that detail in shape and color in the image. The designer of a microscope objective tries to reduce spherical and zonal aberration as well as chromatic aberration and coma to a minimum. As a result of the application of these corrections to an objective, the image is substantially free from haze and color.

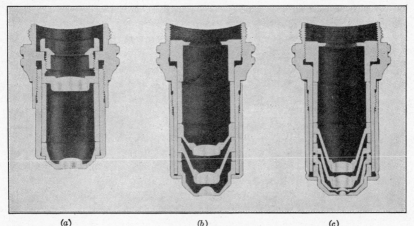

(a)   (b)   (c)

Fig. VIII–6.   (a) 10 × (16 mm) Achromat, 0.25 N.A.
(b) 43 × (4 mm) Achromat, 0.65 N.A.
(c) 97 × (1.8 mm) Achromat, 1.25 N.A.

Note precision of construction and relative position of lenses. (Courtesy Bausch and Lomb Optical Company, Rochester, New York.) ·

Curvature of field depends upon the focal length of the objective, its numerical aperture, and its spherical correction. The long-focal-length objectives, such as the 48-mm and 32-mm objectives, have relatively flat image fields, because of their simple construction and small numerical aperture. The 16-mm objective (Fig. VIII–6a) produces a slight curvature of the image field, noticeable only when the object under examination is very thin. The high-power objectives have still greater curvature of field because of their complex lens system. As seen in Figs. VIII–6 and 7, they are formed of several extremely short-focus lenses.

Chromatism in a microscope objective means that the image of an axial point source of white light has colored rings around it, due to the fact that the focal length of a lens varies with wavelength. This variation of the focal length because of dispersion of a lens is called chromatic aberration. Its existence can be shown by arranging a lens as in Fig. VIII–8, where light from a small white source S falls on a lens of tolerably wide aperture and is received on a white paper screen, first in position A, then in position B. In position A the outer edge of the image will be red; in position B, blue.

Because of this defect it is impossible to obtain colorless images with simple spherical lenses. Since various kinds of glass have different dispersive powers, it is possible with the proper choice of combinations of lens shapes and indices of refraction to obtain an achromatic lens train whose focal length is the same for all colors.

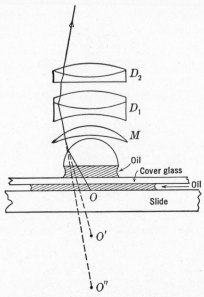

FIG. VIII–7. Typical section of an immersion objective, 2 mm, N.A. 1.25. The object O is embedded in an oil having same index of refraction as lens and cover glass. The first lens is hemispherical; the object is relatively immersed in the lens at one of the aplanatic points, thus forming a virtual image point at O'. The other aplanatic point is at the center of curvature of the lower face of the meniscus lens M; hence no refraction takes place at this lower surface. O' is also the aplanatic point for the upper surface of M so that this lens produces a perfect point image of O' at O''. The diverging beam coming from the virtual focus O'' is brought to a focus by the doublets D_1 and D_2.

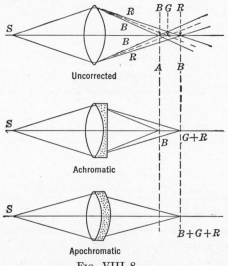

FIG. VIII–8.

The cross section of a typical achromatic 4-mm objective is shown in Fig. VIII–9. It has been designed so that its blue image (F light,

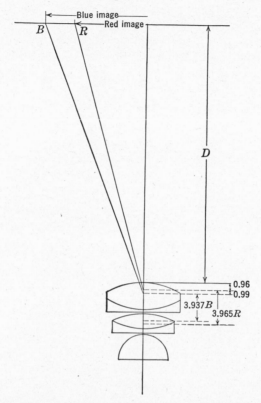

Fig. VIII–9. Section of a 4-mm achromatic microscope objective showing the position of the focal points for B (blue light, λ 4861.4 Å) and R (red light, λ 6562.8 Å) and the values of the equivalent focal lengths for these wavelengths. The blue image is magnified more than the red image, and the ratio of the magnification of the blue image to the magnification of the red image is chromatic difference of magnification. Here

$$f_R = 3.965 \text{ and } f_B = 3.937. \quad \text{Magnification is } M.$$

$$M_R = \frac{D + 0.96}{3.965} = 45.0, \quad M_B = \frac{D + 0.99}{3.937} = 45.3$$

$$\frac{45.3}{45.0} = 1.0065$$

Chromatic difference of magnification is 0.65 per cent. (By courtesy of Bausch and Lomb Optical Company, Rochester, New York.)

λ 4861.4 Å) is 0.65 per cent larger than its red image (C light, λ 6562.8 Å). Its chromatic difference of magnification is said to be 0.65 per cent. The image formed by such an objective is excellent in every respect except that some color is present which becomes disturbing when high-power eyepieces and oblique illumination are resorted to. The residual color which exists in the images produced by achromatic objectives is known as the " secondary spectrum." Its presence is due to the difficulty, if not impossibility, of finding two kinds of glass in which the dispersion is exactly proportionate. By using three glasses it is possible to remove the secondary spectrum.

APOCHROMATIC OBJECTIVES

These objectives are designed to reduce the secondary spectrum characteristic of achromatic systems. Apochromatic objectives consist of several fluorite lenses and contain correcting lenses which remove the secondary spectrum. They are made with large numerical apertures giving the same approximate initial magnification as the achromatic objectives. They are also corrected for spherical aberration for all colors. Much higher-power eyepieces can, therefore, be used so that higher total magnification can be obtained.

IMMERSION OBJECTIVES

The lower faces of immersion objectives are immersed in a liquid instead of air. They are usually designated by the name of the liquid used. *Water-immersion objectives* have water between the cover glass or the object and the face of the lower lens. Homogeneous or *oil-immersion objectives* are immersed in a liquid whose index of refraction must be the same as that of optical glass so that light suffers no refraction in passing from the glass slide and cover glass into the immersing liquid and thence into the objective. The medium below the lens is therefore homogeneous, as illustrated in Fig. VIII–4. Thickened cedar-wood oil has proved very satisfactory. Canada balsam of moderate thickness in connection with white light gives good, though not correct, results. See Table VIII–2 for comparative indices of refraction.

PROPER ILLUMINATION

In working with objectives of numerical aperture greater than 1.0 an important factor must not be overlooked. The cone of light entering the objective must be equal to the numerical aperture of the objective, or a narrow diagonal pencil of light entering at that angle may be used if the full resolving power is to be obtained. For instance, no matter if the numerical aperture of the condenser is greater than 1.0, it cannot send light into air, in contact with its upper surface, at an angle greater that that corresponding with 1.0 N.A.

TABLE VIII–2

INDEX OF REFRACTION RELATIVE TO AIR FOR SODIUM LIGHT

$\lambda = 5893$ Å

Liquid	Temperature, °C	n
Water	18	1.33317
Water	20	1.33299
Water	22	1.33281
Water	24	1.33262
Water	28	1.333219
Glass		
Zinc crown		1.517
Higher-dispersion crown		1.520
Light flint		1.575
Heavy flint		1.650
Heaviest flint		1.890
Fluorite		1.387
Quartz (fused)		1.4584
Canada balsam	20	1.530
Glycerine	20	1.474
Oil of cedar		1.5156 (average)

TABLE VIII–3

NUMERICAL APERTURE (N.A.) AND THE RELATED
MAGNIFICATION AT 160 MM

N.A.	n of Medium	Angular Aperture ($2a$)	Achromatic Objective Magnification ($\times$) at 160 mm
0.10	1.00	11.5°	32 mm ($\times$4)
0.25	1.00	29.0°	16 mm ($\times$10)
0.50	1.00	60.0°	8 mm ($\times$21 or $\times$20)
0.66	1.00	83.0°	4 mm ($\times$43 or $\times$44)
0.85	1.00	116.5°	3 mm $\times$60
1.25	1.52	110.5°	1.9 mm or 1.8 mm oil immersion ($\times$97 or $\times$95)

A COMPARISON OF THE ANGULAR APERTURE REQUIRED TO
GIVE THE SAME N.A. OF 0.50

	($2a$)	n	medium
Dry objective	60°	1.00	air
Water immersion	44° 20′	1.33	water
Homogeneous or oil-immersion objective	38° 28′	1.52	oil of cedar

Whether or not the cone of light is correct can be tested easily by observing the upper lens of the objective. It should be filled with an even illumination. This can be observed if one removes the eyepiece and looks down the draw tube of the microscope. This should be done each time one starts to work with a microscope and each time one changes objectives.

Suppose that an objective of 1.25 N.A. is used with a condenser of 1.4 N.A. If a layer of air (index 1.00) is left between the top lens of the condenser and the slide, the air layer will prevent the condenser from delivering a cone of light greater than 1.00 N.A. By substituting a layer of immersion oil between the slide and the top lens of the condenser the full numerical aperture of the condenser becomes available and the full aperture of the objective will be used. In practice the 1.40-N.A. condenser must be diaphragmed, down to the numerical aperture of the objective, in this case 1.25.

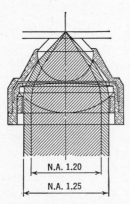

N.A. 1.20

N.A. 1.25

Fig. VIII–10. Abbe or substage condenser, showing the relative size of its 1.20 and 1.25 numerical aperture.

Abbe Condenser

For objectives of numerical aperture greater than 0.25, the ordinary substage mirror is not large enough to provide an illuminating cone of light of sufficient angle to fill the aperture of the objective. This objection is met by introducing a substage condenser or an Abbe condenser between mirror and object slide (Fig. VIII–10). Condensers are usually neither chromatically nor spherically corrected. Their function is to send a sufficiently large cone of light through the object to fill the aperture of the objective.

These condensers may be obtained in various numerical apertures: 1.25 N.A., containing two lenses with top lens removable, or 1.40 N.A., containing three lenses. The condenser mount fits into the substage from below and is provided with an iris diaphragm. If an achromatic condenser is obtained, it is corrected for two colors and spherically corrected for two zones. It is used where it is necessary to have a sharp image of the light source, free from color fringes, projected into the plane of the object. The optical structure of the condenser is such that only parallel rays of light are brought to a focus, in the plane of the object under examination. To obtain this parallel beam of light, a condenser must be interposed between the *plane face of the substage mirror* and an artificial point source, which parallelizes the beam of light.

Mirror

The substage concave mirror is usually so constructed as to deliver light of about 0.25 N.A. Consequently, it will not fill the entire aperture of objectives of higher power than 16 mm, of 0.25 N.A. (See Fig. VIII–2.)

Use of Diaphragm without Substage Condenser

The purpose of the substage diaphragm is to modify the light and by its aid obtain improved results in definition of the object which, without it, are impossible. When the substage diaphragm is essentially in the plane of the object, the limiting factors, so far as numerical aperture is concerned, are the diameter and equivalent focal length of the concave mirror.

An opening in the diaphragm of about the same size as the front of the objective is always used. The last use to which a substage diaphragm should be put is to control the intensity of the illumination. The intensity must be controlled with the aid of filters or dimmers.

In the examination of most microscopic preparations, the problem is to differentiate structure difficult to see, because its color or opacity differs so little from its surroundings, rather than to observe detail at the limit of resolution of the objective. The substage diaphragm is found extremely helpful in examining such specimens by increasing contrast and improving definition. Contrasts in the image can be increased by increasing the size of the diffraction rings around the image. Under these conditions the objective must be used at a lower numerical aperture than that at which it is rated, which is accomplished by closing the substage diaphragm. Care must be taken, however, so as not to confuse diffraction patterns with true details of the specimen.

If the substage diaphragm is closed so as to produce a reduction of working aperture, the resolving power of the lens is lessened. However, it is sometimes desirable to sacrifice some resolving power to improve the contrast and visibility, especially when viewing specimens whose index of refraction differs only slightly from that of the surrounding medium.

In actual practice, the simple substage diaphragm without the condenser can act as a field stop in partly reducing glare and extraneous light, or it can be used to reduce the numerical aperture slightly.

Working Aperture of an Objective

The actual working aperture of an objective is equal to one half the sum of the numerical aperture of the objective and the numerical aperture of the condenser or concave mirror.   Thus, if a 4-mm objective of N.A. 0.65 is used without an Abbe condenser but with the concave mirror, a working numerical aperture equal to $(0.65 + 0.25)/2 = 0.45$ N.A. is obtained.   Unquestionably a substage condenser gives better results, but where no condenser is available the concave mirror limits the cone of illumination.

DRAW TUBE

Some models of microscopes are furnished with draw tubes in place of the fixed eyepiece tube adapter.   The draw tube is graduated on the side in millimeters and normally is set to be used at 160 mm.   The draw tube permits the use of long equivalent focus objectives without the necessity for a length of rack for focussing that would be impracticable for most work.

The draw tube serves three purposes.   The first and most important purpose is to compensate for small differences in cover-glass thickness when high-power dry objectives are used.   An 0.18-mm cover-glass thickness ($n = 1.520$) is used in standard practice.   If the cover glass is not exactly 0.18 mm thick, increasing the tube length 10 mm will compensate a decrease of 0.01 mm in cover-glass thickness.

The second purpose is to permit small changes in initial magnifications so that, in calibrating micrometer eyepieces for purposes of measuring, an even factor may be secured.

The third purpose is to use it as a mount for low-power objectives. In this way a lower magnification can be secured than if the same objective were attached to the nosepiece.   In effect, this is simply using a low-power objective with a shorter optical and mechanical tube length.

EYEPIECES

A microscope ocular or eyepiece consists of one or more converging lenses mounted at the top of the draw tube.   It is used to magnify the real image formed by the objective.   It also serves to correct some of the defects of the image produced by the objective.

In the positive ocular (Ramsden's eyepiece) the real image to be magnified by the ocular lies below the lens train in the plane of the ocular diaphragm.   A positive ocular can be identified by the position of this diaphragm below the field lens.   In its simplest form, Fig. VIII-11, it consists of an eye lens (*EL*) and a field lens (*FL*) of equal focal length, the distance between them being two thirds of the focal length of either lens.   It is equivalent to a single lens whose focal length is three fourths of its component lenses. It is nearly achromatic and gives a flat field with little aberration.

In the best modern Ramsden oculars the simple lenses are replaced by achromatic combinations. They are primarily used in the eyepieces of micrometer microscopes, in connection with cross hairs attached to movable carriages mounted on precision screws, to measure details in an image.

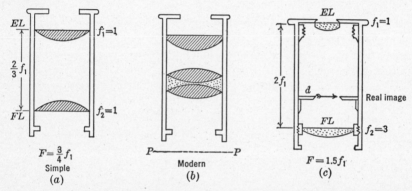

FIG. VIII–11. (*a*) Ramsden eyepiece. Positive ocular. *PP* plane of movable cross hairs. *EL*, eyelens. *FL*, field lens. *F*, equivalent focal length. (*b*) The modern ocular shown with achromatic combination to view image in plane of cross hairs *PP*. (*c*) Huygenian eyepiece. Negative ocular. *EL*, eyelens; *FL*, field lens; *d*, diaphragm; *F*, equivalent focal length.

The negative ocular (Huygenian eyepiece) is the most common eyepiece used in the microscope. It is effectively achromatic if both lenses have the same index of refraction, and it has less distortion and aberration than a single lens. It consists of two convergent lenses, Fig. VIII–11, an eye lens (*EL*) and a field lens (*FL*), whose focal lengths are in the ratio 1 to 3. The distance between them is twice the shorter focal length. In this eyepiece the rays from the objective must pass through the field lens before coming to a focus in the plane of the diaphragm inserted between the lenses. It is equivalent to a single lens whose focal length is one and one half times that of the eye lens.

In practice the ratio of the focal length of the field lens to the eye lens may vary with the power, being 1 to 1.5 or 1 to 2 in low-power, and nearer 1 to 3 in high-power eyepieces.

Huygenian eyepieces as made for modern microscopes are not strictly achromatic but have their focal length for blue light slightly longer than for red light. In order to compensate effectively undercorrection, the achromatic objectives may be designed to have their focal lengths for blue light slightly shorter than for the red light.

The high-power 4-mm achromatic objective discussed above is designed so that its blue image is 0.65 per cent larger than its red image. If the average compensation of a hyperplane eyepiece is 0.80 per cent, this type of eyepiece will very nearly compensate the chromatic difference of magnification in this form of high-power dry achromatic objective.

If the objective is designated as undercorrected (+0.65 per cent) and the eyepiece as overcorrected (−0.80 per cent), then the residual chromatic difference of magnification for this combination is −0.15 per cent. If a 16-mm undercorrected chromatic objective is chosen in which the percentage ratio of the magnification of blue to red image is +0.25 per cent and if the image is viewed with a Huygens eyepiece of average compensating power equal to −0.25 per cent, the image seen through this eyepiece will be quite free from primary color. A slight secondary spectrum will be present, however.

Compensating eyepieces are designed particularly for use with all apochromatic objectives. Unless they are employed in this combination the margin of the field will be quite chromatic.

The residual chromatic difference of magnification for the proper combination of objective and eyepiece in modern microscopes is never greater than 0.5 per cent, even at highest resolution. It should be completely absent in combinations of 16-mm achromatic objective with Huygenian eyepiece, or 4-mm apochromatic objective with compensating eyepiece.

AREA VISIBLE ON SLIDE

With a 7.5× Huygenian eyepiece (draw-tube length 160 mm), and virtual-image distance 250 mm, the diameter of the unmagnified area seen as a magnified virtual image is 4 mm when a 4×, 32-mm achromatic objective is used. The diameter of the area is 1.9 mm with a 10×, 16-mm objective; it is 0.68 mm for a 21×, 8-mm objective, and only about 0.2 mm for an 1.8-mm oil-immersion objective.

THE ELECTRON MICROSCOPE

A considerable increase in the resolving power of optical microscopes or optical micrographic projectors can be obtained if it is possible to substitute for the visible or ultraviolet light, with which the object is illuminated, a form of radiation of much shorter wavelength, which on passing through a deviating medium would come to a focus and produce images.

THE DE BROGLIE WAVES

The modern electron microscope or micrographic projector is a device that uses *matter waves* instead of light waves to make details of structure photographable. High-velocity electrons, according to the de Broglie theory of quantum dynamics, have associated with them so-called matter waves. The lengths of these waves are associated with the momentum of the particle according to the fundamental experimentally verified* relation

$$\lambda = \frac{h}{mv}$$

in which the wavelength λ becomes less as the velocity v of the electron, of mass m, increases. h is Planck's constant.

If the velocity of the electron is small we may use the rest mass m_0 for m. Thus an electron of rest mass $m_0 = 9.11 \times 10^{-28}$ gram moving with a velocity of 5.94×10^8 cm/sec has associated with it a wavelength equal to 1.22×10^{-8} cm.

WAVELENGTHS OF CONTROLLED HIGH-SPEED ELECTRONS

If an electron is placed in a uniform electric field, as for instance the field between two oppositely charged parallel condenser plates, in a vacuum tube, it will move toward the positively charged plate and gain kinetic energy. This gain in energy is proportional to the difference of potential V to which the plates are charged. As the electron emerges from the electric field it will have a velocity v given by $\frac{1}{2}m_0v^2 = eV/300$, if v is not too large. On substituting this relation in the de Broglie equation it is found that

$$\lambda = \frac{h}{m_0\sqrt{\dfrac{V}{150} \cdot \dfrac{e}{m_0}}} = \sqrt{\frac{150}{V}} \cdot 10^{-8} \text{ cm}$$

The wavelength associated with an electron after the electron has moved down a potential gradient of 150 volts is as small as 1 Å, or it may be said that a 1-volt electron has a wavelength equal to 12.3 Å. This result is correct to 0.5 per cent if the velocities of the electrons are not too high.

In order to use the wavelengths associated with very high-speed electrons, of the order of 50 kilovolts (50,000 ev) or more, the relativity

* Experimental confirmation of de Broglie's theory was first achieved in 1927 by Davisson and Germer of the research laboratories of the Bell Telephone Company, New York.

expression for mass $(m = m_0/\sqrt{1 - \beta^2})$ must be used. Then

$$\lambda = \frac{h}{m_0 c}\sqrt{\frac{1 - \beta^2}{\beta^2}}$$

where $\beta = v/c$, $m_0 = 9.107 \times 10^{-28}$ gram, $c = 2.998 \times 10^{10}$ cm/sec, and $(m - m_0)c^2 = \dfrac{eV}{300}$. Thus

$$\lambda = \frac{12.39}{\sqrt{V}} \cdot \frac{1}{\sqrt{1 + 9.72 \times 10^{-7}V}}$$

where the wavelength is expressed in angstrom units (10^{-8} cm) and V in volts. Thus 60-kilovolt electrons have associated wavelengths equal to 4.88×10^{-10} cm or 0.0488 Å, which is about 100,000 times shorter than the wavelength of visible radiation.

RESOLVING POWER

The resolving power of an optical microscope was defined as

$$\text{R.P.} = \frac{2\,\text{N.A.}}{\lambda}\ \text{cm}^{-1}$$

Other things being equal, the resolving power is greater, the smaller the wavelength of light that penetrates the condenser, the object, and the optical lens system. With a numerical aperture equal to 1.00 and with ultraviolet illumination having wavelength 2000 Å the resolving power is 100,000 cm^{-1}. The smallest distance resolved, or the resolution, is therefore 10^{-5} cm.

The numerical aperture of a typical commercial electron microscope is of the order of 0.02; using 60-kilovolt electrons ($\lambda = 4.88 \times 10^{-10}$ cm) a resolution of 1.22×10^{-8} cm is obtained. If it were possible to construct a perfect objective utilizing these short wavelengths we would be able to produce photographable images of some of the giant organic molecules, or obtain an interpretable image of a calcite crystal having a grating space at 20° C of 3.35 Å.

ELECTRON LENSES

Lenses that are built to refract beams of high-speed electrons are called electron lenses. They are either electrostatic- or magnetic-field lenses.

These electron lenses simulate optical lenses in that they may be designed to diverge or converge a stream of electrons. Just as a beam of light can be deviated from its path at the boundary of an air-glass surface, owing to the change in the index of refraction, so a beam of electrons can be deviated from its path where it encounters a change in the intensity of an electric field.

In optics we know from Snell's law that $n_1 \sin i_1 = n_2 \sin i_2$ (Fig. VIII–12a), where n_1 and n_2 are the indices of refraction of the two media. But Snell's law may also be written

$$\frac{n_1}{n_2} = \frac{\sin i_2}{\sin i_1}$$

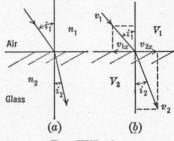

(a)   (b)

FIG. VIII–12.

where n_1 and n_2 are the indices of light in air and glass respectively.

What happens to an electron moving with velocity v_1 (Fig. VIII–12b) as it passes through a region in which the potential alters suddenly from V_1 to V_2? If the electron arrives at the boundary, making an angle i_1 with the normal, it will be deviated and pass into the second medium along the path v_2 making angle i_2 with the normal. The horizontal components v_{1x} and v_{2x} of v_1 do not change in magnitude in passing into the lower medium, so that

$$v_1 \sin i_1 = v_2 \sin i_2$$

If an electric field is used to accelerate the electron, its kinetic energy is determined by

$$\tfrac{1}{2}mv^2 = eV$$

or

$$\frac{\sin i_1}{\sin i_2} = \frac{v_2}{v_1} = \sqrt{\frac{V_2}{V_1}}$$

where a change in the potential at the boundary of the two adjoining media is from V_1 in the upper to V_2 in the lower medium.

The " electric refractive index " is therefore analogous to the optical refractive index in that the $\sqrt{V}$ replaces n.

There is an important difference between the two deviation phenomena, however. In the optical transition from air to glass the index of refraction changes suddenly, and no further deviation takes place in the second medium, whereas in the electron transition the refractive index changes continuously along the path of the electron and as long as it remains in the second medium. A uniform electric field set parallel to the direction of the motion of the electron and a field-free space are the only types of regions which produce no deviation in the path of the electron.

A *thin electron lens* may be defined as a region of non-uniform field extending over so short a distance along its axis that an electron can travel through it in an interval of time small compared to the focal times. The *focal time* is the time elapsing while the electron travels over a path length equal to the focal distance. Thus the optical conjugate focal distances may in a corresponding manner be called the conjugate focal times of an electron lens.

The velocity of the electron, at any point on the axis of an electrostatic electron lens, is obtained from its kinetic energy $\frac{1}{2}mv^2 = eV$. This velocity is

$$v = \sqrt{\frac{2eV}{m}}$$

so that an electron in traveling a distance d along the axis of the lens arrives at a focal point in time t given by

$$d = \sqrt{\frac{2eV}{m}} \cdot t$$

The equation of a thin glass lens of index of refraction n immersed in air is

$$\frac{1}{d_i} - \frac{1}{d_o} = (n - 1)\left(\frac{1}{R_1} - \frac{1}{R_2}\right) = \frac{1}{F}$$

where d_i and d_o are, respectively image and object distances, measured from the optical center of this lens. If this lens is bounded on the object side by a medium of index n_o, and on the image side by a medium of index of refraction n_i, the lens equation reduces to

$$\frac{n_i}{d_i} - \frac{n_o}{d_o} = \frac{1}{F}$$

In the electrostatic electron lens, by analogy, $\sqrt{V}$ is used instead of the optical index,

$$\frac{\sqrt{V_i}}{d_i} - \frac{\sqrt{V_o}}{d_o} = \frac{1}{F}$$

which describes the focal length of a thin electrostatic electron lens in terms of the image distance d_i, object distance d_o, and bounding electric fields which accelerate the electron to the lens under a difference of potential V_o and away from the lens under a difference of potential V_i.

An apertured plate set at right angles to the lines of an electric field practically fulfills the definition of a thin electrostatic electron lens.

Such a lens is shown in Fig. VIII–13 as a small aperture in a thin metal plate separating two fields of different electric intensities. The electric field E_2 on the right side of the hole is of greater intensity than E_1. Note the narrow region around the edge of the hole in which there is a rapid change in electrical intensity. Since the lines of force are continuous, a field parallel to the axis of the lens can change in intensity only

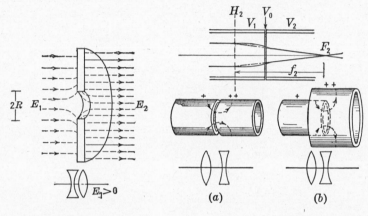

FIG. VIII–13. Lines of force terminating on an apertured plate with field $E_2 > E_1$. Equivalent optical lens system below. (By courtesy of the *Bell System Technical Journal* and F. Gray [1939].)

FIG. VIII–14. Electron trajectory and principal points for cylindrical tube lenses. Lines of force are the broken lines; H_2 second principal plane; F_2 second principal focus. (a) and (b) equivalent optical trains for potential $V_2 > V_1$. (By courtesy of the *Bell System Technical Journal* and F. Gray [1939].)

by lines of force crowding into it or leaving it in a radial direction. These radial components of the fields deviate the electrons in a radial direction. Since the radial components of E_2 are greater than those of E_1 in the region around the hole, a parallel electron beam approaching the hole from the left would converge on the right side of the aperture. In this type of lens the non-uniform field at the aperture covers a distance, along the axis, about equal to its diameter.

Another electrical potential electron lens much favored in the construction of " electron guns " is the coaxial tube type.

These lenses are diagrammatically represented in Fig. VIII–14a and b. The path of the electron is indicated as an unbroken line; the lines of force, as broken lines. The divergent field has the same intensity as the convergent field, but an electron is traveling faster in the divergent field so that it receives a corresponding smaller radial deflection in that field, thus making the total lens system convergent.

ELECTRON GUN

The use of the apertured lens plate as an electron lens unit is illustrated in Law's [1937] design of an electron gun, Fig. VIII–15.   It is composed

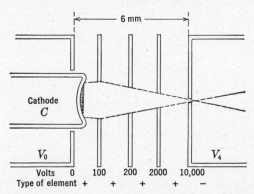

FIG. VIII–15.   Details of a high-density electron gun.   Indirectly heated cathode.   Coated area 0.13-cm diameter.   Electron beam, broken line.   Apertures 3.86-, 2.24-, 1.70-, 1.32-, and 0.10-mm diameter.   (By courtesy of R.R. Law [1937].)

of an oxide-coated cathode (C) with aperture V_0 acting as its " grid." This is followed by a train of aperture anodes.   The potentials of the grid and cathode are V_0, and the others rise in the order indicated.   This lens gives a high-density electron stream with a cross-over at the hole in V_4.

A coaxial type of electrostatic electron lens train as designed by Zworykin [1933] is shown in Fig. VIII–16.   The electrons emitted by the cathode are accelerated by the positive potential of the first anode and converged by the higher positive potential of the second anode. Note that a cross-over of the beam occurs near the aperture of the first anode.

An electron gun, featuring both the circular diaphragm and the coaxial cylinder as parts of an electron lens system to obtain either a divergent or a convergent beam, is illustrated diagrammatically in Fig. VIII–17.   If the electrons are traveling with low velocity near the cathodes as in (b) the field must be perfectly uniform.   If the first aperture lens draws off the electrons with high velocity as in (a), the first cylindrical electron lens acts as a condenser lens; otherwise an accelerating cylinder lens must precede it, as in (b), to impart the necessary velocity before convergence takes place.   In this way a condenser lens

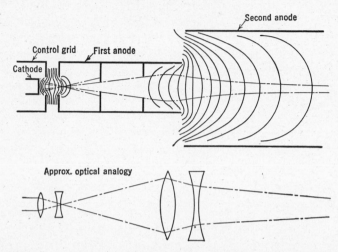

Fig. VIII–16. An electron lens-system due to Zworykin. Sections of the electric equipotential surfaces are shown in solid lines, electron beam in broken lines. Potential of second anode about twice as great as first anode. Approximate optical analogy just below. (By courtesy of V. K. Zworykin [1933 and 1934].)

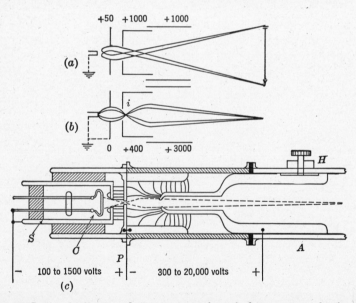

Fig. VIII–17. A diagrammatic representation of electron guns having same physical dimensions but charged as in (a) to give a divergent beam and in (b) to give a convergent beam of electrons. (c) Diagrammatic section of an assembled electron gun. Note cross-over at aperture and subsequent convergence of beam. (By courtesy of R. H. George [1929].)

can either diverge or converge the beam. Figure VIII–17a will give an image of the cathode in the plane of the arrow at the right and can be used to produce a magnified image of the surface structure of the cathode. Figure VIII–17b will give an image of the cross-over area located just to the left of i while the image of the cathode is located at i.

Owing to the non-uniformity of emission, it is not desirable to use the cathode as the electron source. It is more desirable to use an intervening aperture as an electron source since it can be made smaller and denser and also allows some latitude of focusing. This is taken advantage of in George's [1929] design of an electron gun (Fig. VIII–17c).

The beam from the cathode C is concentrated and brought to a focus at the hole in plate P by properly proportioning the spacing between filament C, filament shield S, and plate P with respect to the size of the aperture S. The high-potential field is so shaped, by the anode cylinder, that the electrons are not only accelerated in the direction of the anode but are also given radial components of velocity which crowd them to the axis of the beam. If this radial force component compensates the repulsive force of the beam's space charge it is possible to bring the beam to a sharp focus. If the diameter of the beam is wide, where it starts to converge, the electron gun will have a long focal length. By increasing the radial component, it is possible to change the focal length of the beam. This is done by shifting the anode A by means of the knurled head H which operates a rack and pinion.

The Magnetic-Field Electron Lens

If a moving electron, with its associated magnetic field, enters a static magnetic field it may be deflected so as to change the curvature of its path. The static magnetic field does not change the kinetic energy of the electron. If the electron moves in a direction perpendicular to a homogeneous magnetic field, it is deflected to describe a circular path. If it moves parallel to the direction of the field, it is altered neither in direction nor in speed. If the electron makes an angle with the direction of the magnetic field it will corkscrew down the field as indicated in Fig. VIII–18. This complex motion is more easily understood after considering the motion of an electron which is shot, with velocity v, into a homogeneous static magnetic field of intensity H set at right angles to the direction of motion of the electron. This magnetic field forces the electron to move in a circular path.

The static magnetic field acts at right angles to the magnetic field associated with the moving electron. The electron is therefore acted upon by a radial force $F_r = -evH$. While moving in this circular path the electron is subjected to a centrifugal force $-F_c = mv^2/r$. In equilibrium, the sum of these two forces is equal to zero; hence the radius of the circular path of deflection is

$$r = \frac{mv}{eH}$$

For a given magnetic field of intensity H the radius of curvature is therefore proportional to the velocity of the electron. The time of a complete revolution of an electron, of charge $e = 1.602 \times 10^{-20}$ emu, is

$$t = \frac{2\pi r}{v} = \frac{2\pi}{H}\frac{m}{e} = \frac{3.57}{H} \cdot 10^{-7} \text{ second}$$

If a pencil of electrons, of mixed velocities, leaves a point source and moves at right angles to the magnetic lines of force, each electron will

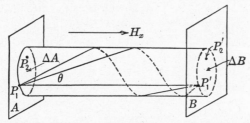

FIG. VIII–18.

describe a circle having a radius proportional to its velocity. If they all start from the same point at the same time, they will all converge at the same point at the end of one complete revolution, because the time of the circular excursion depends only on the field strength.

If an electron is projected into a uniform magnetic field set at some small angle θ with the direction of its motion, the field acts as a focusing device. Under these circumstances the motion of the electron may be resolved into two components, one parallel and the other at right angles to the magnetic field. The parallel-velocity component, Fig. VIII–18, will translate the electron in a direction parallel to the magnetic field with velocity $v \cos \theta$, while the right-angled component $v \sin \theta$ directed perpendicular to the magnetic field will give the electron a circular motion. The composite motion is therefore screwlike. The figure shows two such paths.

Suppose that the point P_1 emits an electron beam in which all the electrons have the same velocity, but leave the point at various small angles θ with the direction of the horizontal magnetic field H_x. They will all arrive at the point P_1' at the same time. A point P_2 in a small circular area in the same plane with P_1, under identical circumstances, will be imaged in the plane B by the point P_2'.   Thus a small area ΔA emitting a stream of electrons with uniform velocity will form a point-for-point image in the plane B at ΔB.

The analysis of the motion of an electron in a short symmetrically distorted magnetic field is beset with mathematical difficulties beyond the scope of this book.   An approximate graphical analysis, therefore, will be used to show how a short magnetic electron lens functions.

A *short magnetic electron lens* is a coil in which the region of magnetic field distribution, along its axis, is small compared with its focal length.

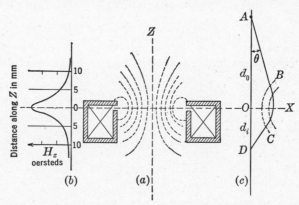

FIG. VIII–19.   (a) Vertical section through a magnetic field of an annular sole-noid enclosed in a 2-mm soft-iron shield.   Condenser electron lens without pole pieces.   (b) Curve showing magnetic field strength in oersteds measured along Z, above and below horizontal plane through X.   (c) Path of an electron leaving A and passing through such a magnetic field, crosses Z axis at D.

In order to compress the field, the coil is encased in soft iron shields about 2 mm thick with an inner annular gap at one end.   This air gap is usually made equal to about one twentieth the diameter of the inside coil.   Such a lens produces an axially symmetrical magnetic field, the intensity of which drops off very rapidly above and below the gap. Figure VIII–19 shows such a coil of 6500 turns of 0.2-mm-diameter wire excited at 220 volts, 0.1 ampere current.   It has a 4-mm annular gap.   If a probe is moved along the vertical axis, to determine the intensity of the magnetic field, it will be found that the magnetic intensity H_z drops to half value at about 3 mm above and below the horizontal plane of the gap.

If a high-speed electron from a field-free space above A approaches this coil and moves down the z axis, it will pass through the magnetic field without changing its speed or direction.   If the electron leaves the point A, however, and moves along the straight line AB making a small angle θ with the z axis, and enters the magnetic field at B, which extends around the equatorial plane OX, it will be continuously deflected until it reaches the field-free space CD. From C onward it will move in a straight line to intersect the z axis at D. The trajectory is not in one plane, however. It is a screw motion which at every complete turn crosses this axis. For a given object distance OA, the image distance OD does not depend on the angle of projection θ, if θ is small.

Busch [1926] and later Davisson and Calbick [1931] showed that for electrons of moderate velocity the focal length f of an electron lens is

$$\frac{1}{f} = \frac{0.022}{V} \int_{-\infty}^{+\infty} H_z{}^2 \, dz \text{ cm}^{-1}$$

where V is the energy per electron in volts and H is the field intensity in oersteds. The value of H along the z axis may be obtained from the currents induced in a miniature probe coil as it is pulled out of the field, from various points above and below the z axis. The resulting distribution of H_z is shown in Fig. VIII–19b. If this curve is replotted in terms of H^2, the area under this new curve is the value of the integral $H^2 dz$.

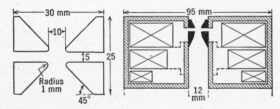

Fig. VIII–20. A typical electron lens pole piece. Electron lens with pole piece in place. The tier of three coils may be used interchangeably to vary the magnetic field in pole-piece gap.

Magnetic Lens with Pole Pieces

Ruska [1934] developed an electron lens of an iron-cored type to be used as an objective in his electron microscope. Two common types of iron pole pieces that may be inserted in the magnetic field of an electron lens are shown in Fig. VIII–20. These pole pieces are about 30 mm in diameter and 25 mm thick, with a 10-mm gap. The lens is designed so that one or two coils may be used to modify the magnetic field between the pole pieces.

In such annular magnetic pole pieces the field intensity may attain 3500 oersteds and will drop to 1000 oersteds in the fifth millimeter below the gap.

Two-Stage Magnetic Electron Microscope Projector

Electron microscopes may be roughly classified as those using electrostatic- or magnetic-field electron lenses. Each of these two types may be designed to use either a hot filament or a cold cathode immersed in a low-pressure gas as a means of generating the electron stream.

In both types the available electrons are accelerated by a controlled electric field to give them the proper energy before they enter the condenser lens. The condenser lens converges the stream of electrons on the miniature aperture of the object stage in which the specimen is supported. The electron lens acting as an objective converges the beams of electrons that have succeeded in passing through the object, and focuses them in the field of the image projector, which in turn takes a small section of this electron pattern and focuses it on a photographic plate or fluoroscopic screen.

The two-stage electron microscope projector probably had its inception in the high-potential laboratory at the Neubabelsberg technical school in Berlin. Various members of this laboratory had been experimenting with high-voltage cathode-ray oscillographs using cold cathodes in low-pressure gas as the sources of uniform-velocity electron beams. Knoll and Ruska by 1930 had successfully adapted one of these to a one-stage magnetic lens microscope. By 1934 Ruska had developed a two-stage, cold-cathode, magnetic lens microscope. The magnetic lenses with their uniquely designed pole pieces made it possible for him to attain exceptionally high resolution. His magnified electron images reached 40,000 diameters. He succeeded in magnifying some organic specimens from 8000 to 10,000 times.

Marton [1934] at Brussels built a two-stage instrument having a hot-filament cathode as source. With his subsequent adoption of a new histological technique to prevent the destruction of organic cells by the intense electron bombardment [Nature, 1934] he obtained excellent microphotographs of Chromobacterium prodigiosum fixed in chromic acid.

A two-stage cold-cathode electron microscope of very elaborate design was completed by Martin, Whelpton, and Parnum [1937], at London. The source of power was a 250-cycle, 20-kilovolt generator with 0.1-microfarad condenser having a ripple voltage as small as 0.1 per cent.

By 1938, Borries and Ruska, at the laboratory of Siemens and Halske, completed their " supermicroscope " and showed that their instrument could produce recognizable structural details in Staphylococcus aureus at 20,400 magnification. A later publication by Borries, Ruska, and Ruska [1938] showed Bacillus enteritidis with internal nuclei at 13,500×, and some viruses appeared to have recognizable shapes at 20,000×.

A commercial instrument has been completed at the RCA laboratories by Zworykin, Hillier, and Vance [1941], based on the design of Marton's original experimental model. A sectional view and full-scale photograph of this instrument are shown in Figs. VIII–21a and b.

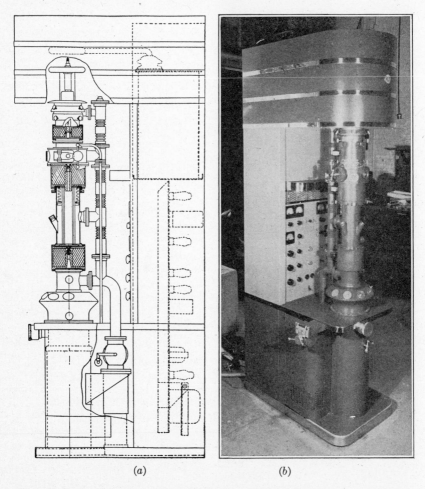

(a)   (b)

FIG. VIII–21. Sectional and external view of the RCA electron microscope. This commercial model was developed in the RCA Laboratories at Camden, N.J. (By courtesy of V. K. Zworykin, RCA Research Laboratories.)

This RCA model is equipped with an electron source in the form of a small tungsten filament which is partly surrounded by a guard cylinder. The anode is enclosed, but the end of the guard cylinder has a hole in it which is coaxial with the opening in the collimator. The full voltage of the microscope (maximum 60 kilovolts) is applied between the cathode and anode, the anode being at ground potential, while the cathode is negative. The electrons emitted from the filament are accelerated towards the anode. A portion of these electrons passes through the aperture in the anode, thence through the condenser, which concentrates them on the specimen.

The magnetic condenser lens consists of an iron-clad coil with pole pieces shaped to converge the electron beam on the specimen placed just below it. The specimen is placed in position through an air lock.

The electrons after passing through the specimen enter the magnetic field of the objective. This lens deviates the emitted electrons, which leave point sources at small angles, in such a way as to focus them in a plane directly above the pole piece of the projection lens. In this focal plane lies the first-stage magnified electron image of the specimen. This first-stage image has a magnification of about 100 diameters.

The final image is formed from that portion of the first-stage electron image which fills the diaphragm stop of the projection electron lens. The electron stream passing through the magnetic field of this lens is deviated to form the second-stage image in the plane of the photographic plate or fluorescent screen. The magnification at this stage can be varied from 20 to 300 diameters by controlling the current in the projection coil. The total magnification varies from 2000 to 30,000 diameters. Supermagnification can be obtained by enlarging the photographic image from 6 to 10 times, depending on the grain size of the photographic emulsion. Under favorable conditions it is possible to attain a magnification of 180,000 diameters. The limiting usable magnification is about 100,000 diameters.

The operating pressure in this instrument is about 10 mm of mercury. No greased joints are used. Alignment is obtained by means of flexible sylphon bellows. The photographic chamber is air locked and is fitted for 2-by-10-inch photographic plates. Such a long plate permits making a number of pictures in a row. Six ports are also provided for viewing the definition of the final image on a removable fluorescent screen.

Figure VIII–22 is a 21,000× photograph of a human tuberculosis bacterium obtained with this electron microprojector.

For the high-voltage power supply, Vance [1941] employed radiofrequency power to actuate the step-up transformer unit, since stray fields are more easily shielded when radiofrequency power is used. The power supply can therefore be mounted as an integral part of the unit. It is claimed that the measured voltage fluctuation in the power supply over a period of half an hour was less than 0.002 per cent. The current supplies for the lenses have a constancy of better than 0.002 per cent for the objective lens, 0.004 per cent for the projection lens, and 0.02 per cent for the condenser lens (Zworyken, Hillier, and Vance [1941]). This stability of the current is necessary if one wishes a resolution of 10^{-7} cm.

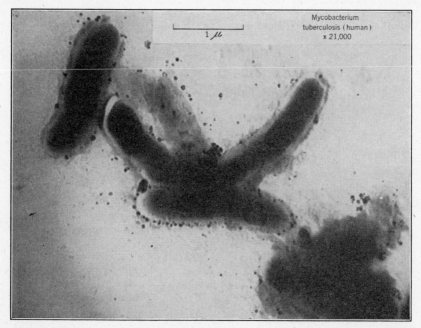

Fig. VIII–22. An electron image of a human tuberculosis bacterium (original magnification was 42,000 ×) obtained with an RCA electron microscope. (By courtesy of V. K. Zworykin, RCA Research Laboratories.)

OPTICAL ANALOGY

A diagrammatic sectional drawing of an electron microprojector incorporating the essential features of a hot-cathode electron source with magnetic field electron lenses is shown in Fig. VIII–23. The train of magnetic lenses conforms to the standard design of the two-stage hot-cathode magnetic lens electron microprojector.

The electron gun G at the top is corona shielded. Its electron beam can be focused by the rack-and-pinion movement F of the anode on the condenser stop. Its cross-sectional area at this point is used as the electronic source. The condenser lens C focuses this beam on the specimen placed in the 0.12-sq-mm cavity of the object stage at S. The first-stage image, after a cross-over of the beam, is focused in the first-image plane I.

This image position is comparable to the position of the magnified real image found in the image plane of the optical microscope. In the optical microscope, the real image is projected with the aid of a lens on

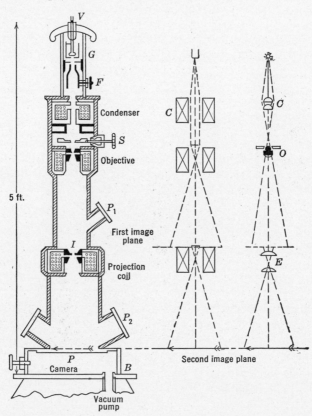

FIG. VIII–23. Diagrammatic section of a typical electron microscope projector with hot cathode. The operation is analogous to the conventional light microscope at right. Suitably shaped magnetic fields take the place of the glass lenses. Condenser lens C, objective lens system O, projection lenses E with final image in second image plane. In the electron microscope the electrons leave the filament, are accelerated between G and F by about 50 kv, are converged by the condenser lens on the specimen at S. After passing through the specimen, the objective lens coil forms a first image at I, enlarged about 100 fold. The projection lens coil again magnifies this image about 100 fold making an overall magnification of 10,000. Image can be photographed at P. P_2 is a port for viewing the fluorescent image, when a movable fluorescent screen is placed in plane of image at P.

the photographic plate of a camera attached to the barrel of the instrument. In the same way the projection coil of the electron microscope allows that section of the electron image covering its stop to be used for reprojection, with its accompanying magnification, into the plane of the photographic plate placed at P. The port P_2 is used with the aid of a movable fluorescent screen to view the composition of the final image. The height of the electron microprojector, from the high-potential voltage terminal V to the base B where the vacuum pump connection enters, is about 5 feet.

RESOLVING POWER OF AN ELECTRON MICROSCOPE

According to Ruska [1934], magnetic field lenses can be constructed to possess larger apertures than electrostatic electron lenses. The practical limit is reached when a magnetic-coil electron lens has attained a numerical aperture equal to 0.02. With a 50-kilovolt electron beam ($\lambda = 0.055$ Å) and such an aperture it is possible to attain a theoretical resolution of 1.4×10^{-7} cm. Ardene [1938], in a detailed analysis of the contributing factors which may reduce this theoretical value, showed that with a 50-kilovolt electron beam the practical limit of resolution is 10^{-7} cm.

ELECTRON IMAGE DEFECTS

The first-stage electron image may possess defects due to: (1) the diffraction of the associated electron waves; (2) the influence of space charge on the electron path; (3) chromatic aberration due to the fact that not all the emission electrons have the same velocity and that electron scattering by the specimen and its support are unavoidable; (4) insufficient magnetic shielding against the earth's magnetic field and other outside influences; (5) fluctuations in the accelerating potential which should be reduced to at least 5 volts in 50 kilovolts.

MAGNETIC CONDENSER

A typical electron lens train, and the effects of the magnetic fields on the electron beams passing through it, are shown in Fig. VIII–24. The electron beam entering the lens from the top is shown filling the aperture of the condenser lens. This beam has a minimum diameter d at a distance a above the equatorial plane of the field of the condenser lens. Its virtual source A_1 has an angular aperture $2\alpha_s$. When no field has been established, a point P in the plane of the object, $(a + b)$ below d, subtends an angular aperture

$$\alpha_c = \frac{d}{2(a + b)}$$

When a magnetic field is established by a current flowing through the condenser coils, the virtual focal point A_1 moves down owing to the constriction of the electron beam by the magnetic field. This lowering of A_1 continues until α_c reaches a maximal value α_c' such that

$$\alpha_c' = \frac{a}{b} \alpha_s$$

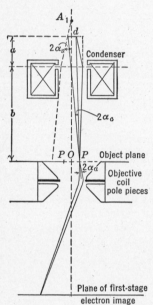

Then the focal point coincides with the source d. A further increase in the field intensity reduces this angular aperture, with an accompanying decrease in the electron density impinging on the object POP. A change in current through the condenser coil can therefore regulate the density of the electron stream "illuminating" the specimen in the aperture POP of the object stage.

If the values of a and b in the electron microscope are 5 and 15 cm, respectively, the maximum angular aperture available for illuminating the point P on the specimen stage would be 0.007. This very constricted beam subtends an angle of 25 seconds of arc and, therefore, fulfills the requirement that the electrons incident on this point make small angles with the axis of the lens.

FIG. VIII–24. A geometrical analysis of an electron beam leaving a small aperture d with electron condenser lens converging a beam at P. Specimen in the object plane at POP. The objective electron lens deviates the beam, it crosses over and comes to a focus in the electron image plane. (Borries and Ruska [1939].)

OBJECT STAGE

The object stage, which supports the specimen in the very small aperture POP, may be centered above the equatorial plane of the pole pieces of the object coil, or it may be placed between the pole pieces, in which event it is designated as an *immersion electron objective*.

The specimen may be placed on very fine-meshed wire gauze or supported on a very thin collodion film suspended in a single mesh of the gauze. These collodion films may have densities as great as 1.6 grams/cc (Ruska [1934]), and they should not be more than 3×10^{-5} mm thick.

The aperture in which the specimen is mounted is about 0.1 mm in radius. It should be made of a gold-platinum alloy to prevent geometrical distortions by oxide particles which may form along its highly polished inner surface. If the apertures are too small, large errors are introduced by reflection of electrons at the side walls of the boring.

MAGNETIC OBJECTIVE

In Fig. VIII–24 is shown an object stage POP, placed just above the pole pieces of the magnetic objective coil. The pole pieces have a clearance of 10 mm. A brass disk, with a boring of 0.1-mm radius, acts as a diaphragm stop. The incident electrons passing through the specimen are scattered through various angles. It is only those electrons that pass through the specimen without appreciable change in path that can be considered as contributing anything to the first-stage electron image, which is formed by the transmitted beam.

The angular aperture of the incident beam is $2\alpha_c$, or $2\alpha_c'$ when it attains its maximum value. The electrons leaving the specimen below P that contribute anything to the first-stage image must be contained in the angular aperture $2\alpha_a$ defined by the resolving power of the magnetic objective, namely

$$\text{R.P.} = \frac{2 \text{ N.A.}}{\lambda} \equiv \frac{2\alpha_a}{\lambda} \text{ cm}^{-1}$$

Without a magnetic field below the plane POP to deflect the emitted electron beam, $\alpha_a = \alpha_c$. The magnetic field of the objective coil constricts the electron beam emitted at P so that a beam of larger angular aperture

$$\alpha_a = \alpha_c + \alpha_b$$

is made available for image formation. Under these conditions α_b is the increase in the angular aperture due to the magnetic field of the objective coil.

Thus the density of the electrons available for image formation, at a given incident electron velocity, depends on the forward scattering properties of the specimen and on the magnetic field strength of the magnetic objective.

If a resolution of 10^{-6} cm is desired with 60-kilovolt electrons ($\lambda = 4.88 \times 10^{-10}$ cm), the angular aperture $2\alpha_a$ should be about 10^{-3}. Under practical conditions the aperture of the diaphragm of the objective coil is made 10 times larger, comparable to a diaphragm stop having a radius of about 0.1 mm.

The very narrow beam of electrons leaving P in the plane of the object is deviated as it passes through the magnetic field of the objective coil to such an extent that it crosses over before it is brought to a focus in the plane just above the pole pieces of the projector lens. This first-stage electron image is usually about 100 times as large as the object.

MAGNETIC PROJECTION LENS

About 35 cm below the magnetic object lens lies the image projector lens. This magnetic projection lens is used to produce the second-stage magnification. The second-stage image lies in the final image-plane 40 cm below the pole pieces of the projector lens.

If a small central portion of the first-stage electron image is further magnified 100 diameters then a total magnification of 10,000 diameters is attained in the second-stage electron image. This image may be viewed through a side port in the instrument and seen in the image plane as it excites a phosphorescent screen, or it may be reproduced by allowing the electron beams to impinge on a photographic plate placed in the plane of the second-stage electron image.

PHOTOGRAPHIC IMAGE

The eye can distinguish detail in an object only when the detail involves dimensions larger than a certain minimum value which at the distance of distinct vision (25 cm) is about 0.074 mm. Its resolving power is thus close to 14 lines per millimeter. The *resolving power of a photographic emulsion* is defined as the number of lines of uniform width, separated by spaces equal to their widths, which can just be distinguished per millimeter on the negative. The average emulsion has a resolving power of about 40 or 50 lines per millimeter. A fine-grained emulsion under most favorable development can attain a resolving power of about 100 lines per millimeter. Magnification of a photographic image by a factor 10 therefore would not destroy the clarity of an image on account of the granular structure of the emulsion.

In the RCA electron microscope the magnification of the second-stage image is about 10,000 to 16,000 diameters. The full useful magnification may then be obtained by enlarging the photographic plate from six to ten times, giving a total magnification of more than 100,000 diameters.

The photographic response of the silver bromide gelatine emulsion to the electron bombardment continues throughout the emulsion as long as the penetrating electron has appreciable energy; thus the depth of penetration of the electrons into the emulsion will determine the practical photographic results obtainable.

It was shown theoretically by J. J. Thomson and confirmed experimentally by Whiddington [1912] that the loss of velocity of cathode rays in passing through matter is expressible by the relation

$$v_i^4 - v_e^4 = ad$$

where v_i is the velocity of the incident and v_e the velocity of the emerging electron after passing through a thickness d, and a is a constant depending on the density of the absorbing substance. Later Terrill [1923] showed that $a = 5.05 \times 10^{42}\rho$, where ρ is the density of the material.

The maximum depth of penetration into a photographic emulsion, here assumed to have a density comparable to that of gelatine,* is therefore approximately $d = v_i^4 \times 10^{-43}$ cm.

If the electrons reach the film with a velocity determined by the accelerating voltage V, the depth of penetration

$$d = 1.2 \times 10^{-12}V^2 \quad \text{cm}$$

If the photographic emulsion is 10^{-3} cm thick, 30-kilovolt electrons would penetrate this film completely, producing a very effective photographic action, since the developed blackening of a photographic emulsion depends on the concentration of the electron beam and on the square of the accelerating voltage.

BIBLIOGRAPHY

1912 WHIDDINGTON, R., *Proc. Roy. Soc. London*, **A86**, 370.

1923 TERRILL, H. M., *Phys. Rev.*, **22**, 101.

1925 WOOD, A. B., *J. Inst. Elec. Engrs. (London)*, **63**, 1046.

1926 BUSCH, H., *Ann. Physik*, **81**, 974.

1929 GEORGE, R. H., *J. Am. Inst. Elec. Engrs.*, **48**, 534.

1930 KNOLL, M., H. KNOBLAUCH, and B. v. BORRIES, *Elektrotech. Z.*, **51**, 966.

1931 DAVISSON, C. J., and C. J. CALBICK, *Phys. Rev.*, **38**, 585.

1932 KNOLL, M., and E. RUSKA, *Z. Physik*, **78**, 318.

1933 ZWORYKIN, V. K., *J. Franklin Inst.*, **215**, 535, or *J. Inst. Elec. Engrs. (London)*, **73**, 437.

1934 BRÜCHE, E., and O. SCHERZER, *Geometrische Elektronenoptik*, Springer, Berlin.

1934 MARTON, L., *Bull. acad. roy. Belg.*, *Cl. Sci.*, **20**, 439; also **21**, 553 and 606 (1935); **22**, 1336 (1936); **23**, 672 (1937).

1934 MARTON, L., *Nature*, **133**, 911.

1934 RUSKA, E., *Z. Physik*, **87**, 580; **89**, 90.

1934 ZWORYKIN, V. K., *J. Franklin Inst.*, **217**, 1.

1935 BEECHING, R., *Electron Diffraction* (elementary de Broglie theory), Methuen and Company, London.

1936 BUSCH, H., *Z. tech. Physik*, **17**, 584. (Electron optics symposium.)

1937 KRAUSE, F., *Naturwissenschaften*, **25**, 817.

1937 LAW, R. R., *Proc. Inst. Radio Engrs.*, **25**, 954.

1937 MARTIN, L. C., R. V. WHELPTON, and D. H. PARNUM, *J. Sci. Instruments*, **14**, 14.

* Gelatine has an average density of 1.27 grams/cc.

1938   ARDENE, M. V., *Z. Physik*, **108**, 38; also **109**, 553.
1938   BORRIES, B. V., and E. RUSKA, *Wiss. Veröffent. Siemens-Werken*, **17**, 99; also *Z. tech. Physik*, **19**, 402.
1938   BORRIES, B. V., E. RUSKA, and H. RUSKA, *Klin. Wochschr.*, **17**, 1; also *Wiss. Veröffent. Siemens-Werken*, **17**, 107; also *Z. Ver. deut. Ing.*, **82**, 1.
1938   FITZSIMMONS, K. E., *J. Optical Soc. Am.*, **28**, 437.
1939   BORRIES, B. V., and E. RUSKA, *Naturwissenschaften*, **27**, 281.
1939   COOPER, F. S., C. E. BUCHWALD, C. P. HASKINS, and R. D. EVANS, *Rev. Sci. Instruments*, **10**, 73.
1939   GRAY, F., *Bell System Tech. J.*, **18**, 1.
1939   KAUSCHE, G. A., E. PFANKUCH, and H. RUSKA, *Naturwissenschaften*, **27**, 292.
1939   KLEMPERER, O., *Electron Optics*, Cambridge University Press.
1939   MYERS, L. M., *Electron Optics*, Chapman & Hall, London.
1939   RUSKA, H., *Naturwissenschaften*, **27**, 287.
1939   SCOTT, G. H., and D. M. PACKER, *Anat. Rec.*, **74**, 17.
1940   ARDENE, M. V., *Elektronen-Übermikroskopie*, Springer, Berlin.
1940   LOOFBOUROW, J. R. (summary of literature), *Rev. Modern Phys.*, **12**, 267.
1940   MARTON, L., *Phys. Rev.*, **58**, 57.
1940   MARTON, L., M. C. BANCA, and J. F. BENDER, *RCA Rev.*, **5**, 232.
1940   ZWORYKIN, V. K., *Elec. Eng.*, **59**, 441; *Science*, **92**, 51.
1941   MARTON, G. A., *RCA Rev.*, **6**, 131.
1941   VANCE, A. W., *RCA Rev.*, **5**, 293.
1941   ZWORYKIN, V. K., J. HILLIER, and A. W. VANCE, *Elec. Eng.*, **60**, 157.
1942   BURTON, E. F., and W. H. KOHL, *The Electron Microscope*, Reinhold Publishing Corporation, New York.

PHYSICAL CONSTANTS*

1 Angstrom unit	$= 1 \text{ Å} = 10^{-8}$ cm
1 micron	$= 10^{-3}$ mm
1 millimicron	$= 10^{-6}$ mm
Velocity of light c	$= 2.99776 \times 10^{10}$ cm sec^{-1}
1 electron volt (ev)	$= 1.6020 \times 10^{-12}$ erg
1 Mev	$= 10^6$ ev

$$\tfrac{1}{2}mv^2 = \frac{eV}{300} = h\nu \qquad = \frac{hc}{\lambda} \quad (V \text{ in volts, } e \text{ in esu})$$

For photons
$$\lambda = \frac{12{,}395}{V} \text{ Å } (V \text{ in volts})$$

For electrons
$$\lambda = \frac{150}{V} \text{ Å } (V \text{ in volts})$$

Electron charge e	$= 4.8025 \times 10^{-10}$ esu
	$= 4.8025 \times 10^{-10}/c = 1.6020 \times 10^{-20}$ **emu**
Mass of electron m_0	$= 9.1066 \times 10^{-28}$ gram
Boltzmann's constant k	$= \dfrac{R_0}{N_0} = \dfrac{8.31436 \times 10^7 \text{ erg} \cdot \text{deg}^{-1} \cdot \text{mole}^{-1}}{6.0228 \times 10^{23} \text{ mole}^{-1}}$
	$= 1.38047 \times 10^{-16} \text{ erg} \cdot \text{deg}^{-1}$
Planck's constant h	$= 6.624 \times 10^{-27}$ erg sec
Mass of H^1 atom	$= 1.6734 \times 10^{-24}$ gram
Mass of alpha particle	$= 6.6442 \times 10^{-24}$ gram
Mass of proton	$= 1.67248 \times 10^{-24}$ gram
Compton shift at 90° h/mc	$= 0.024265$ Å
$\log_e 10$	$= 2.3026$
$\log_{10} 2.718$	$= 0.4343$
Exponential e	$= 2.71828$
Common log	$=$ natural log $\times 0.4343$
Natural log	$=$ common log $\times 2.3026$

* As of August 1941. By R. T. Birge, *Rev. Mod. Phys.*, **13**, 233, 1941.

PROBLEMS

I-1. A peak voltage of 80 kv is applied to an x-ray tube. What is the shortest wavelength emitted? If a tungsten target is used will the characteristic frequencies of tungsten be emitted?

Ans. 0.155 Å.

I-2. What is the longest x-ray wavelength that can penetrate the glass housing of a Coolidge x-ray tube?

I-3. Compute the value of A in Richardson's equation if the electron emission is 2.4 milliamp/cm^2 of tungsten-filament surface when heated to 2000° K.

Ans. 60.2 amp/cm^2/degree^2.

I-4. The work function of tungsten is 4.52 e-volts. How many ergs are expended in removing an electron from a tungsten surface?

Ans. **7**.24 $\times$ 10^{-12} erg.

I-5. What minimum kilovoltage must be used to obtain the shortest wavelength in the K series from an x-ray tube with a tungsten target? ($\lambda = 0.1794$ Å.)

Ans. 69.0 kv.

I-6. A rock salt reflecting crystal is used in a Bragg x-ray spectrometer. An intense reflection is observed to lie 7° 30′ on either side of the central image. What is the wavelength of the x-ray beam forming this image?

Ans. 0.73 Å.

I-7. In surface x-ray doses the incident intensity varies inversely as the square of the skin-to-target distance. What change in time is required to give the same skin dose if the skin-to-target distance is increased from 50 to 80 cm?

Ans. 2.56.

I-8. Find the difference in the doses delivered at 10-cm tissue depth when the x-ray tube is changed from 50 to 80 cm focal-skin distances.

Ans. 1.13.

I-9. An automobile cost $1000. It depreciates 20 per cent in value per year. What is the value at the end of the fifth year?

Ans. $328.

I-10. An automobile costing $1500 depreciated continuously at a yearly percentage rate of 0.30. What was its value at the end of 8 years?

Ans. $136.

I-11. A sample of glass absorbed 2 per cent of the radiant energy passing through it. How much energy will come out of a layer made up of 12 such samples?

Ans. 78.5 per cent.

I-12. A parallel beam of x-rays of wavelength 0.080 Å entered an ionization chamber and its intensity was observed to be 100 units. Calculate the intensities when 1.0-mm sheets of aluminum, copper, and lead are in turn introduced in the beam. Their densities are 2.70, 8.93, and 11.37 grams/cc respectively. What thickness will reduce the intensity to half value?

I-13. How does the penetration in tissue for x-rays of wavelength 0.15 Å compare with those of 0.25 Å?

I-14. The intensity of an unfiltered beam of x-rays, measured by an ionization chamber, was 25 roentgens per minute. After the beam passed through 1, 2, and 3 mm of aluminum the intensities were 20, 15.8, and 10.3 roentgens per minute respectively. Was the beam homogeneous?

II–1. A hospital buys 200 mg of radium element today; how much will remain at the end of 10 years?

II–2. You are given a sample of radioactive material and have found experimentally that the activity has dropped to one-eighth of its initial value in 15 days. What is its half-life? What element is it?

II–3. The rate of change of a radioactive element is represented by the relation $dN/dt = -aN$, where N denotes the number of atoms present at the time t, and a is the constant of proportionality. Show that this is a form of the compound-interest law.

II–4. What is the mass of 1 millicurie of radon?

II–5. A radium emanation tube contains 100 millicuries; how many millicuries are available after 48 hours?

II–6. A radon tube on leaving Philadelphia has a strength of 100 millicuries. If it arrives at your laboratory after 16 hours what is its strength? When is its strength 50 millicuries?

II–7. A radon seed causes the leaf of an electroscope to fall at the rate of 120 divisions per minute. How fast will the leaf move 24 hours later?

II–8. If all the radon is collected every second day from a radon extraction plant containing 500 mg of radium element, what is the strength, in millicuries, of the amount collected, if it is examined 2 hours after collection?

II–9. What is the frequency of a gamma ray if its wavelength is 0.030 Å?

II–10. What thickness of copper will reduce the intensity of a source of gamma rays by the same amount as 2 mm of lead?

II–11. How many alpha particles are emitted by the time a single radium atom has disintegrated into an atom of lead? How many beta particles?

II–12. You are given 2 grams of radium element enclosed in a 0.5-mm platinum cover. What is the tolerance distance with no lead filter if the following lead filters are required to produce a tolerance dose rate of 10^{-5} roentgen per second? Filter thickness of 10.5 cm at 50-cm distance, 7.5 at 100-cm, 4.5 at 200-cm, 1.0 at 500-cm.

II–13. What is the radiation emitted by $_{15}P^{32}$?

III–1. How far from the eye of an observer must a scale be placed in order that 1 cm on the scale will subtend an angle of 1 minute of arc?

Ans. 3438 cm.

III–2. Halftone screens are classified by the number of dots per inch. On coated book paper 200 dots per inch are usually used. If the dot pattern is to be just indistinguishable at the distance of distinct vision, how coarse a screen can be used?

III–3. A given circular sample of gray paper reflects 5 per cent of the incident light. It is fastened to a large piece of white paper reflecting 85 per cent. At what approximate brightness of the white paper will the gray patch be just visible?

III–4. An electric lamp whose intensity is 95.0 candles is placed 250 cm from a wall having a diffusive reflecting power of 80 per cent. What is its brightness in lamberts and in candles per square centimeter?

III–5. If the focal length of a lens is 25.7 cm what is its power in diopters?

Ans. 3.9 dptr.

III–6. The static refraction of an eye is defined as the reciprocal of the distance from the first principal point to the far point. A correcting spectacle lens is +10 dptr. The distance of the anterior principal point of the eye from the second principal point of the spectacle lens is 12 mm. What is the refraction of the eye?

Ans. +11.4 dptr.

III–7. In Gullstrand's schematic eye, with accommodation relaxed, the distance from the image on the retina to the apex of the cornea is 24 mm. A correcting spectacle lens of 5.4-dptr refracting power is used with its second principal point 14 mm from the anterior principal point of the eye. What is the length of the eyeball? What is the static refraction?

Ans. 26.5 mm; +1.01 dptr.

III–8. A common form of "magnifying lens" consists of a +12.0-dptr lens. What is its magnifying power?

Ans. 5.

III–9. A myoptic eye of 10 dptr uses a reading glass of 5-cm focal length. Neglecting the distance from eye to glass, what is its magnifying power?

Ans. 7.5×.

III–10. The refracting power of an eye is 58 dptr. What is the size of the retinal image of an object 200 cm high at a distance of 12 meters?

IV–1. The intensity I of a beam of radiant energy in passing through an absorbing liquid decreases according to the empirical relation $I = 20e^{-10d}$, where d is the depth in centimeters. Draw the semilogarithmic graph of I as a function of d. From this graph interpolate the intensity and its rate of change when the intensity has fallen to 0.1 of its incident value.

IV–2. A given solution of copper chloride, 1.006 cm thick, absorbs 18.1 per cent of the light (5510 to 5540 Å) incident upon it. What percentage will be absorbed by a layer of this solution 7.64 cm thick?

Ans. 78.1 per cent.

IV–3. A population of a colony of bacteria is observed to increase at a rate of 5 per cent per day of the number then living. If the population is initially 100,000 what is the population after 10 days?

Ans. 164,870.

IV–4. It was found that the percentage of the survivors of a radiated colony of organisms was constant during an experiment regardless of the number of cells present. The experiment showed that at time 0, 1, 2, 3, 4, 5, and 6 the survivors numbered 10^6, 10^5, 10^4, 10^3, 10^2, 10, and 1. How many died per day? What percentage died per day? Compute the death rate K where

$$K = \frac{1}{0.4343t} \log \frac{a}{b}$$

where a is the initial number and b the number after time t.

IV–5. The growth of *Bacterium coli* on broth was observed to be 19,000 at 10 A.M., 35,900 at 10:30, 88,000 at 11:00; subsequent data taken at hourly intervals gave 482×10^3; 3.40×10^6; 26.3×10^6; 71.6×10^6; and 118×10^6 counts. What is the form of the growth curve? Which portion of the curve indicates that the nutrients available for growth decreased as the number of organisms increased?

V–1. If the surface energy of water at 0° C is 75.796 ergs/cm², what is it at 20° C?

V–2. What is the total potential surface energy of each of three drops of water whose diameters are 0.2, 0.4, and 0.6 mm? If they are brought in contact to make a single drop, what is the surface energy? How do you account for the difference?

V–3. A drop of water is 2×10^{-4} cm in diameter. To what pressure is the water subjected by its surface energy?

V–4. What force, due to surface energy, is required to remove a clean ring of 2-cm internal and 2.1-cm external diameter through a clean water surface?

V–5. What will happen when two soap bubbles of unequal size are connected with a glass tube?

V–6. Why does a linen towel absorb moisture faster than a cotton one?

V–7. What is the gas pressure inside a 8-cm-diameter soap bubble if the soap solution-air surface has a surface energy of 35 ergs/cm^2 at 20° C?

V–8. Calculate the osmotic pressure of a 1 per cent solution of cane sugar when dialyzed against pure water through a membrane impermeable to the sugar molecules.

Ans. 494 mm Hg.

V–9. In one of his experiments Pfeffer showed that a certain concentration of sugar produced a pressure of 53.5 cm Hg at 20° C. His product pv was 1.82×10^6 dynes $\times$ cm. What was the concentration in grams per liter?

Ans. 10.0 grams/liter.

V–10. If a 0.001 N solution of KCl is completely dissociated, what concentration of KCl in water will be required to give the same osmotic pressure as that obtained from a 10-grams-per-liter sugar solution?

V–11. The freezing point of a solution was found to be −0.93° C. What is its osmotic pressure?

Ans. 11.2 atmospheres.

V–12. Mammalian blood serum gives $\Delta = 0.56°$ C. What per cent NaCl solution gives the same osmotic pressure? What per cent solution of NaCl is isotonic or isosmotic with mammalian serum?

Ans. 0.95 per cent.

VI–1. The following voltages were applied to tissue in order just to produce excitation. Stimulus measured in volts; time measured in milliseconds. Stimulus: 70, 60, 50, 40, 38. Time: 0.10, 0.17, 0.28, 0.49, 1.20. Draw a graph and interpolate the value of the chronaxie.

VI–2. Two idealized axon spikes start in phase. The first has a velocity of 16 meters per second and the second a velocity of 15 meters per second. The first rises to 300 microvolt crest potential in 0.2 millisecond and the second to 200 microvolts in 0.4 millisecond. Draw the resultant compound action potential observed at a point 10 cm from their common origin.

VI–3. Plot the curve $y = a \sin 2\pi t/T$ when the amplitude is 10 cm and the period 4 seconds.

VI–4. A particle is acted on simultaneously by two simple harmonic motions given by $y = 4 \sin 2\pi t/8$ and $y = 6 \sin 2\pi t/4$. Plot a graph showing the resultant motion.

VI–5. Between two points A and B, along whose line a train of simple waves is traveling, there are $8\frac{1}{3}$ cycles. What is the difference in phase between the points A and B?

VI–6. Compound three trains of waves in the ratio 1, $\frac{1}{3}$, and $\frac{1}{5}$ and of amplitude 4, 3, and 2 starting in the same phase.

VI–7. The data for a strength-duration curve showed that when the logarithm of $V/(V-R)$ was plotted against time a linear relation was obtained. Interpret your results if V is the excitation potential, R the rheobase, and t the time. Interpret the slope of the graph.

VII–1. The velocity of sound is 340 meters per second at 16° C. What is its velocity at 50° C?

VII–2. A sounding tuning fork has a frequency of 100 cycles per second. Calculate the wavelength of the pressure disturbance in air at (a) 20° C; (b) −10° C.

VII–3. Calculate the wavelengths of the lowest and highest frequencies that the average human ear can experience as sound.

VII–4. What is the velocity of sound in water if on an increase of 1 atmosphere pressure the water is compressed 4.78×10^{-5} of its volume.

Ans. 1456 meters/sec.

VII–5. Express the ratio of a kilowatt to a microwatt as a simple number and then express this ratio in decibels difference of power level.

VII–6. If 10^{-16} watt/cm^2 is used as the reference level for expressing intensity levels, what is the intensity level of sound having the following intensities: (a) 10^{-3} watt/cm^2; (b) 1 microwatt/cm^2; (c) 2×10^{-10} microwatt/cm^2?

Ans. (a) 130 db; (b) 100 db; (c) 3 db.

VII–7. Explain why the quality of sound emitted by a radio is changed by turning the volume-control dial?

VII–8. Using the normal standard loudness-level contours find the loudness level of each of the following tones:

(1) A 1000-cycle tone having an intensity level of 80 db.

Ans. 80 db.

(2) A 10,000-cycle tone having an intensity level of 80 db.

Ans. 71 db.

(3) A 100-cycle tone having an intensity level of 80 db.

Ans. 75 db.

(4) A 100-cycle tone having an intensity of 10^{-2} microwatt/cm^2.

Ans. 75 db.

(5) A 100-cycle tone having an intensity of 10^{-6} microwatt/cm^2.

Ans. 40 db.

VII–9. You are listening to a source of pure 1000-cycle sound waves, identified as having an intensity level of 50 db at the observer's ear. (1) What loudness level will be observed when two such sources function simultaneously? (2) What is the experienced loudness of one source? (3) What is the experienced loudness of the two simultaneously sounding sources?

Ans. (1) 53 db; (2) 2000; (3) 2600.

VII–10. Construct a deafness audiogram with hearing loss in decibel units plotted as a function of the logarithm of the frequency. Use the following data. At frequencies 128, 256, 512, 1024, 2048, 4096, 8192 the right ear's loss was −5, 0, −5, −10, −10, +10, −2; the left ear's loss was +20, +35, +35, +35, +20, +30, +35 db. Is the right or the left ear defective?

VII–11. For the average of five cases where the tympanic membrane was removed, an air audiogram gave the following hearing losses at the frequencies cited in the previous problem. Hearing loss +40, +50, +45, +65, +50, +45 db. Draw conclusions as to hearing loss of an ear functioning without tympanic membrane.

VIII–1. What is the magnifying power of a reading glass whose focal length is 25 cm, if it is held 15 cm from a book with the eye 50 cm from the lens?

Ans. 1.7×.

VIII–2. Show that the magnifying power of the eyepiece of a compound microscope can be represented by M.P. = $25/f_1$ and that the magnification produced by the objective is $M = L/f_2$, where L is the approximate length of the draw tube, and f_1 and f_2 are respectively the equivalent focal lengths of the eyepiece and objective. Show that the combined magnifying power is $25L/f_1f_2$.

VIII–3. It is desired to have a microscope attain a magnifying power of 1000 diameters. The eyepiece has an equivalent focal length of 1.5 cm and the objective 0.33 cm. What draw-tube length must be used?

Ans. 20 cm.

VIII–4. How small an object would you expect to distinguish visually when using a 32-mm objective of 0.10 N.A.? How small an object can be resolved with a 16-mm achromat of 0.25 N.A.?

VIII–5. An electron is given a kinetic energy of 4×10^5 electron volts. What is its equivalent de Broglie wavelength in centimeters?

VIII–6. Calculate the wavelength associated with an electron moving with a speed comparable to 100,000 election volts. Take into consideration the increase in mass of the electron due to the theory of relativity.

Ans. 0.03 Å.

VIII–7. The unit of magnetic field intensity is called the oersted, formerly called the gauss. The oersted is defined as the intensity at a given point in a magnetic field at which the field would act with the force of 1 dyne upon unit pole placed there; 1 oersted = 1 dyne/1 pole. In a transverse field of 150 oersteds a cathode beam traces a curve of 6-cm radius. What is the velocity of the electrons? $e = 1.60 \times 10^{-20}$ emu.

VIII–8. What magnetic field intensity must be applied perpendicular to a beam of electrons having a velocity of 1.88×10^9 cm/sec so that they will be bent into a circle of radius 4.25 cm?

VIII–9. The numerical aperture of an election microscope is 0.02. Using 50,000 as the accelerating voltage what resolution may be obtained?

Ans. 2.7×10^{-8} cm.

VIII–10. What electron speed must be used to give an electron microscope with magnetic coil lens a resolution of 2.0 Å?

Ans. 90 kv.

361

SUBJECT INDEX

DATE DUE